TEACHING ARITHMETIC

in the

ELEMENTARY SCHOOL

Volume I, Primary Grades

by

ROBERT LEE MORTON

Ohio University, Athens, Ohio

Author of *Teaching Arithmetic in the Primary Grades, Teaching Arithmetic in the Intermediate Grades, Mathematics through Experience,* etc.

SILVER BURDETT COMPANY

NEW YORK BOSTON CHICAGO SAN FRANCISCO

Printed in the United States of America

PREFACE

It is ten years since the author's TEACHING ARITHMETIC IN THE PRIMARY GRADES was published. During this ten-year period many persons have become interested in number work in the early grades of the elementary school. The results of many researches dealing with what to teach, when to teach it, and how to teach it, have been published. The authors of a great many other articles have discussed almost all phases of primary arithmetic and have offered opinions and recommendations as to how number functions in the lives of young children and as to the provision which should be made for it in the curriculum of the early grades.

Two or three years ago, the author started to revise his earlier book. As the work got under way, however, it became apparent that a revision would not be sufficient. As a result, this book is a new book, not a revision. Some of the material in the earlier volume has been used but more than 90 per cent of this book is new material or material which has been completely rewritten. There are very excellent reasons for the decision to produce a new book.

In the first place, the author's point of view has been modified in several respects by his own investigations and the experiences of others. What these changes are will clearly be apparent to the reader, if he is acquainted with the earlier book. There is, in this volume, a much greater emphasis upon number as a series of meaningful experiences. The bond psychology which was conspicuous in the earlier book has given way largely to psychology which emphasizes relationships and which recognizes that new elements may be *discovered* by the pupils by virtue of the fact that these elements are often intimately related to those which the pupils already know. Activities occupy a more important place although it is contended that activities alone are not sufficient as a means of providing a desirable education in number. There is less emphasis upon the early mastery of number facts as such, particularly in the first and second grades, and more emphasis upon experiences which lead gradually to an appreciation of these facts and the eventual learning of them in a really meaningful and significant way.

Secondly, the large number of monographs and articles which have appeared in recent years have added so greatly to the literature of the subject that it was quite impossible to make the proper use of this new material by merely revising a ten-year-old book. In this volume, a serious effort has been made to bring together the findings, the conclusions, and the recommendations of other investigators and to organize them in a form which will be useful and meaningful to those interested in primary education. Naturally, the picture has been colored in places by the author's own point of view. Decisions have been made and recommendations have been offered, rather arbitrarily at times, when the evidence provided by experimental investigations has been in conflict or when evidence has been lacking.

Again, it seemed to be desirable to expand the field covered. For the most part, Chapters 1, 2, and 10 in this book are new. The other nine chapters also contain much that is new and different. The author has found this expansion necessary in his own work with teachers, and he believes that others engaged in the education of teachers will welcome these additions. Teachers in service, supervisors, and directors of elementary education are certain to welcome the new materials and the more extensive treatment of old materials.

In the author's own professional life a great deal of water has gone over the dam since the publication of TEACHING ARITHMETIC IN THE PRIMARY GRADES ten years ago. Whatever that book may have done for those interested in primary education in this and other countries, it has done a great deal for the one who wrote it. It has brought him into contact personally and through correspondence with thousands of persons whom he would not have known otherwise. These persons are widely distributed geographically and they represent many points of view educationally. For the most part they have received the book well, but they have offered suggestions and constructive criticisms which have enabled the author to make this book a much better one than would have been produced without their aid.

To list those to whom the author is indebted is impossible. First, there are those who have sat in his own classes; they number more than six thousand persons. Next, there are those to whom the author has lectured and whom he has met in round table conferences; they are widely distributed and include many with stimulating ideas and refreshing points of view. Those who have written on the subject include many with whom the author is acquainted personally and others whom he would like to know for he is under obligation to all of them. Finally, there are those with whom the author has been in correspondence. They have been users of his book and out of their experience they have offered suggestions which were of great value. To all of these the author wishes to express his grateful appreciation.

The author has been more than gratified with the reception accorded TEACHING ARITHMETIC IN THE PRIMARY GRADES. It has been listed on several state reading circle courses, it has been used as a text in scores of teacher-education institutions, and it has been purchased by many boards of education for teachers' professional libraries and by individuals for their own use. Its use in many countries other than the United States has been extensive. The wide-spread use of that book has been a stimulus in the preparation of this one; it has also left a feeling of grave responsibility. This new volume is offered with the hope that it may be serviceable to those interested in primary education.

ROBERT L. MORTON

Athens, Ohio
September, 1937

CONTENTS

Chapter 1. Developing an Understanding of Number 1

The need for concrete number experience.—Understanding should come before drill.—Primitive man and number.—What can the teacher do?—The object stage.—The picture stage.—The semi-concrete stage.—The abstract symbol stage.—Number rhymes.—Questions and review exercises.—Chapter test.—Selected references.

Chapter 2. The Place of Arithmetic in the Curriculum of the Primary Grades 26

The Buckingham-MacLatchy study.—The Woody investigation.—Other investigations.—Arithmetic in the kindergarten.—Why not ignore arithmetic in the primary grades?—When shall we begin teaching arithmetic?—Arithmetic in an activity program.—Questions and review exercises.—Chapter test.—Selected references.

Chapter 3. Increasing the Child's Understanding of Numbers 57

Rote and rational counting.—Individual differences among young children.—Counting by multiples.—Recognizing the size of small groups without counting.—Cardinal and ordinal numbers.—Reading and writing numbers.—Questions and review exercises.—Chapter test.—Selected references.

Chapter 4. Teaching the Fundamental Combinations of Addition and Subtraction 76

The beginner's knowledge of the combinations.—When should instruction in addition begin?—How to begin the work in addition.—The 45 basic combinations.—Combinations and facts.—The zero combinations.—Difficulty of the combinations.—Order of teaching the combinations.—Teaching the combinations in the easier group.—Teaching the combinations in the harder group.—Providing for drill or practice.—Flash cards.—Games and drill devices.—Undesirable games and devices.—Examples of better games and drill devices.—Problem solving.—Making and using tests.—Recording and using test results.—Questions and review exercises.—Chapter test.—Selected references.

Chapter 5. Elementary Work in Addition 123

Easy column addition.—Other three-digit combinations.—Adding up or down.—Adding longer columns.—Zeros in column addition.—The need for higher decade addition.—The number of higher decade combinations.—Higher decade addition in multiplication. —How to teach higher decade addition.—Practice in higher decade addition.—Further work in column addition.—Addition practice preliminary to carrying in multiplication.—Adding two or more digits.—Introducing the pupils to carrying.—Writing the number carried.—Variety in addition practice.—Addends of unequal length.—Speed versus accuracy.—Checking answers.—Attention span.—Questions and review exercises.—Chapter test.—Selected references.

Chapter 6. Elementary Work in Subtraction 170

Subtraction examples without borrowing.—Methods of subtraction.—The take-away-borrow method.—The take-away-carry method.—The addition-borrow method.—The addition-carry method.—The complementary method.—Borrowing versus carrying.—Subtractive versus additive methods.—The type problems of subtraction.—Teaching the borrowing operation.—Desirable and undesirable habits in subtraction.—Types of examples.—The use of crutches.—Additional sets of practice examples.—Checking solutions.—The use of problems.—Higher decade subtraction.—Cardinal points in subtraction.—Questions and review exercises. —Chapter test.—Selected references.

Chapter 7. Teaching the Fundamental Combinations of Multiplication and Division 213

The use of terms.—The zero combinations.—Writing and speaking the combinations.—The number of combinations.—The effect of going beyond 9 x 9.—Serial memorizing of tables.—The order of teaching the combinations.—The relationship of multiplication to addition.—Teaching the 2's.—Developing the related facts.—Teaching the corresponding division facts. —The need for higher decade addition.—Rate of progress.—Games and practice exercises.—Flash cards.—Solving problems.—Constructing and using tests.—Brief summary of suggestions for teaching the multiplication and the division facts.—Questions and review exercises.—Chapter test.—Selected references.

Chapter 8. Elementary Work in Multiplication . 258

Early use of examples.—Work limited to one-digit multipliers.—Multiplication without carrying.—Multiplication with carrying.—Preparing examples for practice.—The zero difficulties.—Solving problems.—Checking results.—Which way should we multiply?—Questions and review exercises.—Chapter test.—Selected references.

Chapter 9. Elementary Work in Division 281

Division in the primary grades.—Division related to multiplication.—The early use of examples.—Work limited to one-digit divisors.—Using the fraction form in division.—Short division or long division first?—The major difficulty steps in division.—Division without carrying.—The primary facts with remainders.—Division with carrying.—Zeros in the quotient.—Checking results.—The use of problems.—Questions and review exercises.—Chapter test.—Selected references.

Chapter 10. Roman Numerals, Measures, Fractions 321

The broad base of number experience.—Roman numerals. — Comparisons. — Measurement. — Denominate measures.—Measures of length and distance.—Measures of time.—Measures of capacity and weight.—Collective terms.—Developing an understanding of fractions.—Teaching unit fractions.—Other proper fractions.—Questions and review exercises.—Chapter test.—Selected references.

Chapter 11. Problem Solving 346

Distinction between problems and examples.—Problem solving in the primary grades.—Qualities of good problems.—Reality in problems.—Problems having interest.—The language of problems.—The story element in problems.—Problems for practice on basic skills.—A classification of problems.—Method in problem solving.—Questions and review exercises.—Chapter test.—Selected references.

Chapter 12. The Course of Study 370

Preparing a course of study—the old method.—Preparing a course of study—the new method.—Continuous revision necessary.—Provision for individual differences.—Arithmetic in activities.—Arithmetic in the first grade.—Counting and reading and writing numbers.—Measurement.—Addition and subtraction.—Problems and activities.—Arithmetic in the second grade.—Counting and reading and writing numbers.—Addition. — Subtraction. — Measurement. — Problems and Activities.—Arithmetic in the third grade.—The grade placement of arithmetic topics.—Reading and writing numbers.—Addition.—Subtraction.—Multiplication.—Division.—Measurement and fractions.—Problems and activities.—The trend toward a socialized curriculum.—Questions and review exercises.—Chapter test.—Selected references.

Answers for Chapter Tests 405

Index 407

CHAPTER 1

DEVELOPING AN UNDERSTANDING OF NUMBER

Miss Jenkins, the primary supervisor, entered the room at 10:15. She found a flash card drill on the addition combinations in progress. The room was crowded with 44 second grade pupils.

Card after card was "flashed" from the back to the front of the pack in the hands of the teacher. As a card was moved to a visible position at the front of the pack, the name of a pupil was called. If he was hesitant in his response, the teacher moved quickly to another pupil and, after getting the correct answer, back to the pupil who had hesitated. This drill exercise continued for five or ten minutes when the cards were put away and the group turned their attention to other matters.

Watching the pupils closely, Miss Jenkins observed that several were eager and alert and that they apparently enjoyed the exercise. There was just a little tendency for some of them to want to "show off." Others were apparently uncomfortable; they did not know their combinations well and there was evidence of distress on their faces when they did not respond quickly or, worse still, when they failed to respond at all. Several were obviously not interested. And still others did not seem to know what it was all about.

Frequently, a pupil responded quickly when his name was called, apparently desirous of pleasing his teacher, but gave an incorrect answer. Such pupils seemed to think that it was better to answer incorrectly than not to answer at all. Some of these did not seem to be disturbed over the fact that their answers were incorrect. They accepted the corrections complacently.

Miss Jenkins investigated. She discovered that these pupils had had a very limited program of concrete number experience when in the first grade. They had counted but much of the counting had been *rote* counting,—the mere reciting of number names, without reference to concrete objects or meaningful experiences. When they counted, they seldom counted anything. In the second grade, they had been launched promptly into "learning" the addition combinations. A few of the brightest of these pupils who had a special aptitude for arithmetic had done well under this plan but such progress as the majority had been able to make had been decidedly unsatisfactory.

The need for concrete number experience. Many teachers in the primary grades seem to fail to realize the importance of an extensive and varied program of concrete number experience before drill on abstract number combinations is begun. Brownell[1] made a careful investigation of the methods by which children apprehend visual concrete numbers and came to the conclusion that the transition from concrete to abstract number is often too abrupt (p. 47). He found that the kind of teaching done in the first and second grades frequently left the pupils with a very inadequate understanding of the relation of abstract numbers to concrete numbers and that this condition persisted until the pupils reached the fourth grade (p. 57). He concluded

---

[1] Brownell, William A. *The Development of Children's Number Ideas in the Primary Grades.* Chicago: The University of Chicago, 1928. 241 pp.

that deliberate experience with concrete objects followed by the gradual development of work in the addition and subtraction combinations with such semi-concrete materials as number pictures was much better than a program of abstract drill on these combinations before the pupils had had sufficient opportunity to learn the meaning of numbers and the meaning of addition and subtraction (p. 60). Pupils who knew that 4 and 4 are 8 failed to see a connection between this fact and the number picture ●● ●● ●● ●● when it was presented to them. Brownell came to the conclusion that the wide gap between concrete and abstract number, which must be bridged before effective work with the combinations can be accomplished, is not bridged as easily and as simply as many primary teachers seem to believe; that such semi-concrete materials as number pictures in which dots are used are not readily apprehended by pupils who are inexperienced with them; that such abstract methods as counting by 2's, 3's, and 4's, were not generally used by pupils in the third and fourth grades although they had been trained in such methods in the second grade; that it is possible to teach number in the primary grades in such a way that these difficulties are eliminated; and that most of the difficulties in arithmetic in later grades are due to inadequate teaching in the primary grades (p. 61).

De May[2] lays emphasis upon the importance of developing arithmetic meanings in the early grades. Her general outline for instruction in arithmetic recognizes four stages in the pupil's progress from concrete to abstract

[2] De May, Amy J. "Arithmetic Meanings." *Childhood Education,* XI: 408-412, June, 1935.

number experience. The first stage is the purely concrete number stage. In this stage, the pupil deals with concrete objects as he encounters them in his experiences. De May points out that opportunities for this kind of number experience are abundant and that an alert teacher should have no difficulty in discovering them.

In the second stage, the pupil deals with pictures of familiar objects instead of the objects themselves. There are pictures of balls, apples, tops, children, books, chairs, pigs, chickens, etc. Many teachers seem to recognize no difference between these two stages. They seem to think that the picture of a ball, for example, is as real to the pupil as is the ball itself, whereas the picture represents a step on the way to an understanding of abstract number. It is a short step, to be sure, and one which most children will take readily enough if they are not hurried and if they have sufficient experience with the first stage before the second stage is undertaken.

In the third stage, semi-concrete materials are used. These semi-concrete materials take the form of number pictures in which dots, rings, lines, etc. are used. This stage may be broken down into two or more phases when very elementary number combinations are involved. For example, we may have

⁚ and ⁚ are ⁚⁚

Then as the pupils become acquainted with the signs + and =, this item may appear

⁚ + ⁚ = ⁚⁚

The reader will find this topic developed more fully in the chapter dealing with the teaching of the addition and the subtraction facts.

In the fourth stage, the pupil becomes able to use the symbols 1, 2, 3, etc. to represent quantities. When he reaches this stage, he is dealing with abstract number. He has moved slowly and gradually from the purely concrete stage where a number, as four, was represented by four of the actual objects, through the intermediate stages where four familiar looking pictures of the objects in question were seen and recognized, and where four circles or dots or lines represented the four objects, to the final stage where the four objects were represented simply by the abstract symbol 4.

De May regrets that pupils are frequently forced to jump this gap between concrete and abstract numbers. When they do so, they land in what she very properly calls a "wilderness of unknown symbols and meaningless names." They manipulate numbers without an understanding of these numbers. They try to "learn" combinations in addition and subtraction, in which numbers are used in a very abstract way, without a sufficient understanding of number. This understanding which should come early, easily, and naturally may then require years. The pupil has been thwarted in his progress because first things were not made to come first.

Drummond,[3] an English writer, in a discussion of counting says:

> Realization of the nature of Number comes slowly to the child through his own activity in counting. (p. 12)
>
> While he is doing this, he is not only gaining the abstract idea of Number, he is really learning addition, subtraction,

---

[3] Drummond, Margaret. *The Psychology and Teaching of Number.* Yonkers-on-Hudson, New York: 1922. 126 pp.

multiplication, and division, for these are all implicit in the counting. (pp. 12-13)

How these operations are implicit in the counting will be indicated more clearly in later chapters.

Understanding should come before drill. The drill exercise which was described briefly at the beginning of this chapter was not necessarily wrong in itself. It was premature. Although a few of the brighter pupils in this second grade had succeeded in bridging the gap between concrete and abstract number, and had done so in spite of the school program which they had followed in the first grade and the early part of the second grade rather than because of this program, the majority of them had failed to do so. Drill is decidedly harmful if given prematurely although very worthwhile if given at the right stage in the pupil's progress. This point is well stated by Stretch,[4] as follows:

In a word, while drill yields no insight into number and can not make arithmetic meaningful, it does assist the pupil to form efficient habits of number manipulation and to keep these habits at a high level of usefulness. Used for these purposes, to which it is truly adapted, drill must always remain an essential feature in primary arithmetic instruction. (p. 416)

The importance of developing properly an understanding of number before the operations of arithmetic are undertaken has been stressed in printed discussions of the subject for many years. Freeman,[5] in 1916, pointed

---

[4] Stretch, Lorene B. "The Value and Limitations of Drill in Arithmetic." *Childhood Education,* XI: 413-416, June, 1935.

[5] Freeman, F. N. *The Psychology of the Common Branches.* Boston: Houghton Mifflin Company, 1916, p. 209.

out that the child in his study of number is disturbed by difficulties which come from two sources. In the first place, he must understand the number relations and in the second place, he must understand the way in which these relations are represented by number symbols. Frequently, his chief difficulty is with the symbols. If he starts right in with abstract symbols, they are likely to be meaningless to him and what appears to be learning is nothing more than rote memory. Whereas number experiences should be a means of developing the ability of children to think, they often degenerate into the mere memorization of processes and relationships which are not understood.

Wheat,[6] in a chapter on the Psychology of Arithmetic, has a section entitled "Number Facts versus Number Ideas." We quote from pages 142 and 143:

> One may look upon the learning of arithmetic as the learning of separate number facts, or one may view the process as the development in the mind of the learner of interrelated number ideas which may be applied by him both in clarifying the ideas he possesses and in developing ideas of higher orders. Viewed from the former angle, the learning of arithmetic is little more than systematic memorization. Viewed from the latter angle, the process is that of an active mind which not only learns the various number facts but also understands them and their relations and seeks possibilities of their applications.
>
> There are many pupils in school who succeed in learning their arithmetic only as a mass of isolated and unrelated number facts. The number relations in the fundamental

[6] Wheat, Harry Grove. *The Psychology of the Elementary School.* New York: Silver, Burdett and Company, 1931. 440 pp. See especially Chapter IV, "The Psychology of Arithmetic."

operations of addition, subtraction, multiplication, and division are learned only as so many facts to be remembered. Through constant drill and persistent effort, they succeed in acquiring skill in the operations, but fail to recognize withal the nature and the meaning of the operations. As a result, they learn to add, subtract, multiply, and divide with a fair degree of mechanical precision; they learn to perform such operations as they may be directed to perform; but they do not develop the ability to recognize the presence of these operations in the simplest practical situations in which they may be found. In the course of time, however, they succeed in remembering that a statement which includes such terms as "how many," "altogether," "total," "sum," etc., requires addition; that a statement in which such terms as "take away," "left," "how many more," etc., are found requires subtraction; and so on. In other words, they learn to remember the various computations; they come to regard them as so many mechanical and meaningless performances; and finally, they learn such of their applications as can be remembered by formula and rule.

Primitive man and number. It required many thousands of years for man to develop a number system such as that which we have today. Today we find in certain parts of Africa, Australia, and some of the Pacific islands savage tribes whose number ideas and counting practices represent the very primitive stage which our own ancestors must at one time have gone through.[7] Primitive peoples had words or signs for *one, two,* and sometimes *three* but beyond this such vague and general terms as a *heap* or a *flock* or *many* were used. Primitive man

---

[7] See *Numbers and Numerals* by David Eugene Smith and Jekuthial Ginsburg. New York: Bureau of Publications, Teachers College, Columbia University, 1937. 52 pp.

found the development of a more extensive number system to be a very slow process. But he groped his way along and eventually a system adequate for his needs was developed. Conant[8] describes the process as follows:

By the slow, and often painful, process incident to the extension and development of any mental conception in a mind wholly unused to abstractions, the savage gropes his way onward in his counting from 1, or more probably from 2, to the various higher numbers required to form his scale. The perception of unity offers no difficulty to his mind, though he is conscious at first of the object itself rather than of any idea of number associated with it. The concept of duality, also, is grasped with perfect readiness. This concept is, in its simplest form, presented to the mind as soon as the individual distinguishes himself from another person, though the idea is still essentially concrete.

Perhaps the first glimmer of any real number thought in connection with 2 comes when the savage contrasts one single object with another—or, in other words, when he first recognizes the *pair*. At first the individuals composing the pair are simply "this one" and "that one," or "this" and "that"; and his number system now halts for a time at a stage where he can, rudely enough it may be, count 1, 2, many.

There are certain cases where the forms of 1 and 2 are so similar that one may readily imagine that these numbers really were "this" and "that" in the savage's original conception of them; and the same likeness occurs in the words for 3 and 4, which may readily enough have been a second "this" and a second "that." In Lushu tongue the words for 1 and 2 are *tizi* and *tazi* respectively. In Koriak we find

[8] Conant, L. L. *The Number Concept.* New York: The Macmillan Company, 1896, pp. 74-76.

ngroka, 3, and *ngraka,* 4; in Kolyma, *niyokh,* 3, and *niyakh,* 4; and in Kamtschatkan, *tsuk,* 3, and *tsaak,* 4. Sometimes as in the case of the Australian races, the entire extent of the count is carried through by means of pairs. But the natural theory one would form is, that 2 is the halting place for a very long time; that up to this point the fingers may or may not have been used—probably not; and that when the next start is made, and 3, 4, 5, and so on are counted, the fingers first come into requisition.

If the grammatical structure of the earlier languages of the world's history is examined, the student is struck with the prevalence of the dual number in them—something which tends to disappear as language undergoes extended development. The dual number points unequivocally to the time when 1 and 2 were *the* numbers at mankind's disposal; to the time when his three numeral concepts, 1, 2, many, each demanded distinct expression. With increasing knowledge the necessity for this differentiation would pass away, and but two numbers singular and plural, would remain. Incidentally it is to be noticed that the Indo-European words for 3—*three* (English), *trois* (French), *drei* (German), *tres* (Latin), etc. have the same root as the Latin *trans,* beyond, and give us a hint of the time when our Aryan ancestors counted in the manner I have just described.

It seems strange, then, that primary teachers would expect their pupils to know number without its being taught, or to learn number from mere rote counting, and would proceed after a grossly inadequate foundation in the fundamentals of number to drill upon the addition and subtraction combinations. Yet this, in many school rooms, seems to be precisely the case. Children are expected to come unaided into an understanding of a number system which their remote ancestors required thousands of years to develop. If they have had any aid, it has frequently been restricted to counting and often mere rote counting at that.

Ballard,[9] an English writer, describes in this manner the pupil's early number experiences in a good school:

A young child in the infant school or the kindergarten gains his first notions of number through his eyes and his fingers. He handles real things. He counts beans and beads and tablets; he performs simple operations with them; he adds them and subtracts them; he arranges them in groups and disposes them in patterns. . . . The result is that his concepts of the simpler numbers and of their relationships are singularly clear and accurate. The meanings he acquires are real meanings, gained by a living experience. And his knowledge of number, being intelligently gained, can, when need arises, be intelligently applied. In fine, the foundations of arithmetic in a good modern school are well and truly laid.

It was not always so. I well remember the time when the teaching in the infant school was indistinguishable in kind from that of the senior school. . . . The children were always taught *en masse*. When concrete objects were used, the number lesson was just like the drill lesson. The children were asked to do this, and they did this; to do that, and they did that. They obeyed mechanically and collectively. They were invited to think of what they were doing; and they were supposed to think abreast just as they were able to march abreast. Yet there is no time in which the flow of thought is more manifestly fitful and intermittent than when it deals with a problem in arithmetic—and to the young beginner every exercise in number is a problem: it presents a difficulty to be overcome by an act of thought rather than by an act

[9] Ballard, P. B. *Teaching the Essentials of Arithmetic.* London: University of London Press, 1928. 260 pp.

of memory. Hence the children's mode of attack in our most enlightened schools is individual and personal. (pp. 52-53)

What can the teacher do? Usually, it is not difficult to persuade a primary teacher who hastens from concrete number to abstract number that the results are not what they should be. Usually, too, the point which has been stressed in this chapter, that the transition should be gradual and that the pupil should have sufficient experience with each stage before he goes on to the next, is granted if clearly stated and amply illustrated. But what most teachers want to know is what they should have done that they didn't do or what they should be doing but are neglecting to do.

Probably, the question is best answered by referring again to the four stages recommended by De May (pages 3-5) and by others who have talked and written on this subject. They may be summarized briefly as follows:

1. The object stage: purely concrete number.
2. The picture stage: pictures of familiar objects.
3. The semi-concrete number stage: dots, lines, circles, etc.
4. The abstract number stage: number symbols.

The object stage. Many opportunities for counting arise in the work of a first grade. Whether the work of the class be conducted in the conventional manner with fixed seats in straight rows and scheduled "recitation" periods, or in accordance with the more modern and sometimes better "activity" plan, or according to a plan which is at times modern and at times conventional, opportunities for handling and counting materials are frequent and should not be missed. Just what these opportunities are depends upon the school, the room and its equipment, and the program of work.

For a game, four boys and five girls are needed. Instead of selecting them and counting them out herself, the teacher will let the pupils assist with the selection, observe from time to time the number chosen and the number yet needed and when the required number of each has been obtained. Occasionally, while the selections are being made and even after the correct number of each has been chosen, the teacher will ask, "Do we need any more boys? Or, do we need any more girls?"

Books and other materials of various kinds are to be distributed to the pupils. They assist with the distribution and are directed in such terms as: "Mary Jane, give a sheet of this drawing paper to each one at your table. How many will you need? Are you taking one for yourself?" Or, "Ralph, take enough of these books to give one to each child in the *first* row."

It is often observed that the teacher is so much absorbed with the activity or the program that she fails to capitalize on the opportunities for developing an understanding of number. Indeed, many teachers have heard and read so often that there will be no *formal* work in arithmetic in the first grade that they think little about the need for developing number concept. They may even consciously avoid such opportunities when they see them.

The situations requiring the handling and counting of materials should, so far as possible, be situations which naturally arise in the pursuit of worth-while activities. If materials are provided for no other purpose than that they be handled and counted, they should be materials which children enjoy handling, materials which they like to play with. Bright and shining disks which look like coins are much better than beans or grains of corn. Objects, such as blocks, which have bright and contrasting colors are much better than drab, colorless objects. One teacher reached a very low level of objective materials when she saved the tiny bits of chalk which accumulate on the blackboard tray and used them for exercises in counting and grouping objects. Of course, objects which readily roll off a desk surface or table top should ordinarily be avoided.

Some schools have number readers or number primers for use in the first grade. Obviously, the first of these stages in developing an understanding of number can not be accomplished through the use of printed pages. The best that can be found there is pictures of objects. The first stage depends for its successful accomplishment upon the resourcefulness of the teacher.

The picture stage. It has already been suggested that many teachers fail to distinguish between the object stage and the picture stage. They seem to believe that pictures of objects should be as real to children as the objects themselves and that their number should be apprehended as readily. In the picture stage, on the other hand, we are taking the first step from concrete number toward abstract number.

In many schools, a major difficulty lies in the scarcity of satisfactory picture material. Such pictures as the teachers are able to obtain are often poorly suited to this purpose.

Well prepared number books or number readers help greatly in schools where picture materials are scarce.

Many of these books have been prepared for first and second grade pupils in recent years. Some are good and some leave much to be desired. Some make the same mistakes that teachers have been accused of making, the chief of which is the too early introduction of symbols. Before a book of this kind is adopted for use in the first or the second grade, it should be examined critically to see whether it conforms to desirable standards.

The vocabulary of a number book should be examined minutely. The authors of some number books apparently have given more attention to this matter than have others. It is probably permissable to introduce in number books words which the children have not encountered in printed or written form elsewhere but there should not be many of these. When such words are introduced, there should be a real need for them and they should occur sufficiently often to enable the pupils to learn them. For the most part, however, the new experiences which a pupil has when he uses a number book should be number experiences and unless the vocabulary is largely a familiar one, the real issue will be obscured.

Pictures have an advantage over the actual objects in that they are easily handled and in that a much wider variety is possible. For example, children have seen monkeys and elephants and bears at the circus and at the Zoological gardens but the best we can hope for in the schoolroom is pictures of these animals. (One teacher remarked that she had a whole room full of monkeys and that her principal was a bear.)

There is a prevailing opinion that colored pictures are better than plain black or white; they probably are.

So far as is known, however, the difference is not great enough to be very significant. The teacher who can get pictures which are otherwise attractive to children need not be greatly concerned about the matter of color.

Fortunate, indeed, is the teacher whose skill at drawing is sufficient to enable her to prepare her own pictures or, at least, a portion of them. Some teachers do easily and rapidly blackboard and paper sketches which are quite satisfactory.

The semi-concrete stage. It must be obvious by this time that number representations in the form of circles, lines, dots, and the like represent a still greater advance in the direction of abstract number. Such representations are concrete but not in the way or to the extent that pictures of familiar objects are concrete; hence the term "semi-concrete."

Dominoes are an old, well-known, and favorite device. Some teachers hesitate to use dominoes for fear that their use will lead to the development of the counting habit with the addition combinations. As we shall see in a later chapter, however, counting is an indispensable aid in teaching the addition combinations. Of course, we do not want the counting response to be the permanent response with combinations in addition but whether this is to be the case depends more upon how the teacher develops the subject than upon whether such semi-concrete materials are used. Children frequently become much interested in dominoes and simple games which can be played with them. Sets in which numbers up to double nine are represented should be available and should be used.

One does not have to be an artist to prepare very satisfactory materials for children's use. Many teachers use the hectograph and thereby duplicate very good materials at little expense. If a mimeograph is available, still better copies are made and they are made more rapidly and more easily.

In each of the stages so far discussed there will frequently be opportunities for the comparison of small groups to see which is the larger. At first there will be differences of two or more, as:

OO OOOO or OOO OOOOO

and then groups which differ by only one, as:

OOO OOOO and OOOOO OOOO

Such words as *more* and *fewer* will be used.

Later, three groups may be compared and the words *most* and *fewest* may be used.

These are samples of questions which may be asked:

1. Which shelf has the more books on it?
2. At which table are there fewer children?
3. Which plant has the more blossoms on it?
4. Which row has the fewest chairs in it?

In each of these stages the pupils will come gradually to recognize the common quality in groups of different kinds of objects but having the same number. Thus, they will appreciate the "twoness" of

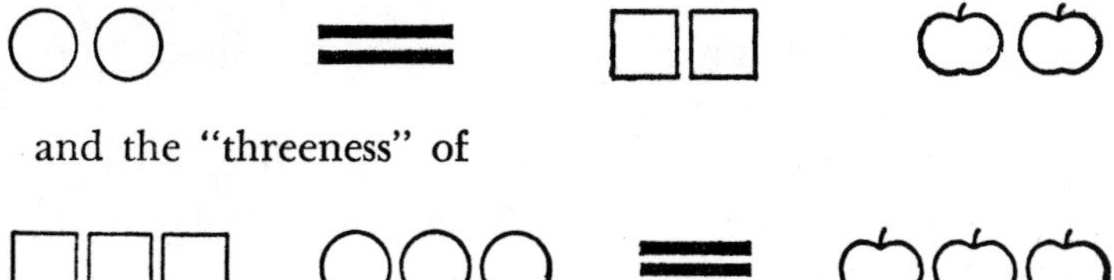

and the "threeness" of

The abstract symbol stage. It will be seen that this stage is reached only after considerable experience in the concrete and semi-concrete stages and after considerable time. Pupils learn what *four* means and they use the word "four" orally long before they learn to read the printed word and the symbol 4.

But eventually the printed or written word *four* and the symbol 4 must be recognized and associated with the idea of four. Gradually, the number words and the symbols come to be associated with the pictures and the semi-concrete objects which they represent. There may be built up gradually some form of number chart such as the following which uses squares.

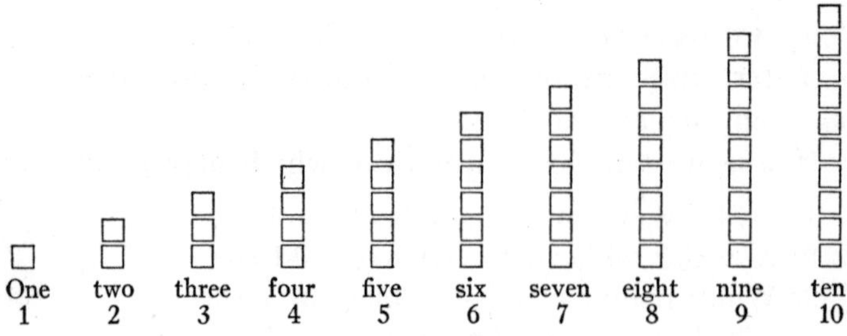

Of course, there is not yet a need for zero as a word or the symbol 0 alone.

Number rhymes. Pupils often become interested in number rhymes. If rhymes are used too early or too much, they tend to induce rote counting at the expense of number understanding. If used judiciously, they may be a pleasant means of helping in the transition from concrete to abstract number.

There are many such rhymes. We give here a few of the most popular. Children enjoy singing the second and the third.

1. One, two, three, four, five,
   I caught a hare alive.
   Six, seven, eight, nine, ten,
   I let him go again.

2.

3. One little, two little, three little fingers,
   Four little, five little, six little fingers,
   Seven little, eight little, nine little fingers,
   Ten little fingers clean.

   Ten little, nine little, eight little fingers,
   Seven little, six little, five little fingers,
   Four little, three little, two little fingers,
   One little finger clean.

These stanzas may be sung to the tune of "Ten Little Indians." Note that the second stanza provides practice in counting backward from ten to one. The song "Ten Little Indians" may be reversed in the same manner and sung to the same tune.

Ten little, nine little, eight little Indians,
  Seven little, six little, five little Indians,
Four little, three little, two little Indians,
  One little Indian boy.

4. One, two, buckle my shoe;
  Three, four, shut the door;
Five, six, pick up sticks;
  Seven, eight, lay them straight;
Nine, ten, a big fat hen.

QUESTIONS AND REVIEW EXERCISES

1. Do you recall your own experiences when a pupil in the primary grades well enough to react critically to the kind of teaching which you received? Summarize the strong points and the weak points of this teaching as you see it now, so far as the development of number understanding is concerned.

2. Whether you are a teacher or a student in a teacher-training institution, you should observe the work of a few primary teachers while the points of this chapter are fresh in your mind. Look for good features as well as for features which you believe you could improve.

3. Are flash card drills, such as that described at the beginning of this chapter, desirable? What is the reason for the obvious ineffectiveness of this drill?

4. If pupils learn addition combinations and learn them well, what difference does it make as to whether they understand the number relationships involved or not?

5. State briefly the four stages in the transition from concrete to abstract number which are recognized by De May.

6. Do you agree that pictures of objects are less concrete than the objects themselves? Discuss.

7. Why do we call such material as circles, dots, and lines semi-concrete material?

8. Do you subscribe to the statement, "Skill in the fundamental operations is worth while but skill with understanding is education"?

9. Is there any reason to expect pupils to be slow in understanding a social institution such as our number system because it has required mankind thousands of years to develop it?

10. Is there any evidence that early names for 1 and 2 were such as to suggest that these two numbers were thought of as a pair? Is there such evidence for 3 and 4?

11. If number is taught in the first grade only as a subject incidental to other subjects, is there danger that teaching opportunities will be missed? Why? So far as the subjects of the elementary school curriculum are concerned, what is the main business of the first grade teacher?

12. If you were a member of a committee to select a number reader or number primer for use in the first grade, what criteria would you employ in making your selection?

13. Why is training in free-hand drawing to be recommended for the prospective primary teacher?

14. What is meant by the "twoness" of several groups of two objects each?

15. When should number rhymes be used? What useful purpose, if any, do they serve?

CHAPTER TEST

Read each statement and decide whether it is true or false. A key for this test will be found on page 405.

1. Understanding of a new process should come before drill.
2. In drill exercises, pupils should be urged to respond quickly even though incorrectly.
3. Brownell discovered that the transition from concrete to abstract number is usually too slow.
4. Many difficulties in arithmetic in later grades are due to inadequate teaching in the primary grades.
5. De May recommends that the first stage in the development of an understanding of abstract number be the picture stage.
6. The figures 1, 2, 3, etc. are concrete.
7. Number concepts grow slowly.
8. The chief value of drill lies in the insight into number which it provides.
9. Drill should be used in the primary grades.
10. Most arithmetic learning should be systematic memorization.
11. Primitive man could count to 10.
12. Our present number system required thousands of years for its development.
13. Early language forms of the words "one" and "two" and the words "three" and "four" suggest that these numbers were at one time thought of as pairs.
14. In the earliest school counting, actual objects should be counted.
15. To children, number should be a mode of thinking.
16. In first grade rooms, opportunities for counting are frequent.
17. Teachers in primary grades frequently miss opportunities for developing an understanding of number.
18. If objective materials for counting are provided, it matters little what the materials are.

19. Good number primers are desirable for accomplishing the first stage in developing an understanding of number.

20. The vocabulary of primary number books should agree in general with the vocabulary of primary readers which are used with the same pupils.

21. Dominoes represent semi-concrete number materials.

22. Pupils should be given practice in comparing groups of objective materials to see which is the larger.

23. Number rhymes should be much used early in a pupil's school experience.

24. Most children enjoy number rhymes.

25. Colored pictures are known to be much better than plain black and white pictures for teaching purposes.

SELECTED REFERENCES

1. Association for Childhood Education, 1201 Sixteenth Street, Washington, D.C. *Foundations in Arithmetic,* 1937. 32 pp. This is an excellent bulletin. Its ten brief articles make interesting reading for the primary teacher or supervisor.

2. Ballard, P. B. *Teaching the Essentials of Arithmetic.* London: University of London Press, 1928. 260 pp. This book, by an English writer, reflects upon conditions and practices prevailing in English schools, some of which differ considerably from those found in the United States. The book is entertainingly written and contains some excellent suggestions. See especially pages 1-68.

3. Brownell, William A. *The Development of Children's Number Ideas in the Primary Grades.* Chicago: The University of Chicago Press, 1928. 241 pp. This monograph reports a high-grade research study. Of especial value, as a supplement for this chapter, are Chapters II, III, IV, V, and VIII.

4. Conant, L. L. *The Number Concept: Its Origin and Development.* New York: The Macmillan Company, 1896. 218 pp. For more than 40 years, this book has been a standard source of information on the evolution of number ideas

and number symbols. Chapters III and IV give an account of the origin of number words.

5. De May, Amy J. "Arithmetic Meanings." *Childhood Education,* XI: 408-412, June, 1935. A short but excellent article. Outlines stages in the transition from concrete to abstract number.

6. Drummond, Margaret. *The Psychology and Teaching of Number.* Yonkers-on-Hudson, New York: 1922. 126 pp. Another of the older books by an English writer. This book offers good suggestions in a number of places. Read especially the chapter from which we have quoted.

7. Freeman, Frank Nugent. *The Psychology of the Common Branches.* Boston: Houghton Mifflin Company, 1916. 275 pp. Chapter IX is devoted to a discussion of "Mathematics: Abstract Thought."

8. Lockhart, Lovine; Eldredge, E. C.; and Brown, J. C. *Number Helps.* Chicago: Rand McNally and Company, 1924. 120 pp. This book contains a collection of games, rimes, and songs for grades 1, 2, 3, and 4. Rimes will be found on pages 65-78 and songs on pages 81-96.

9. Losh, Rosamond and Weeks, Ruth Mary. *Primary Number Projects.* Boston: Houghton Mifflin Company, 1923. 199 pp. This little book contains a list of projects for various phases of primary arithmetic. "Aims and Hints" are given in Chapter I and "Counting Projects" in Chapter II. The second chapter includes several rimes.

10. Morton, Robert L. "What Do Numbers Mean to First-Grade Children?" *American Childhood,* 13: 18-19 and 60-61, May, 1928. This article suggests that children frequently use number words without understanding their meaning and gives suggestions for making them meaningful.

11. Morton, R. L. "Developing Number Ideas." *The Grade Teacher,* XLIX: 770 and 813, June, 1932. Gives briefly suggestions for developing children's ideas of number.

12. Russell, Ned M. "Arithmetical Concepts of Children."

Journal of Educational Research, XXIX: 645-663, May, 1936. Reports a study of the arithmetical concepts of young children. Cautions against formal work on isolated addition and subtraction facts and recommends that initial training in arithmetic be undertaken with concrete materials.

13. Smith, David Eugene and Ginsburg, Jekuthial. *Numbers and Numerals,* Monograph No. 1, Contributions of Mathematics to Civilization. New York: Bureau of Publications, Teachers College, Columbia University, 1937. 52 pp. This is a most interesting account of the subject indicated by the title. It is worth the time and energy of a teacher to read the whole monograph although the first few pages will be of greatest value.

14. Stretch, Lorene B. "The Value and Limitations of Drill in Arithmetic." *Childhood Education,* XI: 413-416, June, 1935. A brief but clear-cut discussion of the function of drill.

15. Tenth Yearbook of the National Council of Teachers of Mathematics, *The Teaching of Arithmetic.* New York: Bureau of Publications, Teachers College, Columbia University, 1935. 289 pp. Chapter I, by William A. Brownell, entitled "Psychological Considerations in the Learning and Teaching of Arithmetic" is very much worth reading.

16. Thorndike, Edward L. *The Psychology of Arithmetic.* New York: The Macmillan Company, 1922. 314 pp. An interesting discussion of the meanings of numbers is found on pages 2-8.

17. Wheat, Harry Grove. *The Psychology of the Elementary School.* New York: Silver, Burdett and Company, 1931. 440 pp. Chapter IV contains an interesting and well-organized treatment of "The Psychology of Arithmetic."

18. Wheat, Harry Grove. *The Psychology and Teaching of Arithmetic.* New York: D. C. Heath & Co., 1937. 591 pp. This is a very stimulating book. Chapter I is entitled "The Beginning of Number."

CHAPTER 2

THE PLACE OF ARITHMETIC IN THE CURRICULUM OF THE PRIMARY GRADES

Of late, much has been said on both sides of the question, Shall arithmetic be taught in the primary grades? Opinions vary greatly; they range all the way from the point of view that there should be a definitely scheduled period for arithmetic with a rigidly prescribed and formally presented course for each grade, including the first, to the point of view that supports the revolutionary suggestion that there be no specific arithmetic program prior to the time when the pupil enters the seventh grade.[1]

Naturally, the primary teacher and the primary supervisor, whatever their own practices may be, are disturbed by such extreme recommendations. And the student in the teacher-training institution is filled with downright dismay when he learns of such extreme variations in practice.

Years ago in most schools (and even today in many schools) the whole program was highly formalized. The material presented was frequently above the maturity levels of the pupils and it was often extremely uninteresting to them. Drill was the prime method of instruction. The typical pupil understood but little of his lessons in arithmetic and he enjoyed none of it. He moved through the grades getting little understanding of, and hence deriving little benefit from, the study of arithmetic

---

[1] Benezet, L. P. "The Story of an Experiment." *Journal of the National Education Association,* 24: 241-244, November, 1935.

and growing to dislike it more and more. Today, as an adult, he nonchalantly dismisses the subject with a remark to the effect that he "was never good at mathematics."

It is not surprising that there was a revolt. Right-minded persons refused to tolerate a condition from which pupils obviously derived very little educational benefit and which left them with a dislike for school. The reformers cleaned house thoroughly. They swept the old drill program as rubbish out the schoolhouse door. And in its place, they offered in some cases an informal so-called "incidental" program of number instruction and in other cases, nothing at all.

Now, there are a good many teachers and far more patrons of the school who believe that the reform has gone too far. They agree that a reform was in order but they are not satisfied with a program which makes number training a mere incident, or sometimes almost an *accident*. They contend that the children who are pupils in the primary grades have so many experiences out of school as well as in school which require understanding and use of numbers that we dare not permit arithmetic to play the role of a kind of byproduct of an activity or to be just an incident in some other sort of educational program. Let us examine some of the evidence.

The Buckingham-MacLatchy study. Buckingham and MacLatchy have reported a study[2] which they made of the number abilities of children when they enter

---

[2] Buckingham, B. R. and MacLatchy, Josephine. "The Number Abilities of Children When They Enter Grade One." National Society for the Study of Education, *Twenty-Ninth Yearbook*. Bloomington, Illinois: Public School Publishing Company, 1930, pp. 472-524.

grade one. They found that 90 per cent of these children could count to 10 while the average could count as far as 25 or 30. This was rote counting, that is, merely reciting the number names. When objects were counted, again about 90 per cent could go as far as 10 while the average could count 20 objects.

More interesting and perhaps more surprising are the results obtained when these children were tested for usable number ideas. The children were required to reproduce numbers by responding to such directions as, "Give me six blocks." This was done for the numbers 5, 6, 7, 8, and 10, and, in case of failures, with smaller numbers. These children not only showed that they could reproduce these numbers in the manner indicated but also in the majority of cases they were successful on all three of the three trials given. Those who failed on all three trials for the numbers 5, 6, 7, 8, and 10, constituted on the average less than 20 per cent of the 1355 children tested.

When the same children were tested on naming numbers by being asked questions such as, "How many blocks are there here?" about 50 per cent were successful on all three trials, on the average, for the numbers 5, 6, 7, 8, and 10, while about 25 per cent failed on all three trials.

Buckingham and MacLatchy also tested the abilities of children entering grade one on some of the easier addition combinations. Ten verbal problems were constructed using the combinations below:

5	7	1	4	1	5	8	4	5	3
1	1	9	4	6	2	2	5	3	5

The per cent correct ranged from 21.8 to 71.5 and averaged 43.6.

Next, objects were used and the pupils were tested on these combinations:

2	8	6	1	3	2	2	2	3	4
2	1	1	7	1	4	8	6	7	6

This was done by an "invisible" method and, in the case of failure, by a "visible" method. By the invisible method, objects illustrating the first term of a combination were shown, identified, and then concealed. The same thing was done for the second term and the pupil was asked to state the sum. If he failed, the objects were reproduced and he was again asked to state the sum; this was the visible method. The per cent of correct responses by the invisible method ranged from 31.8 to 66.0 and averaged 47.0 When the visible method was used on those who had failed by the invisible method, the per cent of correct responses ranged from 54.1 to 68.2 and averaged 59.4. Combining the results obtained on the invisible and the visible methods we find per cents of correct responses ranging from 71.8 to 88.8 and averaging 77.7.

The Buckingham-MacLatchy investigation presents an impressive picture. It indicates clearly that entering first grade children have a readiness for number and that they have already had experiences of such an extent and variety that many of them can respond with an impressive degree of success to situations requiring an elementary understanding of number and number relationships.

The Woody investigation. Another study, somewhat similar to the Buckingham-MacLatchy study, but differing in some respects, has been made by Woody.[3] The

[3] Woody, Clifford. "The Arithmetical Backgrounds of Young Children." *Journal of Educational Research,* XXIV: 188-201, October, 1931.

Woody tests were given to children when in the grade preceding that in which formal instruction in arithmetic was to be introduced. A few of these pupils were in the kindergarten, most of them were in grades 1B and 1A, and some of them were in grades 2B and 2A. The tests required counting, telling time, fractions, and addition.

There were six of the tests in counting but the results from only two will be reported here. The per cent of children who could do rote counting to 100 was 26 in the kindergarten, 38 in grade 1B, 66 in grade 1A, 76 in grade 2B, and 94 in grade 2A. The test requiring that the children count 20 circles was passed successfully by 71 per cent of those in the kindergarten, 79 per cent of those in grade 1B, 93 per cent of those in grade 1A, 98 per cent of those in grade 2B, and 97 per cent of those in grade 2A.

We shall pass over the results of the tests having to do with telling time and consider those involving fractions. Pictures were shown of apples cut into halves, thirds, and fourths. The per cent of those who could select the picture showing halves ranged from 64 in the kindergarten to 87 in grade 2A. For fourths the corresponding per cents were 44 and 74 and for thirds they were 40 and 76. When asked whether a half or a whole apple is larger, 84 per cent in the kindergarten and 98 per cent in grade 2A responded correctly. Forty per cent of the kindergartners and 65 per cent of those in grade 2A knew that a half apple is larger than a fourth apple.

Tests in addition included not only several of the basic combinations but more elaborate addition examples as well. The easiest combination, $\begin{array}{r}2\\ 1\\ \hline\end{array}$, was answered correctly by 40 per cent of those in the kindergarten and 95 per cent of those in the 2A grade. The hardest combination, $\begin{array}{r}9\\8\\\hline\end{array}$, was answered correctly by one per cent of the kindergarten children and by 48 per cent of the children in the 2A grade. Of course, the per cents of correct responses decreased as the examples became more difficult. The most difficult example of all, one in which the addition of 987, 456, 321, and 237 was required, was done correctly by three per cent of the boys and two per cent of the girls in the 2A grade but by none in lower grades.

Woody summarizes by stating that "children possess much ability in the elementary processes of arithmetic even before the time of beginning formal instruction in the subject" and that "the knowledge possessed by children is not limited to counting and adding simple combinations, but includes elementary knowledge of fractions, United States money, units of various types of measurement, and the understanding of the processes demanded in simple verbal problems." To be sure, there was great variation among those in each of the five grade groups. Marked variation in such abilities is always found whether the subject has been systematically taught or not.

In another article,[4] the same author presents similar conclusions. He also suggests the importance of giving the children inventory tests with a view to finding out not only what they know and can do but also what methods they employ in obtaining their solutions. Chil-

---

[4] Woody, Clifford. "Achievement in Counting by Children in the Primary Grades." *Childhood Education,* VII: 339-345, March, 1931.

dren differ greatly in their attainments and, therefore, instruction must be adapted to their individual needs.

Other investigations. Many other investigations of the arithmetic abilities of children in the primary grades have been made in this and other countries. Polkinghorne[5] studied 266 children in the kindergarten, the first, the second, and the third grades of the Elementary School of the University of Chicago. These children were probably somewhat better selected than those in the average school but it was discovered that they knew a great deal more about fractions than most persons would have believed.

Beckmann[6] tested 465 German children, aged two to six years, and found decided evidence of ability to count and of some acquaintance with the elements of addition. Descoeudres[7] gave tests to some 300 Swiss children aged two and a half to six years, and found that counting and other number abilities appeared early and progressed steadily through the ages of those tested. McLaughlin[8] tested 125 children ranging in age from three to six years, and found considerable evidence of ability to do both rote and rational counting.

Those who take the trouble to observe the out-of-school activities of first grade pupils readily find many instances in their experiences in which the elements of arithmetic are conspicuous. They make their own pur-

---

[5] Polkinghorne, Ada R. "Young Children and Fractions." *Childhood Education,* XI: 354-358, May, 1935.

[6] Reported in *Zeitschrift für Angewandte Psychologie,* Vol. 22 (1923).

[7] Reported in *Le Développement de L'Enfant,* pp. 271-294.

[8] McLaughlin, Katherine. "Number Ability of Preschool Children." *Childhood Education,* XI: 348-353, May, 1935.

chases in stores; they play games involving counting; they read numerals in finding pages of books and in telling time; they sometimes read house numbers, numbers on automobile license tags, etc.; they divide candy, fruit, cookies, and other articles with brothers, sisters, and playmates; they play store; they deposit money in toy banks at home and in school banks; and they engage in many other activities in which numbers and number operations are used. Smith[9] studied the uses of arithmetic in the lives of first-grade children and found activities which we have mentioned and many others of less frequent occurrence. The chief activities which she discovered and the percentage frequency of each may be listed as follows:

Activity	Per Cent
Transactions carried on in stores	30
Games involving counting	18
Reading Roman numerals on the clock	14
Reading Arabic numerals in finding pages in books	13
Dividing food with playmates and pets (fractions)	6
Depositing money in and withdrawing money from toy banks	5
Playing store	3
Other miscellaneous activities (15 activities)	11
Total	100

When the same data were tabulated according to the kind of operation which was used, the result was as follows:

[9] Smith, Nila B. "An Investigation of the Uses of Arithmetic in the Out-of-school Life of First-Grade Children." *The Elementary School Journal,* XXIV: 621-626, April, 1924.

Process	Per Cent
Addition	35.0
Counting	23.0
Subtraction	12.0
Fractions	8.0
Reading Arabic numerals	6.0
Measuring	5.5
Comparison	4.3
Reading Roman numerals	3.1
Multiplication	2.0
Division	1.1
Total	100.0

In summarizing her study, Dr. Smith says:

This study furnishes data of considerable importance in solving several problems concerning arithmetic instruction: (1) Which arithmetical processes should receive emphasis in the first grade in order to enable the children to meet the arithmetical needs in their every day lives? (2) What types of concrete situations should be provided for the children in the first grade that they may have practice in making applications similar to those required of them outside of school? Incidentally, the study throws light on the controversy as to whether counting or spatial measurement should be the starting-point in instructing primary pupils in arithmetic. From these data it would appear that counting plays a very large part and that spatial measurement plays a very small part in the ordinary uses of number made by first grade pupils.[10]

Gunderson[11] made a study of the arithmetic found

[10] Smith, Nila B., *op. cit.,* p. 626.

[11] Gunderson, Agnes G. "Nature and Amount of Arithmetic in Readers

in first- and second-grade readers. Ten series of readers were analyzed and 22,916 items relating to arithmetic or quantitative concepts were found. The items may be classified as follows:

Item	Per Cent of Total
Terms referring to size	22.3
Terms referring to quantity	15.8
Terms referring to time	13.6
Terms referring to location	12.0
Numbers expressed in words	9.4
Arabic numerals	8.2
Terms referring to money	4.7
Other terms of lesser importance	14.0
Total	100.0

Arithmetic in the kindergarten. Many kindergartners have been disposed to recognize the fact that their charges have real and numerous out-of-school uses for number by providing number experiences for kindergarten children. In a bulletin prepared by a subcommittee of the Bureau of Education Committee of the International Kindergarten Union,[12] Miss Alice L. Harris discusses briefly the place of number in the kindergarten-first-grade curriculum and makes recommendations for a course of study.

All kindergartners seem to agree on the following quantitative experiences of kindergarten children.

---

for Grades I and II." *Elementary School Journal,* XXXVI: 527-540, March, 1936.

[12] *A Kindergarten-First-Grade Curriculum.* Washington: Department of the Interior, Bureau of Education, Bulletin No. 15, 1922.

1. *Counting:*

To find the number of children in the circle, chairs in the circle or room, blocks used, objects constructed, objects seen on walks, pennies brought in for savings stamps, squares in the 16 square fold, etc. This counting may sometimes be carried on to 100.

2. *Construction:*

Oral expression about the work in construction provides many opportunities for language training in relation to number. The activities as suggested in the Kindergarten Curriculum would afford elementary knowledge of the facts listed under the following headings:

3. *Fractions:*

Wholes, halves, and possibly quarters.

4. *Measurement:*

Length—long or short.

Width—wide or narrow, thick or thin.

Units–cubes, or bricks when used in building.

5. *Games emphasizing number:*

Muffin Man (1 and 1 more, 2 and 2 more, 4 and 4 more, so 8 of us know the Muffin Man).

Chickadees (5—"1 flew away and then there were 4," etc.).

Family, members—parents, children, brothers, and sisters.

Sense games—feeling the number of objects.

6. *Time:*

From clock—short time, long time; how clock looks at 9 o'clock.

From calendar—days of week.

7. *Proportion—in industrial arts:*

Chimney too large for house.

Furniture too small for room, etc.

8. *Recognition of number:*

Groups—4 children here, etc.[13]

---

[13] *A Kindergarten-First-Grade Curriculum,* op. cit., pp. 52-53.

In commenting upon this program, Miss Harris states that the basis for such arithmetic instruction as is given "should be the child's experiences and the knowledge of number obtained through the activities of home, school, neighborhood, and situations arising through these. While for the child it should appear incidental to these situations, *it should be definite in the mind of the teacher.*"[14]

It would be easy to present additional evidence in support of the point of view that children in the primary grades have need for number in their out-of-school experiences; that they have, quite independent of any program of instruction provided by the school, acquired a considerable understanding of number and considerable ability in dealing with number situations; and that these number experiences are neither difficult for the children nor distasteful to them. Successful teachers have discovered again and again that a correctly selected and properly presented arithmetic program can be taught in the primary grades so that the pupils acquire desirable and worth-while number habits and skills and enjoy the experience.

Why not ignore arithmetic in the primary grades? Since children seem to learn so much about number before they enter the first grade or before the school begins to make provision for instructing them in this subject, some students of primary education ask why teachers in these grades should be bothered about number training. They suggest that the pupils are making excellent progress without instruction, as shown by the

---

[14] *Ibid.*, p. 53 (Italics supplied).

tests, and that the teacher's efforts may well do more harm than good.

It is true that arithmetic differs from reading and spelling and handwriting in that much of the former is learned without the teacher's help. But there are reasons why pupils need the assistance which good teachers can give.

In the first place, the teacher soon finds that the progress which the pupils have made is very unequal. Some have progressed much farther than have others because of differences in native intelligence, differences in home instruction, and differences in their environment. There is little that the teacher can do about the differences in native intelligence but she can equalize the amount of instruction and even up the environmental opportunities. To neglect the subject is to increase these differences and to encourage definite retardation in some of the pupils.

Secondly, pupils sometimes gain wrong impressions and begin to acquire habits which are objectionable. For example, pupils sometimes believe that one-half of an object is simply a *part* of the object. They do not understand that to get halves, the apple must be cut into just *two* pieces and that these two pieces must be the same size. They talk about the "littlest" half and the "biggest" half. Bad habits are often begun by parents and others at home whose intentions are good but whose teaching skill is not on a high plane.

In the third place, the pupils will make greater progress with good teaching than without it, even though they may acquire considerable information and skill if left to their own devices. In this respect, the situation is somewhat like that in English. Pupils make truly remarkable progress in learning English before they enter the first grade (What would the teacher's task be if they did not!) but efforts to facilitate the acquisition of desirable speech forms and to correct a few of the most grievous errors are made early in the school program.

To the writer there is no question but that the primary teacher should provide very definitely for a program of number instruction. The difficulty and the basic cause of the current dispute lies in the kind of material included in the program and in the instructional method employed. Certainly, we should not have a highly formalized program made up of abstract materials and presented by a method consisting largely of routine and monotonous drill.

When shall we begin teaching arithmetic? We should begin to teach arithmetic as soon as the child is ready for it. We have seen that there is abundant evidence that he is ready when he enters the first grade. And when we say that the child is ready for arithmetic, we mean that he is well able to learn it, that he is interested in situations in which it is found, and that he has need for it in his out-of-school experiences.

Indeed, the kindergarten child is ready for several kinds of number experience. Kindergartners know this and act accordingly. Buckingham and MacLatchy found that children who had had kindergarten training made higher scores on the arithmetic tests which they gave in the first grade than did those who had not had kindergarten experience. This meant, apparently, that the kindergarten experience had required the use of number and that the pupils had benefited thereby.

Yes, we should begin to teach arithmetic as soon as the child comes to school whether he makes his first appearance in the kindergarten or in grade one. And we should continue to teach arithmetic in all the grades of the elementary school.

Should arithmetic teaching in the primary grades be formal? It certainly should not. Indeed, formalism in arithmetic teaching has no place in any grade. But, in the words of Buckingham,[15] "if by formal we mean systematic, regular, provided for in the schedule, then the answer still remains the same. Teach arithmetic from the time the child enters school. Incidental teaching has its advocates. Few of them, however, apply it to arithmetic. Here is a subject which more than any other in the elementary school is organized and sequential. Let the teacher accomplish all she can through incidental teaching. But let it never be supposed that either in the first grade or elsewhere a satisfactory course in arithmetic can be provided without being planned and systematically pursued."

Now and then, an article appears reporting the results of an experiment in omitting arithmetic from the program of grades one and two. Two groups of entering first-grade children are formed. They are equal in ability. One group is taught arithmetic throughout the first and second grades but the other group receives no arithmetic instruction in either of these grades. In the third grade, both groups are taught arithmetic and at the end of this grade, tests are given to both groups. The two groups do equally well on the tests. Therefore, teaching

[15] Buckingham, B. R. "When to Begin the Teaching of Arithmetic." *Childhood Education,* XI: 339-343, May, 1935.

arithmetic in grades one and two is a waste of time!

If this conclusion is true, it is startling indeed. We know that young children learn about number irrespective of a school program, that they have needs for number, and that they have an interest in it. Yet, when they are helped by a teacher to understand number and to gain number skills, the result is the same as if the teacher remained completely out of the picture! This does not seem to be possible. In discussing this subject Buckingham points out that what has happened is that without intention the dice have been loaded in favor of the untaught group.

When the two groups, the taught and the untaught, entered the third grade the taught group was unquestionably superior to the untaught group in arithmetic. Why did it not remain so? Possibly the kind of arithmetic offered to these children was inappropriate—such, for example, as could not be expected to remain with them as a permanent possession. Unduly abstract material would be likely to be ineffective in precisely this way. But even this merely means that a more appropriate type of arithmetic should have been offered—a type in other words which would have been retained. Waiving, however, the question of the appropriateness of the particular kind of arithmetic which the taught group had received, it is still clear that for whatever work either group would be likely to do in grade three the taught group was superior. Here was something to build upon. And if it were built upon, it is clear that the taught group at the end of grade three would remain superior to the untaught group. In fact, if the same energy and resourcefulness were devoted to the taught group during the third grade it is probable that the two groups would be wider apart at the end of the year than they were at the beginning of it.

No, the experimental evidence does not mean what it has been held to mean. It does not mean that instruction in arithmetic may be neglected for two years. It means nothing so clearly as that the children who were taught arithmetic in grades one and two and who were allowed to fall back to the level of those who began arithmetic in grade three have been defrauded.[16]

Washburne[17] gave tests to 2469 sixth grade pupils located in 15 cities and in four states. Approximately a third of these pupils had begun their arithmetic in the first grade, a third in the second grade, and a third in the third grade. He found that those who began in the first grade had an unmistakable advantage over those who began in the second grade and that those who began in the second grade had the same advantage over those who first studied arithmetic in grade three.

Arithmetic in an activity program. There are those who believe that if the pupils engage in a series of interesting and life-like activities, there will be no need for the teacher to be concerned about arithmetic. Arithmetic, through activities, will take care of itself, as it were.

It is not the function of this book to undertake a thorough-going evaluation of the activity movement in elementary education. It may be said in brief that tremendous good has been accomplished by the activists in breaking down the old lock-step system of formalized drill and in focusing attention on the young learner, his interests, and his capacities. Unfortunately, however,

---

[16] Buckingham, B. R. *op. cit.*, p. 343.

[17] Washburne, Carleton. "When Should We Teach Arithmetic?" *Elementary School Journal*, XXVIII: 659-665, May, 1928.

there are many brands or forms of the activity movement. As a consequence, some of the leading proponents of the activity movement have been making vigorous efforts to secure agreement among the activists on the cardinal principles and elements of procedure in the movement and to salvage from the discarded formalized program a few elements which will provide some system and some definiteness for the program which the teacher is to follow. It has been suggested that teaching is again to be one of the duties of the teacher.

One of the sanest and soundest of the critical appraisals which have been made of the activity program in elementary education is that offered by one of its best friends, Mr. Stanwood Cobb.[18] He devotes a chapter to "The Limitations of Activity Education." A few quotations from this chapter will indicate Mr. Cobb's position.

> The project should convey at least a certain minimum of definite knowledge; the activity project should be a means toward definite educational goals and not an end in itself. (p. 115)
>
> The tools and techniques of learning—such as reading, writing, and arithmetic—cannot be *learned* by the project method but only *motivated* by it. These skills must be made automatic by means of much drill and practice. It is the same situation in learning the three R's as in learning to play the piano. The beginning of piano can be made interesting and attractive to the child by means of a game, a project, an activity; but not until the scales, the fingering, the chords, and the reading of music are mastered by much practice, can anyone perform efficiently upon the piano. And so it is with

---

[18] Cobb, Stanwood, *New Horizons for the Child.* Washington: The Avalon Press, 1934. 212 pp.

the techniques of the three R's; they can be mastered only by repeated drills. (p. 116)

Retarded children definitely above the border line of intelligence need thorough drilling in the techniques of reading and arithmetic more than they need activities. *Right here lies one of the most dangerous temptations of the activity method.* Mental work leading to mastery of the techniques is what such children most need. (p. 116)

The world had had "activity education" for six thousand historical years and knew very little at the end of that period. But during the relatively brief period when the world has been practising education by means of book-learning, its knowledge has grown apace. Humanity has learned a hundred fold more in the last three centuries than it had learned during the previous six thousand years. (p. 118)

Activities and experience, it is true, bear a close practical relation to the gleaning of knowledge from books. They point the way to truth from the firm basis of actuality; they stimulate interest, effort, analysis, discovery, and assimilation; they assure a constant correlation between the world of the ideal and the world of the real. Activity correlated with abstract thinking is the method par excellence of scientific discovery in which observation and experimentation both inspire and verify ideas. We must grant that the educational functions of activity are valuable and indispensable. But we cannot afford to let activity crowd out the functions of abstract education. Certain things can be learned much better through doing than thinking, but other things can be learned only through thinking. (p. 120)

A committee[19] composed of teachers in the Lincoln

[19] Hanna, Paul R. *et al.* "Opportunities for the Use of Arithmetic in an Activity Program." National Council of Teachers of Mathematics, Tenth Yearbook, *The Teaching of Arithmetic.* New York: Bureau of Publications, Teachers College, Columbia University, 1935, pp. 85-120.

School of Teachers College, Columbia University, and other schools in and near New York City has prepared a report on arithmetic in an activity program. The Committee states three viewpoints held by teachers concerning the learning of arithmetic.

According to the first viewpoint, functional experiences are adequate for the teaching of arithmetic. Those who hold this viewpoint would teach arithmetic only as it is needed to accomplish the children's purposes at the time, they would not use textbooks, and they would not have regular periods for drill.

Those who hold to the second viewpoint have systematic arithmetic mastery as their goal. They use textbooks and drill periods and follow a definite schedule laid down long in advance. Activities are used but only as a means of stimulating interest in a formal systematic arithmetic program.

The third viewpoint recognizes two goals. It, in a way, is a combination of the two viewpoints already mentioned. Activities are selected because of their general value to the pupils, not solely because of the opportunities they offer for arithmetic. But the use of arithmetic in solving the problems which arise soon demonstrates the need for systematic practice and indicates that many processes in arithmetic depend upon a mastery of more elementary processes. Those who hold this viewpoint deny that functional experiences alone are adequate, but, on the other hand, refuse to adopt entirely the older program of systematic mastery. This third viewpoint represents the position of the majority of the members of the Committee.

The Committee then proceeded to make a survey in

grades 3 and 6 to determine whether the activity program alone is sufficient as a means of teaching arithmetic. They found that it was not. They found that activities give arithmetic vitality and make it meaningful but that children's functional experiences alone are not sufficient.[20]

Further, the authors recognize that the present activity program does not assure a comprehensive orientation in arithmetic. It is evident from this survey that each classroom found a very small number of experiences per week. In addition, there is a large element of chance operating in the selection of units of work in the present activity school. In the typical activity program, there is no check to assure that the total experiences of the six years of elementary school will introduce a child to most of the significant phases of comprehensive living in our contemporary world. If the activity program had in it some principle guaranteeing the development of a comprehensive understanding of most of the important social areas, then this committee would be willing to leave to the demands of such activities, the development of the necessary arithmetic fact and process, utilizing, of course, those meaningful situations as the occasions for drill sufficient to give the required degree of facility. They do not feel, however, that a survey of the opportunities found in the *present* activities program is a sufficient guide to the selection of arithmetic materials.[21]

Until such time as the activities program is fundamentally reconstructed and a survey of these arithmetic opportunities

---

[20] Results more favorable to the activity program were secured by Harap and Mapes. However, their experiment was limited to multiplication and division of fractions in Grade V. *Cf. Elementary School Journal,* XXXIV: 515-525, March, 1934.

[21] Hanna, Paul R. *et. al., op. cit.,* p. 119.

made, a teacher will find it advantageous to approach the teaching of arithmetic through her own survey of the needs of her own pupils. If no opportunities are found for certain of the present courses-of-study requirements, she will probably do the best she can to build meaning before drill. But constantly, she will urge a revision of the curriculum in terms of a more socially comprehensive experience which will surely present the necessity to gain control over important arithmetic skills and processes.[22]

Arithmetic should find its place in each of the primary grades, including the first. The program of number instruction should keep pace with the developing needs of the pupils. To permit the school program to get ahead of out-of-school needs, or to violate another phase of the Law of Readiness by permitting drill on processes to come before there is an understanding of the processes, is to make the program abstract and difficult because it is not understood; interest lags and an actual dislike for the subject develops. On the other hand, if the school program lags behind the pupil's developing out-of-school needs, the pupil is likely to be instructed by persons, at home or elsewhere, who are not competent to instruct, or he will acquire erroneous ideas and invent ways for handling number situations himself, which are conducive to the formation of undesirable habits.

At every stage of his progress, from the primary grades to the university, the pupil should learn his mathematics as a series of related meaningful experiences. It has already been indicated that there will be a place for drill; however, the drill will not come at the beginning

---

[22] *Ibid.*, p. 120.

of the pupil's study of a topic but after the initial elements have been meaningfully presented. In the words of Betz:[23]

It can no longer be doubted that when primary number work for young children is carried on with a scrupulous regard for their maturity, and when the teaching process stresses understanding and genuine application rather than mechanical drill, there is gratifying retention, and continuous progress becomes a certainty instead of a dubious possibility.

Betz quotes from the account of an expert remedial teacher as follows:

The case of one class was particularly illuminating. We followed and recorded the work of this group from the fourth grade through the ninth year of the high school. The original analysis showed technical rote memory training. The number *facts* in addition, subtraction, and multiplication seemed to have been assimilated. But the *processes* of subtraction, multiplication, and division were *not understood. There was no evidence of conceptual mastery.* The children admitted that they were "very poor in arithmetic" and had a great dislike for it. Problem solving turned out to be an almost impossible hurdle.

It became necessary to rebuild the entire structure of primary arithmetic for these pupils and to give them the thought training which they lacked. For many months, progress was very slow, necessarily so. No child was any longer permitted to go beyond his depth or to proceed without a conscious feeling of mastery. At last, the class began to move forward

---

[23] Betz, William. "The Reorganization of Secondary Education." National Council of Teachers of Mathematics, Eleventh Yearbook, *Mathematics in Modern Education.* New York: Bureau of Publications, Teachers College, Columbia University, 1936, p. 113.

at a more rapid rate. *This was not a spontaneous maturation effect, but was due primarily to painstaking daily instruction.* In the sixth grade, these children forged ahead so rapidly that they went beyond the usual prescribed program of work.[24]

Pupils who follow a carefully formulated and skillfully directed program in arithmetic in the primary grades do not get into such a condition as was this fourth-grade class. Let us plan an arithmetic program which will keep pace with the child's developing needs for number out of school and let us arrange that the elements of this program become meaningful experiences to the child. Doubts as to the place of arithmetic in the curriculum of the primary grades will then disappear.

The elimination of arithmetic from the curriculum of the primary grades may leave the pupil no worse off than he would have been had he gone through such a course as was prescribed in the old-fashioned school with its formally organized program but it will, quite probably, leave him considerably short of a satisfactory grasp of the subject.

---

[24] Betz, William, *op. cit.*, p. 114.

QUESTIONS AND REVIEW EXERCISES

1. What conditions have been responsible for the recent tendency to eliminate from the curriculum of the primary grades all arithmetic except that which is taught incidentally?

2. What are the advantages of incidental number instruction? The disadvantages?

3. Does the fact that a program of number instruction may appear to the pupil to be incidental mean that it must also be incidental to the teacher? Discuss.

4. Why should premature drill cause a pupil to dislike arithmetic?

5. Did Buckingham and MacLatchy find that entering first grade pupils could count about equally far when they did rote and rational counting?

6. The Buckingham-MacLatchy study showed that children vary greatly in their number abilities. What significance does this fact have for the first-grade teacher?

7. What is the difference between the "invisible" and the "visible" method as these methods were used by Buckingham and MacLatchy? By which method were the children more successful?

8. What difference is there between the Buckingham-MacLatchy study and the Woody investigation as to the grade position of the pupils who were tested?

9. Summarize what Woody discovered about children's understanding of fractions. Does this indicate that first- and second-grade teachers should give attention to fractions?

10. What other investigator, referred to in this chapter, tested children on their knowledge of fractions?

11. Do you think that there have been any significant changes in the extent to which first-grade children use number in their out-of-school lives since the time of the Smith study? Are clock faces with Roman numerals becoming less or more frequent?

12. Would you teach multiplication and division in the first grade because Smith found these operations among first-grade pupils?

13. Which is more important in the first-grade pupil's uses of number, counting or spatial measurement?

14. Does the kindergarten outline given by Harris provide that these children shall learn to tell time?

15. What are the chief disadvantages in having the primary teacher neglect arithmetic?

16. When should the teaching of arithmetic begin?

17. How early should arithmetic teaching become formal?

18. What is the apparent fault in the conclusion arrived at experimentally that children who have been taught arithmetic in grades one and two and those who have not get along equally well in grade three?

19. Summarize the advantages afforded to arithmetic by an activity program.

20. What are the probable deficiencies if an activity program is relied upon as the sole means of teaching arithmetic in the primary grades?

21. Suggest other skills which people develop, besides those in school subjects and in music, which require drill.

22. Name some things that can be learned better through doing than through thinking; some that can be learned better through thinking than through doing.

23. State the three viewpoints given by Hanna's committee. Which of the three do you think is the soundest?

24. Think back over your own experiences with arithmetic when a pupil in the elementary school. Were all of these experiences meaningful experiences?

25. Why should the school program in arithmetic not get ahead of the child's out-of-school needs? Why should it not lag behind these needs?

CHAPTER TEST

For each of these statements, select the best answer. A key will be found on page 405.

1. Drill on a new process should come (1) before the elements of it are taught, (2) while the elements of it are being taught, (3) after the elements of it have been taught.

2. Professional opinion as to the place of arithmetic in the primary grades (1) agrees that there should be a definitely organized program, (2) agrees that it should be incidental, (3) disagrees.

3. Benezet suggested that the first specific arithmetic be provided for (1) the first grade, (2) the third grade, (3) the seventh grade.

4. The Buckingham-MacLatchy study showed that 90 per cent of entering first-grade pupils could count to (1) 10, (2) 20, (3) 30.

5. When rote counting was compared with rational counting the same study showed that the average pupil could go (1) farther, (2) just as far, (3) not so far.

6. In the same study, the results of the "visible" method in addition compared with the "invisible" method were (1) equal, (2) better, (3) worse.

7. The first-grade pupils who took the Woody tests constituted (1) all of his subjects, (2) the majority of his subjects, (3) the minority of his subjects.

8. The per cent of Woody's kindergarten children who were able to recognize halves was about (1) one-third, (2) two-thirds, (3) three-fourths of the total.

9. Tests show that children vary in number knowledge (1) slightly, (2) moderately, (3) greatly.

10. The leading number activity discovered by Smith was (1) transactions carried on in stores, (2) games involving counting, (3) reading numerals.

11. The leading process found by Smith was (1) counting, (2) addition, (3) subtraction.

12. The kindergarten outline included (1) counting, (2) addition, (3) subtraction.

13. The number program followed should be (1) definite in the mind of the pupil, (2) definite in the mind of the teacher, (3) definite in the mind of neither.

14. As to the need for teaching in the primary grades, arithmetic was found to be like (1) handwriting, (2) reading, (3) English.

15. First-grade pupils who have had kindergarten experience make (1) lower scores, (2) equal scores, (3) higher scores on arithmetic tests than do those who have not had kindergarten experience.

16. Arithmetic teaching should be characterized by formalism in (1) the lower grades, (2) the upper grades, (3) no grades.

17. Arithmetic is (1) learned by the project method, (2) motivated by the project method, (3) ignored by the project method.

18. The method of scientific discovery consists of (1) activity correlated with abstract thinking, (2) activity alone, (3) abstract thinking alone.

19. Hanna's committee concluded (1) that activities are insufficient as a means of teaching arithmetic, (2) that activities are sufficient, (3) that they could offer no recommendation.

20. The school program in arithmetic should (1) anticipate the pupil's needs, (2) keep pace with his needs, (3) come after the needs have been shown.

SELECTED REFERENCES

1. *A Kindergarten-First-Grade Curriculum.* Washington: Department of the Interior, Bureau of Education, Bulletin No. 15, 1922. A portion of this bulletin, the report of a committee of the International Kindergarten Union, is devoted to Number. The report contains the recommendations of experts in kindergarten-primary education at that time and a bibliography.

2. Betz, William. "The Reorganization of Secondary Education. A Study of Present Problems and Trends, with Particular Reference to Mathematics." National Council of Teachers of Mathematics, Eleventh Yearbook, *Mathematics in Modern Education.* New York: Bureau of Publications, Teachers College, Columbia University, 1936, pp. 22-135. Portions of this chapter make excellent reading for the primary teacher. Part Three discusses "The Present Status of Progressive Education" (pp. 47-58). Some educational psychology and a few suggestions to teachers are given in Part Six (pp. 118-132).

3. Buckingham, B. R. "How Much Number Do Children Know?" *Educational Research Bulletin,* VIII: 279-284, September 11, 1929. An address which reports a portion of the findings of the Buckingham-MacLatchy study.

4. Buckingham, B. R. "When to Begin the Teaching of Arithmetic." *Childhood Education,* XI: 339-343, May, 1935. This article reviews the kinds of arithmetic which may be taught to young children and recommends that we begin teaching arithmetic when the child enters school for he is then ready.

5. Buckingham, B. R., and MacLatchy, Josephine. "The Number Abilities of Children When They Enter Grade One." National Society for the Study of Education, *Twenty-Ninth Yearbook.* Bloomington, Illinois: Public School Publishing Company, 1930, pp. 472-524. A thorough and well-

written report of an extensive study of the number abilities of entering first-grade children. A good review of preceding research is included.

6. Cobb, Stanwood. *New Horizons for the Child.* Washington: The Avalon Press, 1934. 212 pp. A well-written book dealing with the progressive education movement. Chapter VIII is entitled "The Limitations of Activity Education."

7. Gunderson, Agnes G. "Nature and Amount of Arithmetic in Readers for Grades I and II." *Elementary School Journal,* XXXVI: 527-540, March, 1936. Reports an analysis of 10 series of readers (primers, first readers, and second readers) for items relating to arithmetic and quantitative concepts.

8. Hanna, Paul R. *et al.* "Opportunities for the Use of Arithmetic in an Activity Program." National Council of Teachers of Mathematics, Tenth Yearbook, *The Teaching of Arithmetic.* New York: Bureau of Publications, Teachers College, Columbia University, 1935, pp. 85-120. This chapter presents a very sane point of view regarding the use of activities in teaching arithmetic. The entire yearbook is devoted to various phases of arithmetic teaching in the elementary school.

9. MacLatchy, Josephine. "A Phase of First-Grade Readiness." *Educational Research Bulletin,* X: 377-380, October 14, 1931. Presents data resulting from the use of tests which were given to 1242 six-year-olds who were entering Grade I at Cincinnati.

10. MacLatchy, Josephine. "Number Abilities of First-Grade Children." *Childhood Education,* XI: 344-347, May, 1935. Sets up a hypothetical first-grade group of 35 pupils and shows how many will be able to count to 10, 15, 20, etc., and how many will know various numbers of combinations.

11. McLaughlin, Katherine. "Number Ability of Preschool Children." *Childhood Education,* XI: 348-353, May, 1935. Reports the results of administering three series of tests

to children ranging in age from 36 months to 72 months.

12. Polkinghorne, Ada R. "Young Children and Fractions." *Childhood Education,* XI: 354-358, May, 1935. Tests having to do with fraction concepts were given to 266 pupils in the kindergarten and the first three grades of the Elementary School of the University of Chicago. These children had already obtained considerable information about fractions.

13. Reid, Florence E. "Incidental Number Situations in First Grade." *Journal of Educational Research,* XXX: 36-43, September, 1936. Indicates the kind of incidental number situations which may be utilized in the first grade even though there be no formal arithmetic program.

14. Smith, Nila B. "An Investigation of the Uses of Arithmetic in the Out-of-School Life of First-Grade Children." *The Elementary School Journal,* XXIV: 621-626, April, 1924. Using the interview technique, data were collected on out-of-school uses of arithmetic by 500 first grade (1A) children in Detroit. Facts given in this chapter with considerable additional detail are reported.

15. Washburne, Carleton. "When Shall We Teach Arithmetic?" *Elementary School Journal,* XXVIII: 659-665, May, 1928. This is one of the earlier reports of the Committee of Seven on the grade placement of arithmetic topics.

16. Woody, Clifford. "The Arithmetical Backgrounds of Young Children." *Journal of Educational Research,* XXIV: 188-201, October, 1931. Reports the results of tests given in 39 school systems widely scattered over the country. The tests had to do with counting, telling time, fractions, and addition.

17. Woody, Clifford. "Achievement in Counting by Children in the Primary Grades." *Childhood Education,* VII: 339-345, March, 1931. Presents conclusions similar to those arrived at in the preceding reference.

CHAPTER 3

INCREASING THE CHILD'S UNDERSTANDING OF NUMBERS

Counting is the fundamental number experience. Children gain an elementary understanding of number through various experiences which involve the use of number. At first, this experience is confined to objects with which they play; at first, the experience is entirely concrete experience. They count these objects as they look at them and handle them and thus come slowly to know the meaning of two, three, four, and larger numbers.

Rote and rational counting. The child who counts blocks, books, marbles, dolls, pennies, and the like is learning to count in a meaningful way. This is *rational* counting. In rational counting, when the child counts he counts something. It is still rational counting when he counts the steps he takes, the strokes as the clock strikes, or other phenomena which he sees, or hears, or feels, although such counting is a little less concrete and hence a little more difficult than the counting of objects which he manipulates.

Rote counting, on the other hand, consists of the mere recital of the number words without reference to objective experience. In rote counting, the child repeats from memory a series of words which he has learned. The words may be meaningful to him but, on the other hand, they may be meaningless.

The writer, in his capacity as superintendent of schools, happened to be in a first-grade room on a Monday morning in September as the children gathered for their first school experience. Miss Graham, the teacher, stood at the front of the room and the children found seats. She began to speak when Tommy, his face aglow with repressed excitement, waved his hand above his head.

"What is it, Tommy?," asked Miss Graham.

"I can count to a hunderd," Tommy announced proudly.

"Very well, Tommy," Miss Graham replied with a smile, "let's hear you count to a hundred."

Tommy stood and began as fast as he could go, "One, two, three, four, five," and so on. He paused occasionally as he gasped for breath and his face became flushed as he rushed along. At last, he pronounced "hunderd" and dropped into his seat with an obvious air of triumph. Miss Graham smiled again, said "That's fine, Tommy," and went ahead with her plans.

Now, what was back of this performance? Obviously, Tommy's mother, or his father, or possibly older brothers and sisters at home, had spent hours coaching him. And, sure that he was ready on the opening day of school, they also instructed him to show "the teacher" what he could do. They even coached him in the proper method for gaining her attention. Tommy had his day and the family thought that he was making a remarkably fine start at school. Miss Graham, wisely, did not disappoint Tommy or his family but when she got around to some fundamental matters in number, it was not rote counting with which she was concerned.

Teachers are sometimes deceived by facility in rote counting. But what appears to be understanding and appreciation of number may be only appearance. Just as rote learning in general is a poor and an empty substitute for rational learning, rote counting, if permitted to run ahead of number understanding, becomes an empty shell, a meaningless mouthing of words. Early teaching of rote counting usually does more harm than good. Fond and doting parents, ambitious for the welfare of their children, sometimes thwart their progress by stimulating early rote counting.

Individual differences among young children. As we discovered in the last chapter, there is abundant evidence that many children can do both rote and rational counting when they enter the first grade. The average can count to about 25 or 30 by rote and to 20 when objects are counted. But to say that the average can count to 20 means that half of these children can not do this well while half can do better. Some can do *much* better while a few may not be able to count at all. Herein lies the primary teacher's first concern as she plans her program of number instruction. She finds herself confronted with an acute problem of individual differences.

Few teachers seem to appreciate the extent to which children differ in native intelligence, in the richness of their out-of-school experiences, and, hence, in their readiness for number experiences in school. It is the teacher's first responsibility to get well acquainted with each of her pupils so that she may have accurate, first-hand information as to what each pupil knows and does not know and as to what he can do and can not do. Instruction in number can not proceed satisfactorily until the teacher has come to know each pupil well.

When she discovers the appalling degree of individual

differences among her pupils, the teacher soon realizes that instruction must be individual. There are times and places where class teaching is in order, although they are probably not so numerous as many teachers seem to believe, but the time when attention is first given to the development of number concepts is not one of them.

Miss Drummond[1] describes six stages in early counting. These stages are not entirely distinct but mention of them will help one to realize how children may differ in their attainments when they enter school. In the first stage, a pre-number stage, the child does not know number or counting at all. In the second stage, he has begun to understand *one* and sometimes other number terms, such as *two,* to indicate more than one. In the third stage, he knows the order of the first few number names and recognizes small groups. When he reaches the fourth stage, he has considerable knowledge of the number series as far as ten or twenty and can count small groups of objects although not always accurately. The fifth stage shows increasing familiarity with the number series and greater facility in counting although there may be some hesitation or stumbling as he passes from one decade to another. The sixth stage, of course, finds the pupil familiar with numbers and able to count any number of things; errors made are due to inattention.

First-grade teachers may expect to find their pupils in all six of these stages. Obviously, the treatment which they receive must depend upon the stages which they occupy.

A first grade class whose teacher begins with the ap-

[1] Drummond, Margaret. *Psychology and Teaching of Number.* Yonkers-on-Hudson, New York: World Book Company, 1922, p. 35.

parent assumption that all are at the fourth or the fifth stage is headed for catastrophe. Many pupils will come to look upon number as a hard subject and begin to build up a resistance toward it. Gradually, they become convinced that arithmetic and later mathematics is something which they can not learn. And if convinced that they can not learn it, they will not learn it.

The teaching should be individual and, in each case, must be suited to the pupil's stage of advancement.

Counting by multiples. When the pupil has become proficient in counting by 1's, he should be introduced to counting by multiples as a means of increasing his understanding of number. It is a common practice to have him count by 2's, 5's, and 10's.

Counting by 2's, like counting by 1's, at first should be restricted to concrete objects. Handling the blocks, coins, etc., the pupil picks them up or pushes them aside two at a time and learns to count *two, four, six, eight,* etc. He counts books on a shelf or children in a row by pointing at or touching every other one. If suitable pictures are available, as of children marching by twos, he can carry his counting by twos to the picture stage indicated in Chapter I. (See page 14.) Then he goes on to the semi-concrete stage and counts circles, dots, etc. which are printed in such a manner as to facilitate counting by twos. Finally, as he arrives at the abstract stage, he does a limited amount of rote counting by twos. How far the pupil goes will depend upon the materials used but ordinarily, it is sufficient to carry counting by twos to 20 or 30.

It is considerably more difficult to carry out counting by 5's and 10's with concrete objects, especially counting by 10's. Blocks and other small objects can be placed in groups of five each and then counted, five, ten, fifteen, twenty, etc. The number of cents in a group of nickels can be determined in the same way, but this is somewhat more abstract since the cents are not actually present. Likewise, some concrete counting by 10's may be done. If there are ten children at a table and four tables, they may be counted, *ten, twenty, thirty, forty,* but this is a rather long jump from counting blocks by twos and, hence, should come considerably later. Also, money in the form of dimes may be counted, *ten cents, twenty cents, thirty cents, forty cents, fifty cents.* etc.

Abstract counting by 5's and 10's, particularly 10's, to 100 helps the pupil to get in mind the number system. Pupils who hesitate in passing from one decade to another when counting by ones are helped by abstract or rote counting by 10's. The pupil must see the relationship of *thirty* to *three,* of *sixty* to *six,* of *eighty* to *eight,* etc.; rote counting by 10's seems to help with this.

Later, the pupil will learn to count by 3's, 4's, 6's, 7's, 8's, and 9's as he approaches the study of the multiplication combinations. This will be largely abstract, although objects are sometimes conveniently counted by 3's and 4's.

Recognizing the size of small groups without counting. Most persons come gradually to the point where they can recognize the number of objects in a small group without counting. This is easier if the objects are arranged in some definite and familiar pattern, such as ∴ or ∷ or ⁙ than if the arrangement is a chance one; but, regardless of the arrangement, a fair degree of facility in recognizing two, three, four, and sometimes five objects without counting can be developed in primary pupils.

The proper development of number concept in the primary grades will include provision for training in the recognition of the size of small groups without counting. Flashing pictures of two, three, four, or five objects and calling for immediate responses as to the number will reveal the differences among pupils as to the extent to which they have developed this aspect of number concept and will be excellent practice. Doubtless some will always show marked deficiencies in this respect but it is important for the teacher to provide pupils with opportunities for practice in the ready recognition of the number in a small group.

The author is acquainted with well-educated highly intelligent adults who are quite unable to identify a group of four as *four* without counting. One, in particular, a university professor, must not only count the objects in such small groups but also touches them or points at them as he counts. It is an open question, to be sure, whether this condition is due to an innate deficiency or to inadequate training or to both, but pending an experimental study of the question, teachers should give pupils the kind of practice suggested.

Cardinal and ordinal numbers. The distinction between cardinal and ordinal numbers is not one to be taught to children in the primary grades but it is one which the teachers of those children should know and keep in mind in planning exercises to acquaint children with the meaning of number.

Cardinal numbers tell *how many* are being considered.

as *five* boys, *seven* days, *three* dollars. Ordinal numbers indicate position, as *second, third, eighth.* Both of these number ideas are useful and should be taught, but the primary number meaning is the cardinal meaning; it should be emphasized first.

If the teacher is not careful, she may inadvertently represent the ordinal idea of number when attempting to teach numbers in the cardinal sense. Thus, if the first five numbers, beginning with one, are written as symbols and illustrated with such semi-concrete material as circles, the teacher may discover that she is about to represent them as follows:

But this leads, almost certainly, to the ordinal idea of number. It is much better to represent these five numbers as follows:

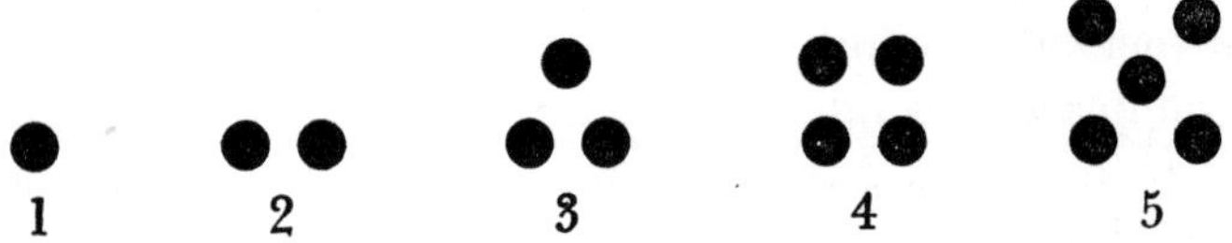

Thus, 3 is learned as the symbol which represents three circles, not the third circle in a row of circles.

Ordinarily, we think of the words *first, second, third, fourth,* as representing ordinal numbers. We also know that they can be represented as 1st, 2nd, 3rd, 4th, etc. But numbers may be ordinal numbers without appearing in either of these forms. Thus, when we write a date as April 6, 1938, we are using ordinal numbers. The number 6 in this case does not refer specifically to six days but to the sixth in a series of 30 days comprising the month of April. Likewise, 1938 refers to a particular year in a numbered series of years. Teachers need to exercise care in planning what they will do and say lest pupils become confused in their early efforts to gain an understanding of number.

Reading and writing numbers. After children have had a rich and extensive experience with numbers and have developed a considerable understanding of numbers, they learn to read the number symbols which represent in an abstract way the numbers which they have come to know in concrete and semi-concrete situations. As was emphasized in Chapter I, the pupils arrive at the stage where they can read and interpret these symbols after passing through other preliminary stages.

The first responsibility of the teacher at this stage is to develop acquaintance with symbols 1 to 9, inclusive. This is difficult and requires time, more time than is sometimes devoted to it. It is difficult because these symbols are all new to the pupils. There is no logical or rational reason apparent to the child why 4 should represent *four,* why 7 should represent *seven,* etc. Hence, the number symbols must be taken up slowly, one at a time, and sufficient practice on each provided to enable the children to remember it. It will help the teacher to appreciate how difficult these symbols are for children if she will represent each of them by a different letter, as *g* for 1, *n* for 2, *r* for 3, *a* for 4, etc., and then try to write two- and three-digit numbers, using these letters. And the teacher will appreciate the children's difficulty still better if she will invent new and strange symbols for these numerals, for to the children at this stage in their progress our numerals 1 to 9 are new and strange symbols.

It is not advisable to begin with 0. Nor is it desirable to introduce 0 until real and meaningful situations requiring the use of this symbol arise. Eventually, 0 may be used in keeping score in games when a child makes no points at a trial but ordinarily it is quite satisfactory to the child, and to the adult too for that matter, simply to refrain from making a record at all when no points are scored. If and when the children normally experience this kind of scoring, as at a baseball game or a football game, the symbol 0 may be taught.

Of course, the child sees 0 in the numbers 10, 20, etc., when these are encountered but here the 0 does not mean *zero* to the child. When 10 is first encountered, it is too early to talk about a ten and no ones or units. This, again, will come later.

When 0 is learned, it should be read *zero* rather than *naught, O, nothing,* or *cipher*. "Naught" is objectionable because it is so often corrupted into *aught,* or worse still *ought*. "Naught" is a perfectly proper word according to the dictionary but it is not the term which most people use. "Naught" is an example of "Pedaguese," the peculiar language of pedagogs. We object to "O" because it is a letter of the alphabet rather than a number symbol. Note the difference between O and 0 as they appear in printed form. Objections are raised to "nothing" for the very simple reason that the symbol 0 does mean something rather than nothing. "Cipher" is a good old-fashioned term, still commonly used in other English-speaking countries, but seldom heard in the United

States. "Zero" is a word which is not readily confused with another; it is commonly used by educated people; and it is especially common in science. After consulting the thermometer on a cold morning in a Northern state, one does not report that it is six below *naught,* or *O,* or *cipher,* but six below *zero.*

After the pupils have learned to read the numbers 1 to 9, and after they have had experiences in which larger numbers are used, the numbers 10 to 19 are taught. Association with the single digits helps here. Thus, the number 16 contains a 1 and a 6, both familiar. Gradually, the pupils learn that 16 means a ten (10) and a six (6). The age-old custom of using splints in bundles of ten and singly helps. Coins are also helpful. Thus, 14 cents is easily represented by a dime, which the pupils have come to know as 10 cents, and 4 cents.

The fact that our number system is a decimal system helps greatly as we go from one decade to another but it is unfortunate that we have such number words as *eleven* and *twelve* and that we say "fourteen" to indicate a ten and four more when later we say "forty-one" and write 41 to mean four tens and one more. But our number words are what they are through no fault of the present generation and all that the teacher can do is to make the best of it. As children increase their knowledge of number and become able to read and understand larger and larger numbers, they see in such a number as 73 7 tens and 3 more and in reading it as "seventy-three" they take their cues from the digits as they appear, but when they read 17 and say "seventeen" they do not take their cues from the digits in the order in which they appear but in the reverse order. We repeat that there is nothing which the teacher can do about this unfortunate condition but she can be on the alert for evidences of confusion and reversal as the pupils learn to read two-digit numbers.

It has already been suggested that rote counting by tens helps in getting an understanding of the number system to 100 and in learning to read numbers. Teachers often prepare a number table and write it in neat and orderly fashion on the blackboard as indicated below. Reading down, the numbers in their natural order are readily seen. Reading across, the decade arrangement becomes apparent; thus, the pupil can count to 100 by tens by reading the bottom line.

1	11	21	31	41	51	61	71	81	91
2	12	22	32	42	52	62	72	82	92
3	13	23	33	43	53	63	73	83	93
4	14	24	34	44	54	64	74	84	94
5	15	25	35	45	55	65	75	85	95
6	16	26	36	46	56	66	76	86	96
7	17	27	37	47	57	67	77	87	97
8	18	28	38	48	58	68	78	88	98
9	19	29	39	49	59	69	79	89	99
10	20	30	40	50	60	70	80	90	100

A similar treatment of three-digit numbers is provided. Here, familiar elements are combined in new and more involved ways. The pupil sees the even hundreds written out in a row and practices reading and writing a few of them until he "gets the hang" of the system to 1000.

100	200	300	400	500	600	700	800	900	1000
101	201	301							
102	202	302							
etc.	etc.	etc.							

He may also go through other hundreds by tens, thus, 300 310 320 330 340 350 360 370 380 390 400 except that he will ordinarily read them and write them in a column, rather than in a row.

There is little to be added concerning the teacher's responsibility in teaching children to write numbers except to add a word of caution as to the numbers 1 to 9. The same principles which apply to teaching children to do writing in an elementary way elsewhere apply here. Some teachers seem to believe that all they need to do is to give the pupils well-formed figures to copy and then leave them to their own resources. On the other hand, close supervision is required. If left to themselves, children will invent strange and peculiar ways to form the figures and will fail to use the economical movements which most people employ. They may use two or more movements in forming a figure, lifting the pencil from the paper after each; they may go backwards as in forming a 7 by starting at the bottom of the figure; and they may develop reversals, writing ε for 3, etc.

As children learn to form these figures, there must be individual instruction and, as has been said, close supervision. There must also be plenty of practice. Naturally, the practice should be motivated so that children enjoy it. There must be many short practice periods. Through all of these periods, as well as the first of them, the teacher should be constantly alert for the appearance of wrong movements. She will be with the children continually as they practice, moving from one to another and giving a bit of help here and a word of encouragement there lest wrong starts be made, or discouragement appear, or interest wane.

QUESTIONS AND REVIEW EXERCISES

1. Have you known first grade teachers who began a program of number instruction by stressing rote counting? What is the probable effect of such a program on the pupils? Does this condition help explain the fact that there are many persons who deny that there should be any conscious effort toward instruction in number in the first grade?

2. Do you know of any real-life situations in which children do rote counting? Of any in which adults do rote counting? When a parachute jumper leaves a plane, his instructions are to count ten before he pulls the ring on his parachute. What kind of counting is this?

3. Do you recommend that parents and others at home coach children in what they believe to be the elements of school work before the children enter school? Give reasons. What should be the teacher's attitude toward the pupil who has obviously been coached to "show off" before the teacher and the other pupils?

4. In general, what value do you think there is in rote learning? Give examples in other subjects and in various grades in which rote learning is often prominent and state the probable effect upon the pupils.

5. Look further into the matter of individual differences among young children by testing a fairly large sampling in counting or by consulting with first-grade teachers who have done so. Do you believe that children differ as much in mental functions as in such obviously physical functions as ability to see, hear, run, or jump?

6. John and Joe enter the first grade at the age of six years and six months. John's I.Q. is 75; Joe's is 130. What are their mental ages in years and months? How long will it be before John reaches Joe's present mental age if his I.Q. remains constant?

7. What should the first-grade teacher do about such differences in mental capacity as that between John and Joe?

8. Review the six stages in early counting as described by Miss Drummond and look for children representing each of them. Do first-grade groups ever include children who are in the first of these stages?

9. Why should early number work in the primary grades be largely individual? What are the probable consequences of class teaching at this time?

10. What is meant by the expression, "Counting by multiples"? How extensively should counting by multiples be developed in the first and second grades? What are the advantages in this type of experience?

11. Should counting by multiples ever be done by rote? Why or why not?

12. What concrete materials would you use in teaching counting by 2's? by 5's? by 10's?

13. Test yourself to see how large a group you can recognize without counting when the objects are not arranged in a definite pattern. One teacher, in reporting on this experiment, said that she could recognize 13 objects without counting. What do you think of this?

14. Test a few other persons, preferably children in the primary grades, to see how large a group each can recognize without counting. Combine your results with those of others to get more nearly adequate information as to what people can do in this respect.

15. Why should the cardinal meaning of number be developed first? How do teachers sometimes inadvertently confuse pupils in using objective materials to develop number understanding?

16. Are the numbers placed on children's lockers cardinal or ordinal numbers? Answer the same question for the numbers on automobile license tags; for the numbers given by

children when asked how old they are; for the answer given to the question, "What time is it?"

17. Which should children be taught first, to read numbers or to write numbers? Why?

18. Why it is probably harder for children to learn to read the numbers 1 to 9 than the numbers 10 to 19?

19. When should the symbol for *zero* be taught?

20. If you could rename the numbers 11 to 19, what would you call them?

21. Look up the number names for 11 to 19 in several foreign languages. Do you find the same difficulty which we have in English?

22. What are the most important suggestions for the teacher who is about to begin teaching children to write numbers?

CHAPTER TEST

For each of these statements, select the best answer. A key will be found on page 405.

1. Rote counting should be taught (1) before rational counting, (2) after rational counting, (3) simultaneously with rational counting.

2. Rote counting in comparison with rational counting is (1) more abstract, (2) less abstract, (3) equally abstract.

3. A child's first number experience should be (1) entirely concrete, (2) entirely abstract, (3) a mixture of the concrete and the abstract.

4. Pre-school teaching by parents and others at home is likely to (1) help the child, (2) hinder the child, (3) have no effect.

5. Experimental studies show that when children start to school the average can do (1) rote counting only, (2) rational counting only, (3) both rote and rational counting.

6. The beginnings of instruction in number should be

(1) individual, (2) group, (3) both individual and group.

7. First-grade teachers may reasonably expect their pupils (1) to know little about number, (2) to know much about number, (3) to vary greatly in what they know about number.

8. In early counting by multiples, the teacher should avoid counting by (1) 2's, (2) 3's, (3) 5's.

9. Counting by multiples should be (1) all rote, (2) all rational, (3) both rote and rational.

10. Recognizing the size of groups without counting when there is a definite pattern is (1) easier, (2) harder, (3) neither easier nor harder, than if there is no definite pattern.

11. The teacher should teach ordinal numbers (1) before cardinal numbers, (2) after cardinal numbers, (3) at the same time that cardinal numbers are taught.

12. The terms "cardinal" and "ordinal" are terms for (1) the teacher to learn, (2) the pupil to learn, (3) both the teacher and the pupil to learn.

13. Pupils should learn to read numbers (1) after learning to write them, (2) while learning to write them, (3) before learning to write them.

14. Learning to read the numbers 1-9 compared to learning 10-19 is (1) easier, (2) harder, (3) equally difficult.

15. The best way to teach children to write numbers is to (1) give them well-formed figures to copy, (2) show them how to form the figures and then let them practice alone, (3) show them how to form the figures and then supervise their efforts closely.

16. Pupils should learn to read numbers when in the (1) second, (2) third, (3) fourth of the four stages outlined in Chapter I.

17. The symbol 0 should be presented (1) before 1-9, (2) with 1-9, (3) after 1-9.

18. The symbol 0 is best called (1) zero, (2) naught, (3) cipher.

19. The number 12 should at first be presented as (1) one ten and two more, (2) just another way to express *twelve,* (3) the second in a series of numbers in the teens which are like the numbers 1-9.

20. In teaching children to write numbers, the teacher should at first give special attention to (1) the accuracy of the results, (2) the neatness of the results, (3) how the figures are formed.

SELECTED REFERENCES

1. Association for Childhood Education, 1201 Sixteenth Street, Washington, D.C. *Foundations in Arithmetic,* 1937. 32 pp. This reference was listed at the end of Chapter I. Several of these short articles bear upon the subject of this chapter.

2. Brownell, William A. *The Development of Children's Number Ideas in the Primary Grades.* Chicago: The University of Chicago, 1928. 241 pp. This monograph reports the results of an interesting research study. Chapters II, III, IV, and V all bear upon the subject of this chapter.

3. Clark, John R., Otis, Arthur S., and Hatton Caroline. *First Steps in Teaching Number.* Yonkers-on-Hudson, New York: World Book Company, 1929. 225 pp. This very readable little book is written for primary teachers. Read particularly pages 22-29 and 59-70.

4. Drummond, Margaret. *The Psychology and Teaching of Number.* Yonkers-on-Hudson, New York: World Book Company, 1925. 126 pp. Chapters II, III, IV, and V, pages 24-76 are recommended.

5. Judd, Charles Hubbard. *Psychological Analysis of the Fundamentals of Arithmetic.* Chicago: The University of Chicago, 1927. 121 pp. This excellent research report gives results of studies of counting and other arithmetic fundamentals. The reader will find that Chapters I, II, III, and IV, pages 1-70, will reinforce this chapter.

6. Knight, F. B. "A Report of Four Studies in Arithmetic." *Journal of Educational Research,* XXX: 325-340, January, 1937. The first of the four studies reported here is entitled "An Experimental Study of the Relative Perceptual Value of Various Configurations of the Numbers Six to Twelve Inclusive."

7. Morton, Robert L. "What Do Numbers Mean to First-Grade Children?" *American Childhood,* 13: 18-19 and 60-61, May, 1928.

8. Morton, R. L. "Developing Number Ideas." *The Grade Teacher,* XLIX: 770 and 813, June, 1932. These two articles, already listed in the references at the end of Chapter I, give observations of the author on the topics discussed in this chapter.

9. Smith, David Eugene. *The Wonderful Wonders of One-Two-Three.* New York: McFarlane, Warde, and McFarlane, 1937. 47 pp. An interesting and simply written account of our numbers. Contains facts as to the history of numbers and hints as to the recreational use of numbers.

10. Smith, David Eugene and Ginsburg, Jekuthial. *Numbers and Numerals.* New York: Bureau of Publications, Teachers College, Columbia University, 1937. 52 pp. Chapter III, "From Numbers to Numerals," gives interesting historical material on the origin of our numerals.

11. Thorndike, Edward Lee. *The New Methods in Arithmetic.* Chicago: Rand McNally and Company, 1921. 260 pp. The reader will find that pages 108-109 and 148 deal with topics discussed in this chapter.

12. Wesley, Marion J. "Social Arithmetic in the Early Grades." *Childhood Education,* XI: 367-370, May, 1935. Gives a valuable list of opportunities for number experience.

13. Wheat, Harry Grove. *The Psychology and Teaching of Arithmetic.* New York: D. C. Heath & Co., 1937. 591 pp. Read especially Chapters II and III.

CHAPTER 4

TEACHING THE FUNDAMENTAL COMBINATIONS OF ADDITION AND SUBTRACTION

The beginner's knowledge of the combinations. We have seen that studies of what children know about arithmetic when they enter the first grade show for many of them a considerable acquaintance with the addition combinations. Ordinarily, it is the combinations which are usually considered to be the easiest combinations that they know,—combinations whose sums are 10 or less. We have referred to the fact that Buckingham and MacLatchy[1] used in verbal problems the ten additions, 5 + 1, 7 + 1, 1 + 6, 1 + 9, 5 + 2, 8 + 2, 4 + 4, 5 + 3, 3 + 5, and 4 + 5. They found that these combinations ranked in difficulty in the order in which we have stated them here, the easiest being given first. The per cent who gave the correct answer to the problem using the combination 5 + 1 was 71.5 while the per cent right on 4 + 5 was 21.8.

When objects were used, the combinations tested were 2 + 2, 3 + 1, 1 + 7, 2 + 6, 6 + 1, 8 + 1, 2 + 8, 3 + 7, 2 + 4, and 4 + 6. Again, we have arranged them in the order of their difficulty as determined by the tests. Combining the results for both visible and invisible addition we find that 88.8 per cent were right on 2 + 2 and 71.8

[1] Buckingham, B. R. and MacLatchy, Josephine. "The Number Abilities of Children When They Enter Grade One." National Society for the Study of Education, *Twenty-Ninth Yearbook*. Bloomington, Illinois: Public School Publishing Company, 1930, pp. 472-524.

per cent on 4 + 6. These investigators had a good sample of all the basic additions whose sums are 10 or less for there are only 45 pairings of numbers which fall in this class and they used 17 of the 45. Note that three combinations appear in both lists but in reverse order.

However, marked differences among the 1356 pupils tested were found. Of the ten combinations used in verbal problems, 143 children, or 10.6 per cent of the total did not get a single one right while on the combinations for which objects were used there were 58 children, 4.3 per cent of the number tested, who failed on all. At the other extreme, there were 91 who were right on all the combinations in the first list and 692 who missed none in the second list (combining the results on the invisible and the visible tests).

Of course, it would be incorrect to assume that the children who gave right answers on these tests really knew the combinations on which they were tested in the sense that we later expect them to know at sight that 2 and 4 are 6, but they did have a fairly well developed understanding of number, they did know something of the meaning of addition, and they were able to give right answers. In many if not in most cases, they probably "figured out" the answers by counting.

When should instruction in addition begin? Apparently, there is no good reason why a program of instruction on the easier additions should not begin in the first grade. The teacher will first work with the pupils individually until she knows with considerable accuracy what they understand about number and what they are able to do. She will take pains to begin with each where he is and to develop his understanding of number in the manner suggested in Chapters 1 and 3. And she will help to provide for him situations which will keep him moving and growing. These situations, for most first-grade pupils, will certainly involve many of the elements of addition.

In the typical first grade, there will be no occasion for instructing the whole class as a group. When the extent of the progress of each individual in the class has been discovered, small groups at or near the same level of development may be formed and instructed as a group. But the levels of development and rates of progress will differ so greatly that there will probably be some who will not be ready for the easier additions by the end of the year while there will be others who will be able to profit from considerable work in addition during their first year in school.

How to begin the work in addition. In the last chapter, we saw that counting is the fundamental number experience. And we have repeatedly insisted that all of the early number experiences of children should be meaningful experiences. Let us take our cue for elementary work in addition from these two statements.

In many schools, there should be less concern about having the pupils *learn* arithmetic in the sense that they memorize addition combinations and their sums and more concern about having the pupils grow in an understanding of arithmetic and in ability to make for themselves new discoveries in arithmetic. At first, their new discoveries in addition are made by reacting to situations with which they are largely familiar by means of a counting response.

MacLatchy[2] has shown that among entering first-grade pupils there is a very definite relationship between ability to count and ability to give correct answers to easier addition combinations. Whether one is the cause of the other or both are due to the degrees of intelligence which the children possess and to differences in their out-of-school environment we do not know, but her results at least suggest two conclusions: (1) that the ability to count should be well developed in children before instruction in addition is begun; and (2) that counting is the proper approach to addition.

Pupils who can count as well as the average pupil can when he enters the first grade are ready for experiences which require the use of some of the easier addition combinations. This does not mean that the teacher must begin to work on addition with such pupils as soon as they start to school; other aspects of the first-grade program may quite well make it advisable for the teacher to delay her attack upon addition. But as number experiences get under way and the abilities of the pupils become known, opportunities for trying them out on some of the easier additions and for increasing their proficiency in this phase of number work should be seized.

The 45 basic combinations. Exclusive of 0, there are, of course, nine one-digit numbers. If each of these is combined with itself and with each of the eight others, we have 45 combinations in addition. They may be arranged in regular and systematic order as shown on the next page.

---

[2] MacLatchy, Josephine H. "Counting and Addition." *Educational Research Bulletin,* XI: 96-100, February 17, 1932.

1	1	1	1	1	1	1	1	1
1	2	3	4	5	6	7	8	9
	2	2	2	2	2	2	2	2
	2	3	4	5	6	7	8	9
		3	3	3	3	3	3	3
		3	4	5	6	7	8	9
			4	4	4	4	4	4
			4	5	6	7	8	9
				5	5	5	5	5
				5	6	7	8	9
					6	6	6	6
					6	7	8	9
						7	7	7
						7	8	9
							8	8
							8	9
								9
								9

Some writers refer to 81 addition combinations; others to 100. To get the 81, we simply reverse each of these 45 except the doubles, and count both forms as a combination. To get 100, we must include the combinations in which 0 appears. If those with 0 had been included in our list, we should have had 55 instead of 45; and if each of these 55, except the doubles, is reversed and both forms counted, we have 100. The reader may satisfy himself that these statements are true by writing out the 81 without 0 and the 55 or the 100 which can be obtained when 0 is included.

Combinations and facts. In recent years, there has been a marked tendency to distinguish between addition *combinations* and addition *facts* and to make a similar distinction in subtraction, multiplication, and division. The purpose of the distinction is to remove the confusion arising from references to 45 combinations and 81 combinations or to 55 combinations and 100 combinations. Those who observe this distinction use the word "combinations" when referring to the 45 or the 55 and the word "fact" when referring to the 81 or the 100. Thus, it is held, the numbers 4 and 3 make only one combination but this combination may be arranged in either of the two ways $\begin{array}{r}4\\ \underline{3}\end{array}$ and $\begin{array}{r}3\\ \underline{4}\end{array}$. The numbers 4 and 3, then, give us but one addition combination but they give us two addition facts. The distinction is not a very important one but it is a convenient one and we shall use it hereafter in this book.

Thus, each of the addition combinations, except the doubles, permits of two arrangements and each of these two arrangements is called an addition fact. To illustrate again, this time with the answers, we have for the numbers 6 and 5 two addition facts, $\begin{array}{r}6\\ \underline{5}\\ 11\end{array}$ and $\begin{array}{r}5\\ \underline{6}\\ 11\end{array}$. The two corresponding subtraction facts are $\begin{array}{r}11\\ \underline{6}\\ 5\end{array}$ and $\begin{array}{r}11\\ \underline{5}\\ 6\end{array}$. These four facts together we refer to as a *teaching unit.*

We may sum up as follows:

Number of addition combinations, without zero	45
Number of addition combinations, including zero	55
Number of addition facts, without zero	81
Number of addition facts, including zero	100

Of course, the number of subtraction combinations or facts in each group is the same as the number of addition combinations or facts in the corresponding group.

The zero combinations. In some schools, the zero combinations are taught along with the others, an occasional zero combination being introduced as the others are being developed, or all the zero combinations are taught as a group at some time while the others are being taught. This seems to be an unwise procedure. Zero combinations as separate, isolated combinations do not occur in ordinary uses of arithmetic. If a child needs a pencil costing 3 cents and a tablet costing 5 cents, he has real use for the addition fact $3 + 5$ or $5 + 3$, depending upon the order in which he thinks of the numbers, but he never has occasion to wonder about the sum of 3 cents and 0 cents. If he has 5 cents and spends nothing he does not subtract to find out how much he has left and if he has 5 cents and spends 5 cents, he knows without the use of a subtraction operation that his money is all gone.

Furthermore, learning the zero combinations is not closely analogous to learning the other combinations in addition and subtraction. Each addition combination which does not include a 0 has a sum which is different from either of the addends and which should eventually be learned and retained. But one can learn any number of zero combinations in one lesson, if his understanding of number permits, by simply observing that the sum of any number and 0 or 0 and any number is the number. Throughout his work in arithmetic and other mathematics, the pupil will learn that zero is unique and that the operations with zero are far from uniform. To scatter the zero combinations through the list of other combinations, making of each of them a separate combination to be mastered, means that we force upon the pupil more or less artificial and meaningless experiences, add considerably to his difficulties, and fail to take advantage of an attractive and easy way to master the zero difficulties.

The proper place to teach the zero combinations is in connection with situations involving their use. Such situations arise in examples where a single addend has two or more digits, one of which is 0, as $\begin{array}{r}20\\ \underline{6}\end{array}$, $\begin{array}{r}640\\ \underline{235}\end{array}$, $\begin{array}{r}325\\ \underline{104}\end{array}$, or $\begin{array}{r}260\\ \underline{130}\end{array}$.

The addition of 0 should be presented when such situations arise. Then is the time to teach that *any number plus zero equals the number* and *zero plus any number equals the number*. Likewise, in subtraction, the pupil discovers when the need arises, that *any number less zero leaves that number* and *any number less itself leaves zero.* These are not rules to be memorized and recited by the pupils, as is too often the case with rules, but principles which are to be discovered through the medium of real problems and examples.

The 19 zero facts in addition may be written without answers, as follows:

0	1	2	3	4	5	6	7	8	9
0	0	0	0	0	0	0	0	0	0

0	0	0	0	0	0	0	0	0
1	2	3	4	5	6	7	8	9

The 19 zero facts in subtraction without answers, are:

0	1	2	3	4	5	6	7	8	9
0	0	0	0	0	0	0	0	0	0

1	2	3	4	5	6	7	8	9
1	2	3	4	5	6	7	8	9

These zero facts are set down here for reference.

The teacher's first and fundamental task in teaching the addition and subtraction facts is the task of teaching 81 addition facts and 81 corresponding subtraction facts.

Difficulty of the combinations. Much has been written on the subject of the difficulty of the combinations. Back in 1914, Holloway[3] wrote his Doctor's thesis on this subject. He did a pioneer piece of work. During the next ten years, others gave some attention to this subject. Then, in 1924, Clapp[4] published a monograph giving results of his study of the difficulty of combinations in addition, subtraction, multiplication, and division. His results have been widely quoted. Four years later, Knight

---

[3] Holloway, Harry Vance. *An Experimental Study to Determine the Relative Difficulty of the Elementary Number Combinations in Addition and Multiplication.* Philadelphia: University of Pennsylvania, 1914. 102 pp.

[4] Clapp, Frank L. *The Number Combinations: Their Relative Difficulty and the Frequency of Their Appearance in Text-Books.* Madison, Wisconsin: University of Wisconsin, 1924. 120 pp.

and Behrens[5] published a little book giving results of an investigation of the same subject. Clapp determined difficulty from the number of errors made after the combinations presumably had been learned. Knight and Behrens, on the other hand, undertook to determine the difficulty which children experienced in learning the combinations and the amount of practice on each which was necessary for mastery.

The results secured by these various investigators are not in agreement. For many of the facts, they differ markedly. The teacher can not accept the conclusions of either investigator without finding herself out of harmony with those of the others. The fact that these investigators used different criteria for determining difficulty probably accounts to a considerable degree for the differences between their conclusions.

The teacher's interest in this matter of difficulty lies in the fact that she naturally wants to teach first the easiest combinations and to leave the hardest until the last. But there are other considerations which should be taken into account in determining the order in which the combinations are to be taught.

Order of teaching the combinations. In the first place, it is recommended that the two facts for a combination be taught together; that is, that $3 + 5$ be taught right along with $5 + 3$. To be sure, there seems to be almost complete transfer if only one of the two facts for a given combination is presented, as has been shown by

[5] Knight, Frederic B. and Behrens, Minnie S. *The Learning of the 100 Addition Combinations and the 100 Subtraction Combinations.* New York: Longmans, Green and Company, 1928. 82 pp.

Olander,[6] and by Beito and Brueckner,[7] but it is as easy to use both forms as only one. Results reported by Knight,[8] however, indicate that it is desirable to include both forms of a combination in drill materials. Now, in these difficulty lists, the two facts for a combination are often widely separated. If we teach them together and take advantage of the economy that seems thus to be made possible, there must be some compromise. Furthermore, each of the difficulty lists has the zero facts mixed in with the others while, as we have seen, there is no good reason why one of them should be more difficult than another or why any of them should be practiced individually.

In the second place, it is recommended that the addition facts and the subtraction facts for a given combination be taught together. Buckingham[9] conducted an experiment on this subject and concluded that there was an advantage in having the addition and the subtraction facts taught together rather than having the subtraction facts taught after the addition facts had been taught.

---

[6] Olander, Herbert T. "Transfer of Learning in Simple Addition and Subtraction." Elementary School Journal, XXXI: 358-369 and 427-437, January and February, 1931.

[7] Beito, E. A. and Brueckner, Leo. J. "A Measurement of Transfer in the Learning of Number Combinations." National Society for the Study of Education, *Twenty-Ninth Yearbook*. Bloomington, Illinois: Public School Publishing Company, 1930, pp. 569-587.

[8] Knight, F. B. "The Superiority of Distributed Practice in Drill in Arithmetic." *Journal of Educational Research,* XV: 157-165, March, 1927.

[9] Buckingham, B. R. "Teaching Addition and Subtraction Facts Together or Separately." *Educational Research Bulletin,* VI: 228-229 and 240-242, May 25, 1927.

That is, when we teach $6 + 7 = 13$ and $7 + 6 = 13$ we would also teach $13 — 7 = 6$ and $13 — 6 = 7$. But, since the addition facts and the subtraction facts for a given combination have not been found to be equally difficult, a compromise is again required if we would teach them together.

Washburne[10] found that in general the combinations in which the larger numbers are used are harder than those in which the smaller numbers are used but that an exception should be made for the doubles. Thus $5 + 4$ will likely be harder than $5 + 2$ but $5 + 5$ will be easier than $5 + 4$. MacLatchy[11] suggests that the easiest facts are those in which 1 is added to a larger number and that the two facts for a combination in which 1 is involved are not equally difficult, that $1 + 7$, for example, is more difficult than $7 + 1$.

After reviewing all of the evidence and considering all of the arguments, we recommend that the primary teacher, in planning work in the elements of addition, divide the 45 combinations into two groups, one to be called the easier group and the other the harder group. This plan has been in use in many schools for many years. The easier group will include the 25 combinations whose sums are 10 or less. This group of 25 combinations gives us 45 facts, for each combination, except the 5 which are doubles, yields two facts. The harder group

---

[10] Washburne, Carleton. "Are Any Number Combinations Inherently Difficult?" *Journal of Educational Research,* XVII: 235-255, April, 1928.

[11] MacLatchy, Josephine. "Another Measure of the Difficulty of the Addition Combinations." *Educational Research Bulletin,* XII: 57-61, March 8, 1933.

will include those 20 combinations whose sums are more than 10. This group provides 36 facts. Of course, the 25 combinations in the easier group are not all equally easy. In general, the easiest of these will be those having the smallest sums and those in which 1 and 2 are added to larger numbers. Likewise, some of the harder group are harder than others.

We may summarize the plan so far developed as follows:

1. Divide the 45 combinations into two groups, putting the 25 whose sums are 10 or less into the easier group and the remaining 20 into the harder group.

2. In teaching a combination, use both forms (the two facts) but present first the form in which the smaller number is added to the larger number.

3. Present the subtraction facts along with the corresponding addition facts, making a teaching unit of the four facts (two in the case of a double). In her first work on the combinations, the teacher may well confine herself to addition but eventually the four facts should be presented together.

4. Postpone the zero combinations until the others have been completed, then teach them as a group by developing the principles which apply to them. Practice on the kinds of examples in which zeros normally occur.

With these considerations in mind, the teacher may proceed systematically to making the pupils acquainted with the 25 easier combinations by taking up these combinations in any one of several orders. The order stated below is given as a suggestion. It is intended that the teacher should first present the combinations in the first line, then those in the second line, etc.

2	2	1	3	4
2	1	1	1	1
3	3	5	4	4
2	3	1	2	4
5	6	4	7	5
5	1	3	1	2
8	6	5	9	7
1	2	3	1	2
6	8	5	7	6
3	2	4	3	4

The exact order is not important. But it is important that the teacher find out what the pupils already know and develop the program accordingly. The teacher will provide many opportunities for practice on familiar combinations and will slowly add other combinations to those with which the pupil is acquainted. Of course, the teacher must keep a careful record of what has been taught to each of the pupils or to each of several homogeneous groups.

The following is one order which may be arranged for the 20 combinations in the more difficult group.

6	9	8	6	8
6	2	3	5	4
9	7	7	7	8
3	4	7	5	8
8	9	8	9	9
5	4	6	5	9
7	9	8	9	9
6	6	7	7	8

Teaching the combinations in the easier group. A city superintendent of schools once told the author that he would not permit the primary teachers in his schools to use objects in teaching the addition combinations. He said that the use of objects always meant the development of the counting habit and that, as a consequence, the pupils never really learned their combinations. When wanting the answer to such a combination as $5 + 3$, he said that the pupils would always count "five, six, seven, eight," before announcing "eight" as the result. "Tell them what five and three are," he said, "and then drill them until they know it."

For all but a few choice pupils, who would learn their arithmetic about as well without a teacher as with a teacher, such teaching as this leads to disaster. Pupils do not *learn* arithmetic in this manner; they merely memorize meaningless materials. We can not emphasize too strongly the point which has been made repeatedly in this book, namely, that a real educational experience is a meaningful experience and that number experiences which are to be meaningful must be concrete long before they are abstract.

This superintendent had in mind an important point. He wanted his pupils eventually to know the addition combinations. So do we all. Surely, no one will recommend the lame and halting counting methods which many adults use as they laboriously find the sum of a column of numbers. But whether one develops a permanent counting habit for addition combinations depends less upon how he is taught the combinations than upon what is done by him and his teacher after the initial presentation of the combinations to enable him to give immediate responses.

By all means, the teacher should begin with concrete experiences. Objects should be used and at first the pupil should *discover* sums by counting. As he becomes increasingly familiar with a combination the counting response should be gradually discontinued and be displaced by an immediate, direct response. This will be done if the teacher sees to it that there is enough practice and enough encouragement.

Some teachers talk too much and leave too little for the pupils to discover for themselves. Pupils should have an opportunity to think things out and to make discoveries. For example, a teacher says, "Now, children, I have two pencils in this hand and three pencils in this hand. When I put them together, I have five pencils. Then two pencils and three pencils are five pencils. How many apples are two apples and three apples?" And she believes that if the children can answer, "Five apples," they are learning satisfactorily. It is much better if the teacher will place more responsibility upon the pupils. Thus,

TEACHER. How many pencils have I here?

PUPIL. Two.

TEACHER. And how many pencils have I here?

PUPIL. Three.

TEACHER. *(Putting them together, but leaving each one clearly visible so that they may be counted.)* Now, how many pencils have I altogether?

PUPIL *(After counting if he does not know.)* Five.

The pupils are already familiar with counting and they use what they know to discover something new in addition.[12]

[12] See Wheat, Harry Grove, *The Psychology and Teaching of Arithmetic.* New York: D. C. Heath and Company, 1937, Chapter X.

Opportunities will be found for making the pupils acquainted with all of the combinations whose sums do not exceed 10. Sometimes, these opportunities may be deliberately set up by the teacher, as in the case of the pencils, but more often, so far as the program of the first grade is concerned at any rate, the opportunities arise in connection with other situations. The alert teacher will find many such opportunities but it may be necessary to supplement with such deliberately planned episodes as that of the pencils. She will keep a careful record of the combinations which appear and will at all times know just what has been done.

Pupils' number understandings grow surely but slowly. Hence, the teacher dare not hurry the pupils on this work with the basic additions. Much of it can and probably should be done in the first grade but the first grade is not the place for such abstract drills as those which are carried on with flash cards. Throughout the year, the teacher should give frequent attention to the elements of addition that the pupils' understanding and growth may be assured.

After the pupils become able to react easily and accurately to situations requiring the addition of concrete materials, they should move on to semi-concrete materials. These have been discussed briefly in Chapter 1. The pupils use dominoes, specially prepared cards and mimeographed sheets showing groups of dots, circles, lines, and the like, and other semi-concrete materials which the teacher is able to provide.

It has been suggested that both the addition and the subtraction facts of a teaching unit should be taught together. At first, however, the teacher may well devote her attention entirely to addition lest the simultaneous introduction of the two processes cause confusion. Attention should be given to several addition combinations before the corresponding subtraction facts are introduced.

Suggestions given for teaching the addition facts apply also to the teaching of the subtraction facts. Problems should be drawn from real and interesting situations. The pupil should discover the results for himself. Many and varied situations requiring subtraction should be used.

When the addition and the subtraction facts are taught together, there is an opportunity to effect an economy of time and energy. The pupil comes to see $5 + 3$, $3 + 5$, $8 - 3$, and $8 - 5$ as an integrated whole. This is especially likely to be true if these four facts are all developed through the use of familiar concrete or semi-concrete materials.

Teaching the combinations in the harder group. At least a year should elapse between the first work on the easier combinations and the first attention to the harder combinations. During this time the pupils grow steadily in their understanding of number, they learn more and more about addition and subtraction from concrete and semi-concrete experiences and they come finally to the place where they are able to give fairly promptly the answers to the easier combinations.

Objects may be used for the harder combinations also, but it is not necessary to teach each and every one of these harder combinations through the use of objects. The number of objects required may be rather hard to handle and it may take so long to count them that the pupil loses sight of what it is that he is trying to do. Furthermore, by this time there is another approach that may be used advantageously.

The success of this second approach depends upon the pupil's understanding of the numbers in the teens. The pupil should understand that 14, for example, means 10 + 4. Then, to add 9 and 5, he thinks "9 + 5 is 10 and how many? 9 is 1 less than 10, so 9 + 5 must be 1 less than 15, or 14." Here, again, the pupil uses what he already knows as a means of discovering something new.

Any combination in which 9 appears may be conveniently learned in this manner. The combinations in which 8 appears can be developed almost as well by this method. The pupil sees 8 as 2 less than 10 and then thinks of 8 + 7, for example, as 2 less than 17 (10 + 7), or 15. Now, since 14 of the 20 combinations in this group contain 9 or 8 or both of these numbers, it is obvious that it will not be very difficult to develop all but 6 of the 20 harder combinations in this manner. The 6 combinations of this group in which neither 9 or 8 appears are:

6	6	7	7	7	7
6	5	4	7	5	6

Of course, objects may be used with these or they may be presented as is suggested for those containing 9's and 8's. Some teachers prefer one method for these and some the other. Probably both should be used eventually.

Not only should these combinations be seen in their relationship to 10 but they should also be seen in their relationship to each other. Thus, the sum of 7 and 8 should be seen with reference to 7 and 7 and to 8 and 8. Frequently, a pupil knows a combination such as 8 + 8 but is completely lost on 9 + 8 because he has forgotten the sum. If numbers are meaningful to him and he has come to understand the meaning of addition, he should have no difficulty in seeing that 9 + 8 must be one more than 8 + 8.

Those who object to this method on the ground that it may make permanent the use of round-about habits of response should remember that arithmetic which is not meaningful to children is worse than no arithmetic at all and that it is a short-sighted policy which causes children to memorize combinations which they do not understand and to depend upon memory in situations which they might think out for themselves. Eventually, the combinations should be learned so that responses are direct and immediate, but while they are being learned the pupil's reactions should be thoughtful and meaningful reactions rather than the mere reproduction of something which has been memorized. The teacher who begins with drill or introduces drill too early soon finds that the pupils do not do what she hoped they would do and that their insight into the subject does not become what it might have become had better instructional methods been employed.[13]

This method of perceiving relationships between combinations can also be applied to the combinations in the easier group. The pupil who knows the sums of 2 and 2, 3 and 3, 4 and 4, and 5 and 5, should see the relationship between these facts and 2 and 3, 3 and 4, and 4 and 5, and should discover other relationships between combinations.

Thus, the pupil comes to make generalizations about

[13] See Brownell, William A. and Chazal, Charlotte B. "The Effects of Premature Drill in Third-Grade Arithmetic." *Journal of Educational Research,* XXIX: 17-28, September, 1935.

combinations and to profit from these generalizations.[14] The combinations are learned slowly, to be sure, but they are learned well. They are meaningful. If enough concrete and semi-concrete situations are found, the time will come when drills can be introduced. If drills are used at the right time and in the right way, they help to fix what the pupil has learned and they increase his efficiency by helping him to arrive more quickly at sums and differences. But if used too early, they becloud his thinking, dim his understanding, and thwart his progress.

Providing for drill or practice. We have indicated that drills on the fundamental number combinations serve a valuable purpose if used at the right time and in the right manner. Those who object to drill object to the form which the drill lesson takes or to the stage in the pupil's progress at which drill is introduced rather than to the mere fact of drill istelf.

There are many phases of human learning which require practice or drill. The student of a musical instrument, for example, must not only learn *how* to use his hands in playing the instrument but he must also *practice* to perfect his technique, to fix as habits the desired types of response, and to maintain his technique at a satisfactorily high level of performance. The same is true of athletic activities, as golf, football, etc., of sedentary games, as contract bridge, and of many other kinds of human behavior.

---

[14] See Thiele, C. L. "The Mathematical Viewpoint Applied to the Teaching of Elementary School Arithmetic." The Tenth Yearbook of the National Council of Teachers of Mathematics, *The Teaching of Arithmetic.* New York: Bureau of Publications, Teacher's College, Columbia University, 1935, pp. 212-224.

At many points in the study of mathematics, from the primary grades of the elementary school to the university, practice exercises are indispensable. This is true of the combinations and other phases of the four fundamental processes in the primary grade, of operations with fractions in the intermediate grades, of applications of percentage and of square root in the junior high school, of linear and quadratic functions in the senior high school, of methods of solving higher degree equations in college algebra, and of differentiation and integration in the calculus, to mention only a scattered few of the numerous places where drill is required.

It seems best to avoid the use of drills in the abstract form in the first grade. But if there have been many opportunities for developing an understanding of number and many contacts with the easier combinations in concrete and semi-concrete form in the first grade, the second-grade teacher may gradually introduce practice exercises of a more abstract form. She may have the pupils write the number combinations with their answers on paper and on the blackboard and state them verbally as opportunities for their use are found. She will employ various games which put a premium upon success with the combinations. And, finally, she will use flash-card and other forms of abstract drills.

After reaching the abstract stage in drill work, however, it is desirable that the pupils be taken to concrete number situations frequently, lest interest wane and the drill lose its value. Many problems arising out of the experiences of the pupils in and out of school will be used and the teacher will propose other problems in which the number skills find their application and which occur or might reasonably be expected to occur in children's affairs. This kind of program, in which the concrete and the abstract are intermingled, will be continued through the second and the third grades.

Resourceful teachers have developed many excellent games and other drill devices for making children's practice on the addition and subtraction facts pleasant and profitable. A few of these are described in these pages; others are found in the references listed at the end of the chapter.

Flash cards. When the pupils are ready for it, a short, snappy drill period with flash cards is valuable. This drill period should ordinarily be provided for a small homogeneous group at a time. Individual differences among the pupils make it virtually impossible to conduct a drill exercise of this kind for a whole roomful of pupils at one time. Some may not need it, others may not be ready for it, and those who do need it may need it on different combinations and in varying amounts.

Flash cards may be purchased from school supply houses or they may be made by the teacher. A card nine inches long and three inches wide is a very satisfactory size for group use. They may be made of light Manila cardboard and the numerals made with India ink. For the number facts without zeros, 81 will be needed in addition and 81 in subtraction. Each of these larger groups may be conveniently divided into two smaller groups, one group containing the 45 easier facts and the other group the 36 harder facts. Each card should be printed on both sides—one side without the answer and the other side with the answer. For example, a card may show $\begin{array}{r}3\\ \underline{4}\end{array}$ on one side and $\begin{array}{r}3\\ \underline{4}\\ 7\end{array}$ on the other side.

The author has prepared for individual pupil use a set of cards which have certain advantages not found in the ordinary flash cards.[15] One of these cards is reproduced herewith in the form and size in which it appears in the set. The other side of the card shows the same facts without the answers. These cards have the following unique features:

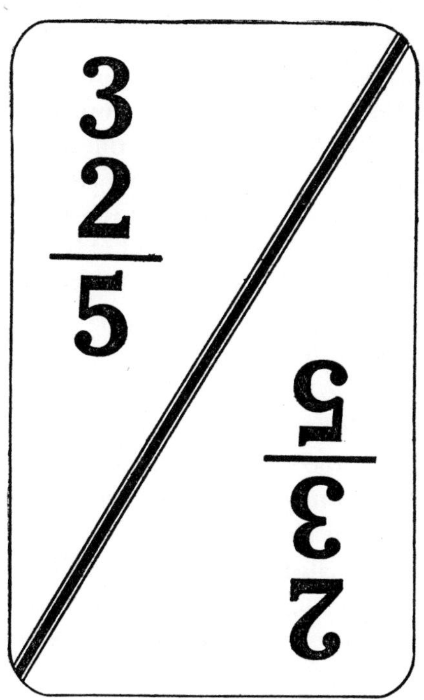

1. The cards are small and easily handled. They are to be placed in the hands of the pupils, a pack for each pupil.

2. Since the two facts for a combination are placed on one card, these facts are closely associated in practice. Also, the number of essential cards is reduced from 81 to 45.

3. The cards are printed in black

[15] Published by the School Specialty Press, 87 West Main Street, Columbus, Ohio. Price, 50 cents per pack; $4.50 per dozen packs.

ink on one side (the answer side) and in red ink on the other side. This arrangement makes it easy for the teacher to distinguish the side which the pupil has exposed.

4. The inclusion of a set of answer cards, called Master Cards, greatly increases the possibilities of the use of the cards.

5. An instruction sheet supplies directions and suggestions for use. Games which may be played, such as "Sorting Mail," are described. In this game the Master Cards are used and the combination cards are sorted into piles, those in a pile all having the same answer.

As the teacher conducts drills with flash cards, she must observe the individual pupils closely and be constantly on the alert not only for the appearance of wrong answers but also for the appearance of undesirable methods of arriving at answers. By the time the pupil is ready for practice exercises of this kind, he should have discontinued or be discontinuing such elaborate ways of arriving at answers as counting. One purpose of such drills is to let the pupil see that it is an advantage to be able to give his answers immediately. If he does not know an answer, he should rediscover it for himself and then be helped to remember it. Counting as a method of obtaining sums or differences should not become a permanent habit.

Patience is required. Pupils often have to be taught and retaught. The wise teacher goes slowly, provides an abundance of meaningful experience before abstract drills are introduced, drills a small carefully selected group at a time, encourages immediate responses, gives much practice but sees to it that the practice fits the needs of individual pupils, and reverts frequently to familiar situations in which a knowledge of the combinations is required.

GAMES AND DRILL DEVICES

The teacher should have at hand a large number and variety of games to be used for practice purposes. In selecting a game or a device for a particular purpose, care should be exercised to see that the game or device really accomplishes the purpose. We have space here for a description of only a few games but these few are selected to illustrate both the undesirable and the desirable kind.

Undesirable games and devices. Some games require a great deal of activity on the part of the pupils but this activity may contribute but little to their understanding of arithmetic. The game may be harmless and even desirable for the accomplishment of other purposes but if it has been chosen to increase skill in number fundamentals, most of the activity involved should work directly toward that end. Consider, for example the game, "Blind Man."

The children form a circle leaving one child in the center blindfolded. Each child has a card hung from his neck containing a number not greater than 9. The blind man catches someone. The one caught gives the sum of his number and that of the blind man. The blind man then guesses the number of the one caught. If he guesses the right number, the one caught becomes the blind man.

This game requires addition on the part of those in the circle and subtraction on the part of the blind man. But as a drill device in addition it is poor, for each pupil has but one combination—the sum of his own number and that of the blind man—and he knows in advance what that combination is and has an abundance of time in which to find the answer by a method of his own choosing. The teacher will not know what that method is. As a device for giving training on the subtraction combinations, it is but little better. The sole recipient of the benefits of the drill is the "blind man," unless the others check him, and he has but one combination to consider. This is a very small return for the amount of time consumed by the game. Furthermore, the directions state that the "blind man" *guesses* the number of the one caught. This is not the time or the place for guessing.

A somewhat more desirable but still faulty game is that of "Bursting Balloons."

> Draw a number of balloons on the blackboard, bringing the strings together at the bottom. Put a combination on each balloon. When a child gives the correct answer to a combination, he "bursts" the balloon and it is erased. Continue until all the balloons are gone.

If this game is designed to give practice on the combinations which the pupils are already supposed to know, it fails to accomplish its purpose. It does not spot weak places in the preparation of the individual pupils. If a pupil does not know an answer, he has plenty of time to figure it out and the teacher will not know the method which he employs. Furthermore, it is a rather far-fetched application of children's interest in toy balloons.

Examples of better games and drill devices. There is an adaptation of the age-old game, "Pussy-in-the-Corner," which children in the second and third grades seem to enjoy.

All the pupils, except one who is "it," are arranged in a circle. Each pupil in the circle is given a number, not greater than 18, the same number being given to two pupils. The pupil who is "it" takes his place in the center and announces a combination, as 8 and 6. The two pupils who have the number 14 exchange places and the pupil who is "it" tries to get the place of one of them. If he is successful, the one displaced becomes "it." If he is unsuccessful, he announces another combination.

This game requires close attention and alertness from all pupils. One must recognize immediately any combination whose sum makes his number. If the pupils' numbers are changed frequently, each receives practice on a wider variety of combinations. The teacher may use this game with smaller groups and limit the practice to a certain portion of the combinations, as those with sums from 6 to 10, or those with sums greater than 12.

This game may also be used for subtraction combinations. The numbers assigned will not be greater than 9. The one who is "it" then says "6 from 13," for example, and the two pupils having the number 7 exchange places.

Another old-time favorite is "Fox and Geese."

The fox stands in the center of a circle of geese. He calls on a goose by name and announces a combination. If the sum or the difference is not given correctly, the goose is caught and joins the fox. Then another goose is named and another combination is called. A goose who has been caught may escape to the circle by giving a correct answer when the fox accepted a wrong answer, or he may be allowed to return to the circle by giving any answer before the goose called upon can give it, in which case the goose called upon is caught.

If prompt answers are to be encouraged, the name of the goose should always be called *before* the combination is announced.

Many teachers like the game called "The Guessing Game."

TEACHER. I am thinking of two numbers which make 12. Ruth.

RUTH. Are you thinking of 8 and 4?

TEACHER. No, I am not thinking of 8 and 4. Mildred.

MILDRED. Are you thinking of 7 and 6?

TEACHER. No, Mildred, 7 and 6 make 13. I am thinking of two numbers which make 12. Betty.

BETTY. Are you thinking of 7 and 5?

TEACHER. Yes, I am thinking of 7 and 5.

Betty then takes the teacher's place and the game proceeds.

Another one which is frequently used and which seems to be fairly interesting to pupils is called "Stepping Stones."

Draw a stream with stepping stones so arranged that there are several different routes from one shore to the other. Each stone will have a combination written on it. Children choose routes and cross the stream by answering the combinations on the stones, being cautioned not to fall into the water by making a mistake. Children at their seats watch for mistakes.

There is a rather wide variety of games which are generally referred to as racing games. Two pupils have a race to see which can give the answers to a series of combinations in the least time. Each has the same number of combinations and they are carefully selected so as to be of approximately equal difficulty. The "Stepping Stones" game just described can easily be used as a racing game since there are several different routes from one side of the stream to the other. When two pupils race, each pupil may choose the route which his opponent is to take.

Sometimes the combinations are simply arranged in a column or placed in a ladder arrangement as shown. Here we have two ladders each containing 14 combinations. These combinations have been selected from those whose sums do not exceed 10. The reader will note that 12 of the combinations given in the two ladders are the same but are expressed in different order. In half of these, the one ladder has the larger number stated first while in the remaining half, the other ladder has the larger number stated first. Two of the combinations in each ladder are doubles which do not differ very greatly in difficulty.

4 + 2	2 + 4
6 + 3	3 + 6
3 + 7	7 + 3
4 + 1	1 + 4
6 + 4	4 + 6
2 + 3	3 + 2
1 + 9	9 + 1
1 + 1	2 + 2
5 + 5	3 + 3
3 + 5	5 + 3
7 + 2	2 + 7
4 + 3	3 + 4
2 + 6	6 + 2
1 + 8	8 + 1

The ladders may be drawn on the blackboard and two pupils may be selected to race to the top. They will be cautioned to be careful not to fall by giving wrong answers. The pupils may be timed with a stop watch or any other watch having a second hand, two seconds being added to each record for each mistake, if any. The answers are written along the right hand side of the ladder.

The combinations may be written in ladder form with plus signs, as shown, or they may be written in vertical form and arranged in rows. Both forms should be used but probably the greater emphasis should be given to the vertical form since this is the form in which most adding is done.

If one pupil only is "climbing the ladder," he can give his sums orally, the teacher timing him and the other pupils watching for mistakes.

Each teacher can make up a large number of sets of such ladders for the combinations whose sums do not exceed 10, for those whose sums do exceed 10, and for the two groups combined. These sets of ladders can be saved for use with later classes. Care should be taken to see that each combination appears occasionally and that the combinations which are most often missed are given special emphasis. Of course, subtraction combinations can be practiced with similar devices.

A simple but valuable device makes use of a circle as shown on page 107. Ten or a dozen addition combinations (or subtraction combinations) are set down and the numbers representing their sums (or differences) are written inside the circumference of the circle. One pupil acts as leader and two other pupils are selected for a race. The leader points to a combination below the circle and the pupil indicating first the correct answer wins a point. The same two pupils may race for several combinations and then be replaced by two new racers.

6	4	9	8	7
8	7	6	8	5
—	—	—	—	—
9	8	3	9	6
4	9	7	9	6
—	—	—	—	—

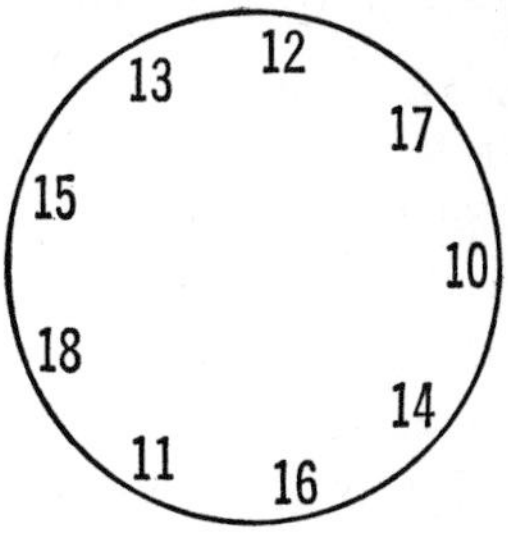

13 12 17 15 10 18 14 11 16

The circle suggests the number wheels, sometimes called race tracks, which are often used. A large wheel with spokes is drawn on the blackboard. The combinations are written in the spaces between the spokes and pupils run races around the wheel or the race track.

If games and devices are well selected and judiciously used, they help considerably in attaining a satisfactory degree of mastery of the fundamental combinations in addition and subtraction. If interest is to be kept at a high level, the teacher must have an extensive repertoire of games and devices that a wide variety may be employed and that the selection may be satisfactory for the particular group and at the particular time when practice is to be provided.

Problem solving. The processes of addition and subtraction are not of importance in themselves. They are a means to an end; the end is problem solving.

We are using the word "problem" to indicate an arithmetical situation which is stated in words and which requires the pupil first to decide what operation to perform. Arithmetical situations in which the operations to be performed are indicated are conveniently called "examples." The addition combinations alone are the simplest of addition examples.

Arithmetic which arises out of activities in which children engage is problem arithmetic. To be sure, the solution of a problem requires the solution of an example but the problem is the main thing. A pupil who needs 3 cents to mail a letter and 5 cents to buy a pencil has a problem to solve if he would know how much money is required for both. It is a very simple problem, but one must understand the conditions and know something of the meaning of addition if he would solve it.

Problems arise out of concrete situations. Examples are pure abstractions. Hence, the problem is likely to be the more interesting and the more meaningful. Pupils who are held for very long on a program of example solving are almost certain to lose interest in arithmetic. When they solve problems, especially problems which arise out of their own experiences, they find their arithmetic to be a vital, functioning thing, full of interest and meaning.

Obviously, the problems which appear in books do not arise out of the experiences of the children who solve them. They may have arisen out of the experiences of some other group of children and they may be interesting to the children to whom they are supplied but they are necessarily a little less interesting and a little less real than are the children's own problems. The teacher should have rich sources of printed problem material and she should use such material to supplement the material which comes out of activities in which her pupils engage. Such supplementary problems are needed because of the probability that an insufficient number will come from children's activities and because a better balance, a better distribution of practice, can thereby be provided.

The teacher needs to be alert if she would catch the opportunities for problem solving which come up in children's school and out-of-school affairs. They are more numerous than some teachers seem to believe. But even if they are all seen and used there will still be a place for the supplementary problems which the teacher and the textbook can provide.

The first problems used should be simple, one-step problems. They will require the use of the basic facts of addition and subtraction. They should be used, and used frequently, as these facts are made the object of a program of systematic practice. Every fact should receive attention in this kind of practice as well as in the more abstract kind of practice.

Frequently, a single situation, a real one or a make-believe one, can furnish several problems. Running through the series will be the thread of a story which ties them together and helps to make them interesting. For example, the story of Lucile and the eggs may provide these problems.

1. When Lucile was visiting her grandmother, who lived on a farm, she went hunting for eggs. She found four eggs in a nest in the haymow but when she picked them up, she dropped one and broke it. How many eggs did Lucile have then?

2. Carrying her three eggs very carefully, Lucile found two more under the corn crib. How many eggs did she have then?

3. Lucile's grandmother was very glad to get these five eggs. She used two of them in baking a cake and put the rest of them in the refrigerator. How many eggs did she put in the refrigerator?

These three problems will suggest what can be done. Many others will come to mind as the story develops and Lucile continues to look for eggs. The problems suggested here are to be read or stated to the pupils, of course, for they contain words which the pupils will be unable to read when at this level of advancement in arithmetic.

Many other situations of similar kind will supply additional problems. They will deal with children's activities in earning and spending money, with the fish which Tommy caught, with the dolls which Jane had, with the pieces of candy in the box, with the cookies remaining on the plate, with the marbles which Dick had, with the papers which Dan sold, with the story books which Anne read, with episodes arising out of nursery rimes and stories which children read and hear, and with the multitudinous other situations in which children are interested.

Making and using tests. There are persons who say that tests have no place in the primary grades. To them, tests are such formal and formidable things that little children should not be brought into contact with them.

But we should have some way to evaluate our teaching efforts. If children can learn addition and subtraction facts in the primary grades, they can be tested on their knowledge of those facts. At first the tests will be oral. That is, the teacher, as she works with the pupils on the elements of arithmetic, will make mental and written note of what they as individuals can and can not do and of what they know and do not know. But after the pupils have learned to read and write numbers, after they have developed a considerable degree of proficiency with the fundamental combinations, and after they have become accustomed to abstract drill forms, written tests containing abstract examples may be used.

At first, a test will be devoted to a single process, as addition. Later the two operations may be mixed in one test and signs used to indicate the process to be used for each combination. In mixed tests, it is hardly necessary to use plus signs for the pupils readily learn that if the combinations are set down in a column form they should add if there is no sign and subtract if there is a minus sign. Let us suppose that we wish to construct an addition test for the first five of the 25 easier combinations. There are only eight facts and they may be arranged for test purposes as follows:

2	2	1	1	3	1	1	4
2	1	1	2	1	4	3	1

Note that the two facts for a combination are not given in direct sequence. They should come together for teaching purposes, as has been stated, but they should be separated in a test.

Again, suppose that we wish to construct a test for the last five of the 20 more difficult combinations and that we wish to include all four facts for each teaching unit. There will be 20 items. They may be arranged in miscellaneous order in some such manner as the following:

6	7	16	15	9	17	7	15	13	9
7	8	–7	–9	7	–9	6	–8	–6	8

6	16	15	13	9	7	15	8	8	17
9	–9	–6	–7	6	9	–7	9	7	–8

Tests may also contain problems. Indeed, a set of problems may be made up to include all of the facts of a group of teaching units, miscellaneously arranged, as sets of examples have been made up to accomplish the same purpose.

Recording and using test results. The least that the teacher can do with a pupil's test paper is to grade the paper and assign him a mark on, let us say, a percentage scale. But a teacher who goes to the trouble of preparing a test and giving it to pupils should get much more out of the results than the mere percentage grades of the pupils.

The test papers should be analyzed minutely and the specific items missed by each pupil should be discovered if further drill work is to be properly planned. A sheet of paper should be ruled into as many columns as there are items of the test and as many rows as there are pupils, or vice versa, with additional columns and rows for the test items, the pupils' names, and the totals. The form on the next page was prepared for the 20 items of the second test given and for a group of 12 pupils. The test items are listed at the left and, for the sake of convenience, are written with signs. The pupils' names are recorded at the top of the form. There is a column of totals at the right and a line of totals at the bottom of the form.

The analysis of the test results shown by this form reveals at a glance that 10 of the 20 test items were missed by none of the pupils, that 8 were missed by one pupil each, that 1 was missed by two pupils, and that 1 was missed by four pupils. Obviously, this item, 15 — 6, has not been taught as well as have the others. The analysis also shows that 7 of the 12 pupils tested missed none of the test items, that 1 missed one item, that 1 missed two items, that 2 missed three items each, and

Results of a Mixed Test on Five of the More Difficult Combinations

Test Item	Anne	Arthur	Bonnie	Clara	Dick	Esther	Henry	John	Mary J.	Mary S.	Richard	Robert	Total
6 + 7													0
7 + 8													0
16 — 7		√											1
15 — 9													0
9 + 7			√				√						2
17 — 9		√											1
7 + 6										√			1
15 — 8		√											1
13 — 6							√						1
9 + 8										√			1
6 + 9													0
16 — 9													0
15 — 6		√	√				√					√	4
13 — 7		√											1
9 + 6													0
7 + 9													0
15 — 7										√			1
8 + 9													0
8 + 7													0
17 — 8													0
Total	0	5	2	0	0	0	3	0	0	3	0	1	14

that one pupil missed five items. It may be a coincidence, but Arthur, the pupil who missed five items, missed nonc but subtraction items. Some further individual diagnosis of his difficulties and some additional teaching are in order.

Such an analysis of the results of a test shows far more than can be learned from percentage grades alone. The analysis points the way to further corrective measures and to further practice exercises.

Some of the testing must be done individually. The results of a test such as this show which pupils made errors on what test items but they do not show the pupils' methods of work. Only tests of the pupils as individuals can reveal faulty procedures unless wrong answers are obtained. Occasionally, the teacher should sit down with each pupil individually and observe his methods of work as he adds or subtracts and says aloud what he thinks as he does so. After all, individual testing and diagnosis are the most important for they not only reveal the errors which pupils make but also the nature of those errors and the idiosyncrasies of the individual pupils.

QUESTIONS AND REVIEW EXERCISES

1. Why is it important that the teacher discover what the pupils already know about the combinations before she begins to teach them?
2. If the first-grade teacher discovers that some of her pupils already know many of the combinations and that others know none of them, what kind of a program in number instruction should she set up?
3. What arguments can you give in favor of beginning instruction in addition in the first grade? What arguments

against this? In your opinion, which side has the better of the argument?

4. When children are tested on the combinations with objects, why do they do better by the visible than by the invisible method?

5. Which is the more fundamental number experience, counting or addition? Which should come first? Can one aid in learning the other? If so, how?

6. Do you know adults who count to find sums? Is it desirable that one have this habit? What is the probable cause of it? How would you prevent it?

7. How many combinations of one-digit numbers, exclusive of zero are there? How many facts? How many combinations and facts if zero is included?

8. What does the word "combination" mean? According to this meaning, can one make two combinations from two numbers? Look up the word "permutation." How does a permutation differ from a combination? Would you call addition facts "addition permutations"? Why or why not?

9. Using the numbers 5 and 9, state the addition facts and the subtraction facts which make up a teaching unit.

10. Do you know of any practical situations in which pupils must react to addition or subtraction facts involving zero and in which there are no numbers of two or more digits? What disadvantages are there in teaching the zero facts of addition and subtraction separately?

11. Ordinarily, how many combinations can a pupil be expected to learn in a lesson? When he is ready for them, how many zero combinations can he be expected to learn in a lesson?

12. What bases have been used in classifying combinations according to their difficulty? Which is better?

13. If investigators find that $1 + 9$ is much harder than $9 + 1$, should we avoid teaching these two facts together?

14. What advantages do you see in teaching the addition

facts and the subtraction facts of a teaching unit together? Should this be done for the first combinations studied? Why?

15. Which combinations did we place in the easier group? In the harder group? How many combinations and how many facts are there in each of these groups?

16. Have you known teachers to teach the combinations by simply telling the pupils the answers and then drilling? Do you see any advantages in this method? Any disadvantages?

17. Someone has said, "Telling is not teaching." Is this true? Is it always true?

18. Describe briefly how you would use objects in teaching that 5 and 4 are 9.

19. How can pupils use what they already know to discover something new in learning addition combinations?

20. Would you use objects in teaching all of the 45 basic additions? What other method can be used for the combinations in the more difficult group?

21. What advantage is there in having a pupil see that 9 + 8 must be 1 less than 10 + 8? Should the addition of 9 and 8 by this method be made a permanent habit? If not, how can it be avoided?

22. Is it better for a pupil to see that 9 + 8 is 1 more than 8 + 8 than that it is 1 less than 10 + 8? Is there any advantage in having him see both of these?

23. Have you known teachers to whom the word "drill" is very distasteful? What is responsible for the disrepute into which drill has fallen?

24. Would there be a serious loss if all drill in all subjects were eliminated?

25. When should abstract drills first be introduced?

26. Summarize instructions as you would give them for making and using flash cards. In this connection, read again the first part of Chapter I.

27. Describe a game which you have known teachers to use in arithmetic but which seems to you to be faulty. Point out the faults.

28. Write up the descriptions of several good games for use in providing practice on the addition and the subtraction combinations. Use games other than those described in this chapter.

29. What is the difference between a problem and an example? Which is the more important? Why?

30. What is the advantage in having a series of problems based upon the same situation. Are you accustomed to seeing problems of this kind in books designed for use in grades three and four?

31. Write a series of problems which you would use in grade one; a series which you would use in grade two.

32. What is the function of tests on the fundamentals of arithmetic in the primary grades? When should such tests be used? How should they be constructed?

33. Do you believe that it pays to make such a detailed analysis of the results of a test as is suggested in this chapter? Should this be done for all tests?

34. Why is it important that the pupils' methods of work be studied? If a pupil obtains right answers, does it matter as to how he obtains them?

CHAPTER TEST

On a sheet of paper, write a column of numbers to represent these statements. After each number write the word "True" or "False" as the case may be. Score your paper by using the key on page 405.

1. All entering first-grade pupils know some of the addition combinations.

2. First-grade pupils do better on tests on the combinations when objects are used than when problems are used.

3. When first-grade pupils give right answers to questions on addition combinations, we can assume that they know these combinations.

4. All first-grade pupils are ready for instruction on the easier addition combinations.

5. When work on the combinations is begun, the whole class should be instructed as a group.

6. Adding is the fundamental number experience.

7. Objective materials should be used in teaching the addition combinations.

8. The number of basic addition combinations without zeros is 81.

9. The zero combinations should be taught along with the rest.

10. The number of combinations, without zeros, whose sums do not exceed 10 is 25.

11. Each teaching unit includes four facts.

12. A subtraction fact belonging in the same teaching unit as $4 + 3 = 7$ is $4 - 3 = 1$.

13. The method of teaching the zero combinations should be different from the method of teaching the other combinations.

14. Usually, the combinations having smaller sums are easier than those having larger sums.

15. In general, it is easier to add a smaller number to a larger number than a larger number to a smaller number.

16. Clapp's difficulty list agrees closely with that of Knight and Behrens.

17. If a pupil has been taught $5 + 6$ but not $6 + 5$, it is probable that he will be able to give the sum for the latter if he knows the sum for the former.

18. Buckingham concluded that it is better to teach the addition and the subtraction facts together than separately.

19. All of the addition combinations must be presented through the use of objects.

20. The exact order in which the combinations are taken up is important.

21. Pupils should discover for themselves the answers for unfamiliar combinations.

22. Suggestions for teaching the addition facts apply also to the teaching of the subtraction facts.

23. Pupils' number understandings grow slowly.

24. The interval between the first work on the easier combinations and the first work on the harder combinations should be not less than a year.

25. Second grade pupils can learn that 16 means 10 and 6 more.

26. Pupils who know that 7 and 7 are 14 should see 8 + 7 as 1 more than 7 + 7.

27. Drills should not be used in the primary grades.

28. There are many phases of human learning which require drill.

29. Abstract drills were recommended for use in the first grade.

30. When pupils have reached the abstract stage in drill work, they have no further need for concrete number situations.

31. Flash card drills are best used with small homogeneous groups at a time.

32. Flash cards should have the combinations both with and without answers.

33. If a game is interesting to the pupils it is always valuable as a drill device.

34. The game "Bursting Balloons" was recommended.

35. Example solving is more important than problem solving.

36. Problems arise out of concrete situations.

37. Examples are pure abstractions.

38. Problems which appear in books arise out of the experiences of the children who solve them.

39. Printed or written problems should have an attractive story element.

40. The best use which the teacher can make of test papers is to assign percentage grades to them.

SELECTED REFERENCES

1. Beito, E. A. and Brueckner, Leo J. "A Measurement of Transfer in the Learning of Number Combinations." National Society for the Study of Education, *Twenty-Ninth Yearbook*. Bloomington, Illinois: Public School Publishing Company, 1930, pp. 569-587. Shows a large measure of transfer from one form of a combination to the other form.

2. Brownell, William A. and Chazal, Charlotte B. "The Effect of Premature Drill in Third-Grade Arithmetic." *Journal of Educational Research,* XXIX: 17-28, September, 1935. Shows that drill which comes ahead of understanding has little value.

3. Buckingham, B. R. "The Difficulty of the Number Combinations." *Journal of Educational Research,* XII: 387-391, December, 1925. Summarizes difficulty studies and suggests uses which teachers can make of such studies.

4. Buckingham, B. R. "Teaching Addition and Subtraction Facts Together or Separately." *Educational Research Bulletin,* VI: 228-229 and 240-242, May 25, 1927. Shows an advantage in teaching the facts together.

5. Buckingham, B. R. and MacLatchy, Josephine. "The Number Abilities of Children When They Enter Grade One." National Society for the Study of Education, *Twenty-Ninth Yearbook*. Bloomington, Illinois: Public School Publishing Company, 1930, pp. 473-524. Shows that entering first-grade pupils already have considerable ability with the addition combinations.

6. Clapp, Frank L. *The Number Combinations: Their Relative Difficulty and the Frequency of Their Appearance*

in Text-Books. Madison, Wisconsin: University of Wisconsin, 1924. 120 pp. This monograph reports in detail a study of the difficulty of number combinations in addition, subtraction, multiplication, and division.

7. Holloway, Harry Vance. *An Experimental Study to Determine the Relative Difficulty of the Elementary Number Combinations in Addition and Multiplication.* Philadelphia: University of Pennsylvania, 1914. 102 pp. This is the pioneer study of the difficulty of the number combinations and still quite worth reading.

8. Knight, F. B. "The Superiority of Distributed Practice in Drill in Arithmetic." *Journal of Educational Research,* XV: 157-165, March, 1927. Reports that an investigation made by Dr. Eva M. Luse indicates that it is desirable to include both forms of a combination in drill materials.

9. Knight, Frederic B. and Behrens, Minnie S. *The Learning of the 100 Addition Combinations and the 100 Subtraction Combinations.* New York: Longmans, Green and Company, 1928. 82 pp. Probably the best of the difficulty studies since it is concerned primarily with learning difficulties.

10. Lockhart, Lovine, Eldredge, A. C., and Brown, J. C. *Number Helps.* Chicago: Rand McNally and Company, 1924. 120 pp. Games for grades I, II, III, and IV, are described on pages 1-62.

11. Losh, Rosamond, and Weeks, Ruth Mary. *Number Helps.* Boston: Houghton Mifflin Company, 1923. 199 pp. Addition projects are given on pages 73-104 and subtraction projects on pages 105-112.

12. MacLatchy, Josephine H. "Counting and Addition." *Educational Research Bulletin,* XI: 96-100, February 17, 1932. Indicates a relationship between counting and acquaintance with addition combinations.

13. MacLatchy, Josephine H. "Another Measure of the Difficulty of Addition Combinations." *Educational Research*

Bulletin, XII: 57-61, March 8, 1933. Shows that the combinations in which a small number is added to a larger number are easier than those in which a larger number is added to a small number.

14. Olander, Herbert T. "Transfer of Learning in Simple Addition and Subtraction." *Elementary School Journal,* XXXI: 358-369 and 427-437, January and February, 1931. Indicates that those who are taught one form of a combination experience almost complete transfer to the other form. The facts are not learned as separate feats of memory but as a system of interrelated experiences.

15. Thiele, C. L. "The Mathematical Viewpoint Applied to the Teaching of Elementary School Arithmetic." National Council of Teachers of Mathematics, Tenth Yearbook, *The Teaching of Arithmetic.* New York: Bureau of Publications, Teachers College, Columbia University, 1935, pp. 212-232. Reports an experimental study which indicated that it pays to develop generalizations in teaching the basic combinations. Pages 215-223 contain results on the addition and the subtraction combinations.

16. Washburne, Carleton and Vogel, Mabel. "Are Any Number Combinations Inherently Difficult?" *Journal of Educational Research,* XVII: 235-255, April, 1928. Shows that difficulty is related to the size of the numbers but that the doubles are easier.

17. Wheat, Harry Grove. *The Psychology and Teaching of Arithmetic.* New York: D. C. Heath & Co., 1937. 591 pp. Chapter X offers suggestions for teaching the number facts up to 9. Those whose sums or minuends are 10 are developed in Chapter XII. Chapter XIV contains the remaining combinations.

CHAPTER 5

ELEMENTARY WORK IN ADDITION

Addition is not a single, simple ability; it is a complex of several abilities. To be able to add successfully, a pupil must not only know the 81 fundamental addition facts. He must also be able to do *column addition.* This soon leads him into *higher decade addition.* After a time he must know about *carrying.* Eventually, he may find himself temporarily baffled by *addends of unequal length.* And, finally, long columns will reveal that he has difficulties with *attention span.*

Easy column addition. When the pupil has learned the addition facts, he is ready for easier examples in column addition. The first of these will be three-digit columns and the digits will be selected so that the second addition in the column requires nothing more than one of the addition facts. Thus, if the digits 2, 3, and 4 are arranged in a column and in the order stated, the pupil will not only need to know that 2 and 3 are 5 but also that 5 and 4 are 9, if he is to add the column successfully. If he adds in the other direction, he must know that 4 and 3 are 7 and also that 7 and 2 are 9. In either event, to add the column one must know no more than the basic facts.

However, there is a difference between this and what the pupil has been accustomed to and there is an added difficulty. The difference and the added difficulty lie in the fact that the pupil must add a visible 4 to an invisible 5 in the one case and visible 2 to an invisible 7 in the other case. It is harder to react correctly to two addition facts when they appear in column addition examples as shown at the right than when they are stated separately, thus,

2	4
3	3
4	2

2	5		4	7	
3,	4,	or	3,	2.	

The pupil's first step forward from the basic facts in the direction of column addition should be to examples such as these in which there are three digits in a column and in which the sums do not exceed 10. Such column addition examples can be used after the 25 easier combinations have been taught. The teacher should attempt to prepare systematically a list of the possible three-digit column addition examples whose sums are 10 or less. The following 31 combinations of three digits each are all that can be written to conform to these requirements.

1	1	1	1	1	1	1	1
1	1	1	1	1	1	1	1
1	2	3	4	5	6	7	8
1	1	1	1	1	1	1	1
2	2	2	2	2	2	3	3
2	3	4	5	6	7	3	4
1	1	1	1	2	2	2	2
3	3	4	4	2	2	2	2
5	6	4	5	2	3	4	5
2	2	2	2	2	3	3	
2	3	3	3	4	3	3	
6	3	4	5	4	3	4	

In other words, there are no other combinations of three digits each whose sums do not exceed 10. But most of these columns can be formed into additional examples. If the three digits in a column are all the same number, no additional examples can be formed. There are three such in the group of 31, so these three columns make only three examples. If a column contains two digits which are alike and a third which is different, it gives us three examples. Thus, the second in the list provides the three examples,

$$\begin{array}{ccc} 1 & 1 & 2 \\ 1 & 2 & 1 \\ \underline{2} & \underline{1} & \underline{1} \end{array}$$

Since there are 17 of these in the list, they will make a total of 51 examples. A column containing three digits which are all different will make six examples. Thus, the second column in the second line provides the six examples,

$$\begin{array}{cccccc} 1 & 1 & 2 & 2 & 3 & 3 \\ 2 & 3 & 1 & 3 & 1 & 2 \\ \underline{3} & \underline{2} & \underline{3} & \underline{1} & \underline{2} & \underline{1} \end{array}$$

Since there are 11 of these in the list, they will make a total of 66 examples. Then, these 31 combinations of three digits each will make a total of 120 examples $(3 + 51 + 66 = 120)$.

In developing skill on examples of this kind, it is better for the teacher to provide practice on a wide variety of examples rather than to give concentrated practice on a few and to neglect others. Since there are only 31 three-digit combinations whose sums are 10 or less and since these produce only 120 examples, the teacher should write out the entire 120 in her notebook as a supply from which to draw in the preparation of sets of examples for practice. If a particular combination of three digits produces six examples, one of these six can be used on each of six days when it is desirable to give practice on examples of this kind. It will probably be feasible to use all of the 120 examples, eventually.

Other three-digit combinations. When the entire 45 addition combinations have been taught, three-digit column addition may be extended to include many more examples. The only requirement is that the sum of the first two numbers in the column shall not exceed 9. There are 79 additional three-digit combinations which satisfy this standard, that is, 79 in which the sum of the first two numbers does not exceed 9 and in which the sum of all three does exceed 10. These 79 three-digit combinations may be stated as follows:

1	1	1	1	1	1	1	1	1	1
1	2	2	3	3	3	4	4	4	4
9	8	9	7	8	9	6	7	8	9

1	1	1	1	1	1	1	1	1	1
5	5	5	5	5	6	6	6	6	7
5	6	7	8	9	6	7	8	9	7

1	1	1	1	2	2	2	2	2	2
7	7	8	8	2	2	2	3	3	3
8	9	8	9	7	8	9	6	7	8

2	2	2	2	2	2	2	2	2	2
3	4	4	4	4	4	5	5	5	5
9	5	6	7	8	9	5	6	7	8

2	2	2	2	2	2	2	2	3	3
5	6	6	6	6	7	7	7	3	3
9	6	7	8	9	7	8	9	5	6

3	3	3	3	3	3	3	3	3	3
3	3	3	4	4	4	4	4	4	5
7	8	9	4	5	6	7	8	9	5

3	3	3	3	3	3	3	3	4	4
5	5	5	5	6	6	6	6	4	4
6	7	8	9	6	7	8	9	4	5

4	4	4	4	4	4	4	4	4
4	4	4	4	5	5	5	5	5
6	7	8	9	5	6	7	8	9

Of course, these 79 three-digit combinations will produce more than 79 examples. In fact, they make possible just 204 arrangements in which the sum of the first two numbers does not exceed 9. Many of the possible arrangements can not be used until higher decade addition has been taught. Consider, for example, the last column in the set, that in which the numbers 4, 5, and 9 appear. Since these numbers are all different, we can make from them six possible examples of three digits each:

4	5	4	5	9	9
5	4	9	9	4	5
9	9	5	4	5	4

But only two can be used. These are the first two if we add downward and the last two if we add upward. The remaining four require the use of higher decade addition, a phase of addition for which the pupil is not yet prepared. The teacher will find it profitable to write out these 204 examples which may be formed from this set without the use of higher decade addition.

Naturally, when examples from these two sets are given for practice, they should be arranged in a miscellaneous order rather than in the systematic order in which they are given here.

These two sets, then, make possible 324 three-digit column addition examples which may be used for practice after the 45 fundamental combinations have been taught and before the pupil has been introduced to higher decade addition. It may not be necessary to use the entire 324 but it is well to have them at hand as a source of practice material.

Adding up or down. It is interesting to listen to the arguments which develop over whether one should add up or down. Cole[1] once undertook an investigation of the subject but his results were inconclusive. Buckingham[2] discusses the matter at some length, points out that we need an experimental attack on the subject to determine the method by which children learn better, and gives arguments in favor of adding downward. These are: (1) When we add downward, our eyes move as in ordinary reading; (2) we write our figures downward; (3) when we add downward, we arrive at the point where the answer figures are to be written when we are

---

[1] Cole, Lawrence W. "Adding Upward and Downward." *Journal of Educational Psychology,* III: 83-94, February, 1912.

[2] Buckingham, B. R. "Adding Up or Down: A Discussion." *Journal of Educational Research,* XII: 251-261. November. 1925.

ready to write them; and (4) upward adding means a complicated series of eye movements in carrying. In a later article, Buckingham[3] reports an experiment on upward and downward adding, carried on in seven centers, the results of which favored downward adding. Manuel[4] points out, however, that we should train pupils to add both ways.

It seems probable that the question as to which way one should add is not one of much importance. Eventually, one should learn to add both ways with equal facility for adding two ways provides a very valuable check on one's work. It seems to the author that in the light of the results of Buckingham's study, it is better to begin by adding downward, since a choice must be made and, as soon as possible, to add in both directions.

For the primary teacher, however, there is an important point here, namely, that in his early work in column addition the pupil should select one way to add and stick to it. We have just seen that many of the examples which can be formed from the three-digit combinations in the second set can be added in one way but not in the other until the pupil has had instruction in higher decade addition. And we shall see that many of the column addition examples that are provided to give practice on various higher decade combinations are constructed according to a definite plan as to the direction in which the pupil is to add. To add such columns in the direction opposite to the one intended means that the pupil

[3] Buckingham, B. R. "Upward versus Downward Addition." *Journal of Educational Research,* XVI: 315-322, December, 1927.

[4] Manuel, H. T. "Adding Up or Down: Another Consideration." *Journal of Educational Research,* XVII: 297-298, April, 1928.

gets practice on an entirely different series of combinations, fundamental and higher decade.

Adding longer columns. Pupils who have not yet been instructed in higher decade addition may also add four or more numbers in a column. If the column contains four one-digit numbers, the sum of the first three must not exceed 9. The fourth number can be any one of the one-digit numbers. The easiest approach to the preparation of such examples is to take the 120 examples which are derived from the 31 three-digit combinations in our first set, eliminate those for which the sum is 10, and add another digit to each of the others. Those for which the sum is 10 are:

1	1	1	1	2	2	2	3
1	2	3	4	2	3	4	3
8	7	6	5	6	5	4	4

These yield 36 examples. So, there are 23 three-digit combinations remaining and these make possible 84 examples. Since we may add any one of the numbers from 1 to 9 to each of these, we have 9 × 84, or 756 possible four-digit columns suited to our purposes.

However, it is probably not worth while for pupils to work very extensively on columns of more than three digits until training in higher-decade addition has been provided. Such work as is done, if any, should be done on examples selected from these 756 so as to give a desirable distribution of practice. The smallest sum for three digits in this group is 3 and the largest is 9. It is suggested that the most that we should want to do would be to provide for the addition of each of the numbers from 1 to 9 to each of these sums from 3 to 9. This can be done with 63 examples. The reader will find it worth while to prepare such a set of 63 examples.

Zeros in column addition. While teaching easy column addition, some teachers like to introduce zeros. This may be done, of course, *provided that there is a real setting for the examples.* The best plan seems to be to let the column represent scores on a game in which a score of 0 may be made at a turn. In this case, each pupil keeps his scores in a column and, in case he fails to score, represents the fact by a zero. Then the pupil is simply taught to skip the zeros in adding his column of scores. As already indicated, however, the author prefers to postpone the treatment of zeros in addition until examples containing numbers of two or more digits are taken up.

The need for higher decade addition. A pupil can not go very far in column addition until he has learned higher decade addition. A higher decade combination is defined as one in which a one-digit number is added to a number of two or more digits, usually only two digits. Ability to handle such combinations is absolutely necessary in most work in column addition and, as we shall see, in carrying in multiplication.

Suppose, for example, that a pupil is to add the example shown. If he adds downward, he must know first the sum of 4 and 7. This is one of the 81 basic addition facts. But he must also know the sum of 11 and 3, of 14 and 8, of 22 and 5, and of 27 and 6. The last four are higher decade addition combinations. The fact that a pupil knows the 81 addition facts does not guarantee at all that he will know the higher decade combinations also.

```
 4
 7
 3
 8
 5
 6
--
```

Until recently, many of the textbooks gave very little

space to the subject of higher decade addition. Even today, there are schools in which the subject receives scant attention. Pupils trained in such schools usually fall into one of two classes: (1) the few self-taught individuals, those who discover for themselves what to do about higher decade addition; and (2) those who count their way along after the partial sum becomes 10 or more. These counters often leave their footprints behind them, as it were, in the form of pencil dots sprinkled along the column.

The number of higher decade combinations. Theoretically, there is no limit to the number of higher decade addition combinations since such a combination has been defined as one in which a one-digit number is added to a number of two or more digits and there is no limit to the number of numbers containing two or more digits. Practically, however, one seldom adds a column the sum of which is more than 100, and pupils in the primary grades do not go this far, so there is a practical limit to the number of such combinations. If we add each of the numbers from 1 to 9 to each of the numbers from 10 to 90 and to the numbers in the 90's so that the sum does not exceed 99, we have 765 higher decade addition combinations whose sums are less than 100. There will be nine combinations for each number from 10 to 90 inclusive, making a total of 9×81, or 729 combinations. To 91 we add each of the numbers from 1 to 8, inclusive, making eight more combinations; to 92 we add each of the numbers from 1 to 7, inclusive; to 93, each of the numbers from 1 to 6, inclusive; and so on until the last combination, $98 + 1$, is reached. There will be in all, then, $729 + 8 + 7 + 6 + 5 + 4 + 3 + 2 + 1 = 765$ combinations.

But, as we shall see later, this does not mean 765 new combinations for the pupil to learn in the sense that he learns the basic 45. Furthermore, these 765 combinations are not equally important. Those which the pupils encounter most often are those in the teens, the twenties, the thirties, and, less frequently, in some of the higher decades. Those used in carrying in multiplication go as high as the eighties but most of them are in lower decades. Hence, the pupil's practice should be confined largely to those in the lower decades.

There are 45 of these higher decade combinations whose sums are in the teens. They may be set down systematically as the 45 fundamental combinations were arranged near the beginning of the last chapter. They are:

10	10	10	10	10	10	10	10	10
1	2	3	4	5	6	7	8	9
11	11	11	11	11	11	11	11	
1	2	3	4	5	6	7	8	
12	12	12	12	12	12	12		
1	2	3	4	5	6	7		
13	13	13	13	13	13			
1	2	3	4	5	6			
14	14	14	14	14				
1	2	3	4	5				

$$\begin{array}{rrrr} 15 & 15 & 15 & 15 \\ \underline{1} & \underline{2} & \underline{3} & \underline{4} \end{array}$$

$$\begin{array}{rrr} 16 & 16 & 16 \\ \underline{1} & \underline{2} & \underline{3} \end{array}$$

$$\begin{array}{rr} 17 & 17 \\ \underline{1} & \underline{2} \end{array}$$

$$\begin{array}{r} 18 \\ \underline{1} \end{array}$$

The sum of each of these higher decade combinations is in the same decade as is the larger addend. If the sum is in the next higher decade, "bridging" is required. That is, one is said to bridge from one decade to the next. This is often referred to as "bridging tens."

The combinations which require bridging are considerably more difficult for pupils than are those in which no bridging is required. Buswell and John[5] found that the average amount of time required for a higher decade combination in which bridging is involved is approximately twice as great as the average amount required for a combination without bridging.

There are 45 higher decade combinations requiring bridging from the teens to the twenties. They are shown on the next page.

In the same manner, one can continue producing sets of combinations. There are 45 in the twenties, 45 in which one bridges from the twenties to the thirties, etc. Up to 100, there are 17 of these sets of 45 combinations each.

---

[5] Buswell, G. T. and John, Lenore. *Diagnostic Studies in Arithmetic.* Chicago: The University of Chicago, 1926, Chapter III.

								11
								9
							12	12
							8	9
						13	13	13
						7	8	9
					14	14	14	14
					6	7	8	9
				15	15	15	15	15
				5	6	7	8	9
			16	16	16	16	16	16
			4	5	6	7	8	9
		17	17	17	17	17	17	17
		3	4	5	6	7	8	9
	18	18	18	18	18	18	18	18
	2	3	4	5	6	7	8	9
19	19	19	19	19	19	19	19	19
1	2	3	4	5	6	7	8	9

Higher decade addition in multiplication. In carrying in multiplication, many higher decade addition combinations are used. In multiplying 697 by 8, for example, one must carry 5 to 72 and 7 to 48. In other words, the higher decade addition combinations, 72 + 5 and 48 + 7 are involved in the solution of this example.

697
8

All of the higher decade addition combinations which are used in carrying in multiplication may also be used in column addition but not nearly all of those which may be used in column addition can be used in carrying in multiplication. The combination, 23 + 5, for instance, is frequently used in column addition but never in carrying in multiplication for the simple reason that 23 is not the product of any one of the multiplication combinations.

The higher decade addition combinations which are used in carrying in multiplication contain two-digit numbers which are products of multiplication combinations and one-digit numbers which are possible carry numbers. Let us see what these are.

The two-digit numbers which are products of multiplication combinations are easily seen to be 10, 12, 14, 15, 16, 18, 20, 21, 24, 25, 27, 28, 30, 32, 35, 36, 40, 42, 45, 48, 49, 54, 56, 63, 64, 72, and 81. They are the two-digit numbers which are factorable into two one-digit factors. These are the numbers to which carry numbers are added in multiplication, making higher decade addition combinations.

Now, the largest carry number which may arise from the use of any multiplying figure is one less than the number represented by that figure. Thus, if we are multiplying by 6, the largest carry number which we can have is 5; if we are multiplying by 8, the largest carry number possible is 7; etc. The reader may test this statement by multiplying 999 by 6, 8, and other one-digit numbers. Then, to determine what carry numbers may be used with each of the two-digit product numbers given in the last paragraph, we examine the product number to see what its largest one-digit factor is and conclude that the carry numbers run from 1 to one less than that factor. Consider, for example, the product number, 24. Its largest one-digit factor is 8. One less than 8 is 7. Then, the carry numbers which can be added to 24 in multiplication are 1, 2, 3, 4, 5, 6, and 7.

Table 1 presents in compact form the whole story of the higher decade addition combinations which are used in carrying in multiplication. The table (see page 138) is read as follows:

When the product number is 10, the possible carry numbers are 1, 2, 3, and 4. This means four higher decade addition combinations. They are 10 + 1, 10 + 2, 10 + 3, and 10 + 4. Bridging is required in none of these.

It will be seen that there are, in all, 175 higher decade addition combinations which are used in carrying in multiplication and that bridging is involved in 60 of these.

How to teach higher decade addition. It has already been stated that the higher decade addition combinations are not so many new combinations to be learned. Each higher decade combination, on the other hand, represents an opportunity for the pupil to extend the knowledge of the basic combinations which he already has. Thus, if the pupil encounters the combination, 15 + 3, he should know its relation to the familiar combination, 5 + 3. He knows, or should know, that 5 and 3 are 8. Then, he should easily see that 15 and 3 are 18. Likewise, when a pupil sees or thinks 18 + 4, he should recognize that 8 and 4 are 12 and think of a number above 18 which resembles 12. The number is 22; so 18

Table 1. Higher Decade Addition Combinations Used in Carrying in Multiplication.

Product Number	Carry Numbers	Number of Combinations	Number Requiring Bridging
10	1 – 4	4	0
12	1 – 5	5	0
14	1 – 6	6	1
15	1 – 4	4	0
16	1 – 7	7	4
18	1 – 8	8	7
20	1 – 4	4	0
21	1 – 6	6	0
24	1 – 7	7	2
25	1 – 4	4	0
27	1 – 8	8	6
28	1 – 6	6	5
30	1 – 5	5	0
32	1 – 7	7	0
35	1 – 6	6	2
36	1 – 8	8	5
40	1 – 7	7	0
42	1 – 6	6	0
45	1 – 8	8	4
48	1 – 7	7	6
49	1 – 6	6	6
54	1 – 8	8	3
56	1 – 7	7	4
63	1 – 8	8	2
64	1 – 7	7	2
72	1 – 8	8	1
81	1 – 8	8	0
	Total	175	60

and 4 are 22. Higher decade addition is often called "adding by endings" because of this relationship to the basic addition facts.

Furthermore, these higher decade combinations come in families. Thus, 15 + 3 is not only related to 5 + 3 but also to 25 + 3, 35 + 3, 45 + 3, etc. When the pupil studies higher decade addition, he should see these family relationships as well as the relationship of each family to one of the fundamental addition facts.

Those higher decade combinations in which the two-digit number is 10, 20, 30, etc., are related to basic zero facts. But we have recommended a postponement of the teaching of the zero facts. These higher decade combinations should present no difficulty, however, if the pupil has a fairly well developed understanding of our number system. The pupil should not find it hard to see that 10 and 4 are 14, that 20 and 3 are 23, that 40 and 6 are 46, etc. With these, there need be no reference to the basic addition facts.

Special attention should be given to those combinations which require bridging. There are 45 of these up to thirty, 90 up to forty, 135 up to fifty, etc. They are the more difficult combinations and are, therefore, the trouble makers. The related basic facts must be well known before these are attacked, that is, before the pupils are given columns to add whose sums are in the twenties or higher decades.

The teacher should keep in mind the fact that there is no carrying in higher decade addition. When the pupil adds 7 to 18, whether this combination occurs in a column or in carrying in multiplication, the result should be arrived at as a single act of thought and not by adding

7 and 8 and then carrying 1. Only in this way can one be efficient in column addition or in multiplication requiring carrying. Of course, at first the sum, 25, is arrived at by a more indirect route, just as the sum of 7 and 8 may at first be arrived at indirectly, but eventually the sum should come at once.

The chief use of higher decade addition lies in column addition; its secondary use, so far as frequency of occurrence is concerned, lies in carrying in multiplication. But higher decade combinations may also arise directly out of problem situations. For example, if Harry sold 22 papers before supper and 6 more after supper, he must add 6 to 22 to find the number that he sold that evening. Such problem situations are fairly frequent but higher decade addition will not occur nearly so frequently in situations such as this as in column addition and in carrying in multiplication. Most of the practice exercises which the teacher provides, then, should be in the form of column addition examples and multiplication examples. In the beginning, the practice should be confined to column addition for multiplication will not have been taught when the pupil is first ready for the type of column addition in which higher decade addition combinations are used.

Practice in higher decade addition. Practice in higher decade addition may be provided in both oral and written form. The oral drills may be conducted with flash cards, as were the drills in the fundamental combinations, or the teacher may simply dictate the combinations, calling upon individual pupils for responses. In these oral drills, the relation to basic addition facts and the family relationships should be emphasized. Thus, the teacher may ask for the sum of 3 and 6, then

13 and 6, 23 and 6, 43 and 6, etc.; or for the sum of 5 and 8, then 15 and 8, 35 and 8, 25 and 8, etc.

Written drills are better than oral drills in that they make possible a larger measure of participation on the part of each pupil. For written practice, it is well to prepare mimeographed or otherwise duplicated sheets of higher decade combinations. These will emphasize the relationship indicated in the last paragraph, particularly in the earlier practice periods. At first, practice may be limited to those which do not require bridging, then lessons may be devoted to those in which bridging is required, and, finally, the two kinds may be mixed. Practice should be distributed fairly evenly over the various family groups but gradually an increasing amount of attention should be given to those requiring bridging.

The higher decade combinations should be written in vertical form with the smaller number below if the pupil is being trained to do his first adding downward, as shown at the right. If he is being trained to add upward at first, with the larger number below, as shown.

```
32    24
 6     9
——    ——

 6     9
32    24
——    ——
```

If the fundamental combinations have been well taught and the higher decade combinations have been presented as an extension of these fundamental combinations, the pupil should have little difficulty with higher decade addition. He should not develop the counting habit, as so many do when they get beyond the fundamental facts, but should be able to give immediate responses.

Further work in column addition. When the pupil is learning higher decade addition, he should have an opportunity to use it as soon as possible in column addition examples. When he has learned 11 + 5, for instance, the column addition example on the right may be given (assuming that he adds downward) as a means of putting to use his recently acquired skill.

$$\begin{array}{r} 6 \\ 2 \\ 3 \\ \underline{5} \end{array}$$

Further work in column addition should be very carefully planned so as to give practice on each of the higher decade combinations which have been taught. Furthermore, these column addition examples may well be so constructed as to give practice on each of the fundamental addition facts. Since these fundamental facts must be used in column addition, the columns might as well be constructed so as to give practice on all 81 of them at first and then so as to give special emphasis to those which are the more difficult. The mere random arrangement of digits in columns is likely to mean that some of these combinations, primary and higher decade, are given an undue proportion of attention in the drill lessons and that others are neglected.

This means that a series of practice sheets should be arranged so as to provide drill on the fundamental facts and on the higher decade combinations in a systematic manner. The following sets of column addition examples have been devised to illustrate how this may be accomplished. The first set contains 45 examples and provides practice on each of the 81 primary facts and on each of the 45 higher decade combinations whose sums are in the teens. To prepare this set, the 81 fundamental facts were written out on one sheet of paper and the 45 higher decade combinations on another. Then they were checked off as they were worked into examples. The first 36 examples contain two facts each and the last 9 one fact each. Of course, each example contains a higher decade combination. Zeros have been omitted. The assumption is again made that the pupil will add downward but each column may be reversed if it is desired that he add upward.

Practice Examples in Column Addition. Set 1

Higher Decade Combinations in the Teens

3	2	1	1	1	7	5	5	3
5	5	7	1	2	1	2	3	6
6	5	2	8	7	3	6	7	5
3	4	7	2	1	6	3	2	4
2	1	2	1	8	6	6	4	2
6	8	1	3	1	2	3	4	7
4	1	8	6	2	5	6	8	3
5	8	1	3	7	4	3	1	6
3	1	7	4	5	2	4	1	2
1	4	2	5	4	2	1	5	3
7	5	4	7	8	8	6	4	7
2	4	5	2	1	1	3	5	2
3	3	5	1	2	4	3	4	6
3	2	1	6	4	3	4	2	1
8	8	5	3	6	7	8	7	4
1	1	4	6	3	2	1	2	5
1	3	5	4	2	6	9	7	8
9	9	9	9	9	9	9	9	9
9	7	5	6	8	4	1	3	2

The second set also contains 45 examples. It is designed to give practice on those 45 higher decade combinations whose sums are in the twenties and which involve bridging from the teens to the twenties. This set uses only 45 of the 81 primary facts. These 45 facts are those whose sums are 10 or more. Each of the 45 higher decade combinations whose sums are in the teens are also reviewed in this set. In other words, a pupil makes three additions in each of these 45 examples. The first of these is a primary fact with a sum equal to or greater than 10; the second is a higher decade combination with a sum in the teens; the third is a higher decade combination with a sum in the twenties. No primary fact or higher decade combination occurs twice in this set. If the purpose of the set is to be realized, the pupil must add downward. If he is to add upward, each column should be reversed.

Practice Examples in Column Addition. Set 2

Sums in the Twenties

9	2	7	9	6	5	7	8	6
2	8	8	4	6	5	4	4	8
5	5	1	3	1	2	6	5	1
8	9	4	6	9	8	5	7	5

7	8	5	7	6	3	6	5	9
3	2	6	9	7	7	5	7	8
1	7	2	1	6	9	7	7	2
9	4	7	8	7	4	6	1	9

7	4	4	3	6	4	8	3	8
7	6	9	9	9	7	5	8	6
3	8	1	6	3	1	2	8	4
6	7	8	2	4	9	7	6	3

8	6	4	9	5	9	9	9	1
8	4	8	6	8	5	9	3	9
3	4	2	2	4	2	1	4	3
8	7	6	9	3	7	2	9	8

8	9	9	8	8	7	2	5	7
3	7	1	7	9	6	9	9	5
3	2	6	4	1	5	4	5	3
9	9	5	3	8	5	6	5	8

It may be added, parenthetically, that it is not intended that all 45 examples in either of these sets be given in a single practice period. These sets of practice examples are intended for the teacher's use in such numbers and at such times as seems best. They illustrate how such sets of examples may be prepared. Later an entire set may be used as a review test.

Set 3, which also contains 45 examples, provides practice on 135 higher decade combinations—the 45 in the teens, the 45 in which bridging to the twenties is required, and the 45 in the twenties. The 45 primary facts whose sums are 10 or more are again reviewed in this set. Set 3, in other words provides for further drill on the 45 higher decade combinations in the teens and the 45 which bridge to the twenties and also provides for practice on the 45 which are in the twenties.

Practice Examples in Column Addition. Set 3

Sums in the Twenties

8	9	6	7	9	8	4	7	5
4	2	6	4	6	2	7	7	8
3	6	7	2	2	4	5	3	1
7	3	4	9	9	6	6	4	7
5	8	1	6	2	2	3	6	4

3	8	6	8	1	7	9	5	9
7	8	5	3	9	6	9	5	1
2	3	4	1	6	3	1	3	9
8	1	6	9	7	8	7	7	2
4	5	1	2	5	4	3	1	5

2	7	6	9	3	9	8	5	4
9	9	8	4	8	7	5	6	9
8	2	1	5	7	1	2	3	6
9	4	8	7	2	7	5	8	6
1	2	3	4	7	2	6	4	1

8	9	7	6	7	9	6	5	4
6	3	3	7	5	5	4	7	8
2	6	1	4	2	5	7	1	5
9	8	9	8	9	8	5	8	6
3	1	3	2	2	1	7	7	4

7	8	6	9	4	5	2	8	3
8	9	9	8	6	9	8	7	9
3	1	4	2	5	4	8	1	4
6	9	3	5	9	3	5	4	5
5	2	1	1	3	8	6	9	3

In this manner, cumulative practice on the higher decade combinations can be systematically provided while a thorough review is given to the fundamental facts which are most likely to need it. The preparation of such sets of examples requires painstaking care and is somewhat laborious but the advantage gained is worth the effort.

Longer columns, providing practice on combinations in the thirties and higher decades, may be prepared. Naturally, it is not necessary in each set to include reviews of all items previously considered. Emphasis should be given to those which require bridging since they are more difficult than the others. Set 4 is arranged primarily to give practice on combinations whose sums are in the thirties. Each of the 45 in which one bridges from the twenties to the thirties and each of the 45 whose sums are in the thirties without bridging in the last addition are included in this set. This set also provides for practice on 23 of those higher decade combinations whose sums are in the teens, for 30 which involve bridging from the teens to the twenties, for 12 which have both addends in the twenties, and for the 45 primary facts whose sums are greater than 9.

Practice Examples in Column Addition. Set 4
Higher Decade Combinations in the Thirties

1	9	9	5	6	7	5	6	8
9	1	2	5	5	4	8	7	6
2	3	3	4	6	6	6	8	7
9	9	8	9	7	8	8	7	6
9	8	9	8	8	7	6	5	8
6	3	7	3	7	2	4	2	1

9	8	9	5	8	2	7	7	6
6	7	5	7	3	8	9	6	6
7	5	8	5	5	4	7	7	7
6	9	7	9	8	9	4	5	8
7	6	4	6	7	7	9	9	5
4	2	5	6	1	2	2	3	3

3	8	9	5	4	8	3	8	6
8	2	7	9	9	4	7	8	8
5	5	6	7	6	6	6	5	4
9	9	6	5	9	8	9	8	9
6	6	8	8	4	5	5	7	7
5	9	1	1	5	2	7	3	4

8	3	7	9	7	5	4	4	8
5	9	3	9	7	6	8	6	9
8	6	7	5	5	7	8	8	6
8	9	9	5	9	6	8	9	6
3	4	4	9	6	9	3	3	8
1	6	1	1	2	3	8	4	2

6	7	9	6	9	7	9	4	2
9	5	3	4	8	8	4	7	9
8	6	8	9	5	4	5	4	9
6	7	9	9	7	7	8	8	9
5	8	2	2	9	9	7	9	1
5	1	4	8	1	3	6	4	5

Addition practice preliminary to carrying in multiplication. We have seen that there are 175 higher decade addition combinations which are used in carrying in multiplication and that in 60 of these, bridging is required. There is nothing about these combinations which makes them intrinsically harder than other higher decade addition combinations but they come to the pupil in a form which differs somewhat from the others. It seems desirable, then, to give special attention to these when the pupil is ready to take up multiplication with carrying.

When a higher decade addition combination occurs in column addition, the two-digit number is not visible to the pupil but the one-digit number is. In carrying in multiplication, however, neither of the two numbers is visible. It is well, then, that the pupil be given practice on these combinations in a form which provides that neither of the two numbers is visible.

Again, we should remember that those combinations which require carrying are the combinations which are most likely to cause difficulty. We have seen that there are 60 of these. They are:

14 6	16 4	16 5	16 6	16 7	18 2	18 3	18 4	18 5	18 6
18 7	18 8	24 6	24 7	27 3	27 4	27 5	27 6	27 7	27 8
28 2	28 3	28 4	28 5	28 6	35 5	35 6	36 4	36 5	36 6
36 7	36 8	45 5	45 6	45 7	45 8	48 2	48 3	48 4	48 5
48 6	48 7	49 1	49 2	49 3	49 4	49 5	49 6	54 6	54 7
54 8	56 4	56 5	56 6	56 7	63 7	63 8	64 6	64 7	72 8

There will be a benefit in giving these in written form but if the oral form is used, we have a condition more nearly approximating that which prevails in carrying in multiplication; that is, both numbers are invisible.

Another interesting form of drill exercise for this purpose is one which has been suggested by Thorndike.[6] It may be stated as follows:

6 9 3 7 4 8 5

(a) Multiply each of these numbers by 2 and add 1 to the product.

(b) Multiply each of the numbers by 3 and add 1 to the product.

(c) Multiply each of the numbers by 3 and add 2 to the product.

(d) Multiply each of the numbers by 4 and add 1 to the product; add 2 to the product; add 3 to the product.

(e) Continue in this manner, adding to the product any number from 1 to the number which is one less than the multiplier.

It will be seen that this exercise provides practice both on those combinations which require bridging and on those which do not.

Not all of this exercise should be used at the beginning of the pupil's work in multiplication with carrying. When he is ready to use 2 as a multiplier, he should have the practice indicated by (a); when he is ready to use 3 as a multiplier, he should have the practice indicated by (b) and (c); etc.

This exercise is quite difficult at first but no more difficult than carrying in multiplication. It is an excellent device in that it duplicates almost exactly the

---

[6] Thorndike, Edward Lee. *The New Methods in Arithmetic.* Chicago: Rand McNally and Company, 1921, p. 92.

conditions which prevail in a multiplication example; both of the numbers to be added are invisible. Furthermore, the device gives excellent review practice on the multiplication combinations.

Addends of two or more digits. Long before the pupil has gone as far in column addition as the examples in the preceding sets of practice exercises indicate, he will have his attention directed to examples having fewer addends but two or more digits in an addend. The first of these will be pairs of two-digit numbers arranged so as to avoid carrying but so as to give practice on each of the primary addition facts. If zeros have been introduced, and they may well be introduced at this time, the entire 100 primary facts can be included in a single set of practice examples. If the examples are made up of two two-digit numbers, it will require a minimum of 50 examples to include all of these. The following set does just this.

24	37	86	63	64	26	50	71	70	82
91	82	51	45	65	20	74	74	61	86
44	50	15	44	82	70	91	66	96	73
72	50	90	34	75	36	41	82	53	93
88	50	41	97	50	67	91	52	51	30
20	99	62	31	62	72	80	43	98	98
73	94	42	25	69	10	91	73	98	82
42	10	91	81	50	53	23	86	91	30
83	41	70	95	87	63	30	31	85	52
90	86	57	73	40	91	75	47	62	84

In the same manner, practice may be systematically distributed over the basic facts with addends of more than two digits. However, the emphasis upon the easier facts should be gradually reduced and that on the harder facts gradually increased. Also, examples containing more than two addends of two or more digits each may be used before carrying is taught.

Introducing the pupils to carrying. A common procedure when the pupils are introduced to carrying, is for the teacher simply to tell the pupils that when the sum of the first column is a two figure number they should write down the right-hand figure only and carry the other figure to the next column. Superficially observed, this seems to get results. That is, the pupils do what they are told to do and they get right answers. But here, as in many other places, in elementary education, *telling is not teaching.* The pupil whose early acquaintance with carrying is limited to this type of experience follows blindly where his teacher leads; he does not understand what he does or why he does it.

There is no one best way to rationalize the process of carrying. The explanation to be offered will have to depend upon the pupils and what they already understand about our number system. A pupil who understands that 18 means 1 ten and 8 ones and that 14 means 1 ten and 4 ones can probably see that when 18 and 14 are added we first get 12 ones, that is equal to 1 ten and 2 ones, and that it is reasonable to write down a 2 to represent the 2 ones and count the ten in with the other tens. But this explanation will probably be "over the heads" of most pupils at the time when addition with carrying is usually introduced.

$$\begin{array}{r} 18 \\ \underline{14} \end{array}$$

A much more concrete explanation can be set up by using coins. The teacher says, "If Tommy made 18 cents selling papers Monday evening and 14 cents Tuesday evening, how much money did he make in the two evenings? We can write down 18 cents and 14 cents this way:

18 cents. This is the same as 1 dime and 8 cents.
14 cents. This is the same as 1 dime and 4 cents.

Then we place 1 dime and 8 cents (8 one-cent pieces, not a nickel and three cents) on the table and beneath the dime we place another dime and beneath the 8 cents we place 4 more cents. Now, we see that we have altogether 2 dimes and 12 cents. But we know that 12 cents is the same as 1 dime and 2 cents so we can exchange 10 cents for a dime. We pick up 10 of the 12 cents and place a dime on the table in their place. Now we see that we have 3 dimes and 2 cents and we know that this is the same as 32 cents. Then we can show what we have done on the blackboard in this way:

18 cents. This is the same as 1 dime and 8 cents.
14 cents. This is the same as 1 dime and 4 cents.
32 cents. This is the same as 2 dimes and 12 cents.

Or, again, we may write:

18 cents. This is the same as 1 dime and 8 cents.
14 cents. This is the same as 1 dime and 4 cents.
32 cents. This is the same as 3 dimes and 2 cents."

This statement about the equivalence of the 18 cents and the 14 cents will not have to be written three times. It need be written only once. Then the third line may be added when we are ready for it and later changed as shown.

An old-time device, and still a very useful one, for teaching the meaning of carrying is the use of bundles of splints. The number 18 is represented by a bundle of 10 splints and 8 loose splints. This scheme is often used to show the meaning of such a number as 18. Likewise, the number 14 is represented by a bundle of 10 splints and 4 splints more. When the two numbers, 18 and 14, are added we have the process concretely represented by two bundles of 10 splints each and 12 splints more. But 12 splints will make a bundle of 10 splints with 2 splints left over. The teacher then proceeds to tie up 10 splints into a bundle. We have in all, then, three bundles of 10 splints each and 2 splints more, or 32 splints. Then 18 and 14 are 32.

The coins probably make a more realistic and better understood illustration. However, the use of both devices will do no harm. Whichever device is used, one or two additional examples should be worked out in the same way. Eventually, however, the pupil should be able to break away from such concrete representations and see the carrying operations in terms of the abstract numbers alone. If such numbers are understood, the example above may be reviewed as follows:

TEACHER. How many tens in 18?
PUPIL. One.
TEACHER. How many units (*or ones*) in 18?
PUPIL. Eight.
TEACHER. How many tens in 14?
PUPIL. One.
TEACHER. And how many units (*or ones*)?

$$\begin{array}{r} 18 \\ \underline{14} \\ 32 \end{array}$$

PUPIL. Four.

TEACHER. Then, if we add eight units and four units, how many shall we have?

PUPIL. Twelve.

TEACHER. But how many tens in twelve?

PUPIL. One.

TEACHER. And how many units?

PUPIL. Two.

TEACHER. Let us, then, carry our one ten over to the other tens and write our two units under the 8 and 4. Then, how many tens do we have?

PUPIL. Three.

TEACHER. And our answer is 32, which is what we got with the coins (*or splints*). Let us remember, then, that if the sum of the first column is ten or more, we should write down the right-hand figure only and carry the other figure to the next column.

The first work with carrying may well be limited to examples in which the number carried is always 1, but pupils should quite early be given practice in carrying 2 and 3. If they are held very long to examples in which the number carried is always 1, they are likely to associate "carry" with "carry one" regardless of the examples, and, from force of habit, carry 1 when a larger number is to be carried.

When three-digit addends are taken up, there can be no carrying, there can be carrying from the first column only, from the second column only, and, finally, from both columns. It is well, in such examples, to provide for each of these conditions. Eventually, the various kinds of examples should be mixed freely in sets of practice exercises.

Writing the number carried. Opinion differs as to the

wisdom of writing the number which is to be carried. In examples that will be used in the primary grades—examples of few addends and few digits in each addend—writing the carry number will, of course, not be advisable. The carry number will, of course, be added in at once in the next column. In the addition of long columns, however, it is probably best to write the carry number at the top of the next column. This not only permits one to take up his work where left off, if interrupted, but also makes it possible to check the columns separately to detect errors.

Whether examples long enough to justify writing the carry numbers should be given in the elementary school is again a question. Perhaps this crutch should not be used at all in the elementary school until its benefits have been experimentally determined.

Variety in addition practice. An extensive variety of kinds of addition examples may be prepared by varying the number of addends and the number of digits in each addend. If, for example, we have addends of two, three, or four digits each and two, three, four, five, or six addends, we can have fifteen kinds of addition examples. Considerably greater variety may be introduced by using addends of different lengths in the same example.

It is usually necessary for the teacher to prepare sets of addition examples to supplement those provided by a textbook. Lack of space prohibits our supplying them here but the method of preparation is similar to that employed in preparing the sets of examples in column addition. The teacher should keep in mind the following suggestions:

1. Use a wide variety of examples, as suggested above.
2. Provide that the pupils shall frequently carry numbers other than 1.
3. See that each of 81 primary facts is given occasional practice and that the harder facts are used more often than are the easier facts.
4. Provide for a variety of practice on the higher decade combinations and see that special practice is given to those which require bridging.
5. When zeros have been introduced, use them frequently and in a variety of situations.

Addends of unequal length. Some pupils have difficulty in addition when the addends are of unequal length. Tests show that pupils sometimes become confused and make mistakes when compelled to jump gaps in addition columns as in the example shown. This difficulty exists when printed test forms are used and the figures are equally spaced, of uniform size, and placed in straight columns. If the pupil writes his own examples, he is still more likely to have difficulty with addends of unequal length because of irregularities in the way he sets down his numbers.

```
4625
  14
 372
   6
  25
----
```

If the pupil pauses at a blank space in a column and wonders what to do, there is a chance that he may lose the partial sum which he has obtained to that point. In the example shown, for instance, if the pupil has added the first column, recorded a 2 in the answer space, carried a 2 to the next column, and then, adding downward, has obtained a partial sum of 12, the confusion which he experiences upon reaching the blank space may cause him to lose the 12. In this way, errors are sometimes produced.

Teachers sometimes try to avoid the difficulty which is caused by addends of unequal length by having the blank spaces filled in with zeros so as to make all the addends have the same number of digits, as shown. This device may be quite harmless as a means of showing that certain orders are unoccupied but it should be used sparingly, if at all, lest the practice become a permanent one with some pupils. Like most crutches, it may quite well do more harm than good. The author occasionally finds students in college classes who still follow this practice.

```
4625
0014
0372
0006
0025
----
```

However, teaching children to add numbers of unequal length is, in a way, like teaching them to add zeros. Eventually, the pupils learn to jump the zeros—to ignore them completely as if they were not there. In the same way, they learn to jump the blank spaces.

It will be apparent that it is quite important that the pupils learn to write figures that are neat and of uniform size and to write them in straight columns and to space them equally. Careless figure writing is often the cause of the mistakes of pupils who have no trouble with printed examples. Some teachers seem to assume that since figure writing has been taught in one of the lower grades they need give the matter no further attention. On the other hand, through the years of the elementary school, there should be occasional brief periods devoted to practice in writing numbers. The difficulties which children have in adding addends of unequal length will help to motivate such practice periods.

Speed versus accuracy. Speed is much less important than accuracy. Accuracy should be the primary objective. It is important to remember, however, that the same habits which yield accurate results will also produce speed, and *vice versa.* Elaborate and roundabout methods of work reduce speed and they also produce errors. Speed is merely a symptom of mastery; that is, if the pupil shows satisfactory speed, this is a pretty good sign that he has mastered the fundamentals of addition. And, if he has mastered these fundamentals, he will make few mistakes. If the pupil is well taught, speed will probably take care of itself and will be determined largely by the individual's reaction time.

Some pupils are naturally much slower than others in any thing which they do. Efforts to drive the slow-reacting, deliberate pupil to greater speed will be ruinous to his results in addition if they have any effect at all. But if a pupil is slow, the teacher must be sure that she knows *why* he is slow. His slowness may be due to bad habits which do not appear on the surface. Hence, the importance of individual work with pupils to find out just what they do when they add, that is, just *how* they add. If bad habits are discovered, they should be corrected. Mere efforts to speed up the work will not correct them. Thus, if a pupil counts his way up or down a column, the most that insistence upon greater speed is likely to do is to make him count faster. As the corrective work gets under way, a little pressure on a pupil as to the speed of his work will help to prevent his slipping back into his old habits, but the corrective work must precede efforts to increase the pupil's speed.

When the teacher works with a pupil individually and asks him to "say out loud what you think as you add this example," she often discovers the presence of elaborate language responses. In adding the column 4
shown, for example, the pupil may say, "Four and 8
eight are twelve, and twelve and six are eighteen, 6
and eighteen and five are twenty-three, and twenty- 5
three and seven are thirty, and thirty and nine are 7
thirty-nine." This is wasteful. 9

When the pupil is learning to add columns, he may not be able to go any faster whether he makes this elaborate language response or not. But later, when he can add with greater speed, so far as his knowledge of the combinations is concerned, he is likely to be held down to the speed with which he can make the language response. Hence, early in the pupil's experience with column addition the teacher should encourage him to cut short his language responses and eventually to say, simply, "Twelve, eighteen, twenty-three, thirty, thirty-nine." Many teachers are surprised when they make individual diagnoses of pupils' methods of work and discover that they have been making implicitly such elaborate responses.

Checking answers. The habit of checking answers is of fundamental importance. The place to develop and fix this habit is in the primary grades. In the intermediate grades and in the upper grades, pupils are often supplied with textbooks containing answers, and, as a result, there may be little incentive for checking. Whatever we may say of the use of prepared sets of answers in higher grades, we can most heartily condemn them in the primary grades where the curriculum consists largely of simple problems and examples requiring the use of the fundamental operations with integers. Because the habit of checking should be established early and because there is an incentive for checking where pupils are not supplied with answers, it is incumbent upon the primary teacher to see to it that the pupils regularly and systematically check all of their addition examples, except, perhaps, when tests allow insufficient time.

Checks in the primary grades should be very simple and should be easily applied. In addition, there are probably only two checks which the primary teacher will wish to use. They are: (1) repeating the addition in the same direction; and (2) repeating the addition but in the opposite direction.

Repeating the addition in the same direction is the more easily applied check, for it is simply a repetition of what the pupil has already done. Its objection lies in the fact that when a pupil has made an error, he tends to repeat that error on the second and later addings. Since the sum, up to the point where the error was made, is the same each time, adding the number represented by the next digit is likely to give the result secured before on account of the association which has been established between that result and the previous sum.

It is better, then, to check by adding in the opposite direction. If the first adding was downward, check by adding upward; if the first adding was upward, check by adding downward. This combining of numbers in a different order gives partial sums different from those secured by the first adding and thus makes it highly improbable that a former error will be repeated.

In early work in column addition given before higher decade addition has been learned, however, this check can not be applied. The example shown can be added downward by using none but the basic addition facts, but if it is added upward, the higher decade combination, 13 + 2, is involved. In such cases, the only check which can be used satisfactorily is a repetition of the former adding process. It is quite important that the teacher should not lose sight of details such as this in planning practice exercises in the fundamental operations.

$$\begin{array}{r} 2 \\ 6 \\ \underline{7} \end{array}$$

Attention span. Attention span difficulties do not often develop in the primary grades. Columns which are ordinarily added in these grades are seldom long enough to cause attention span difficulties. This subject should be treated in a volume devoted to arithmetic teaching in the intermediate and higher grades.

QUESTIONS AND REVIEW EXERCISES

1. What is meant by the statement that addition is a complex of several abilities? What are these abilities?

2. A superintendent once said, "Addition is very simple. Either you can add or you can't add." Have you known teachers to develop their programs on the apparent assumption that addition is such a simple matter? What is the probable effect of such a program on pupils?

3. In what respect may it be more difficult for a pupil to add 2, 3, and 4 in a column than to add 2 and 3 and then 5 and 4 separately?

4. Can you satisfy yourself that the 31 three-digit com-

binations given are all of the three-digit combinations whose sums do not exceed 10?

5. How many three-digit examples can be made from three digits if they are all different? If two and only two are alike? If all three are alike?

6. Is it desirable that one be able to add upward and downward with equal facility? Why? Do you find one way easier than the other?

7. Why is it important that the primary teacher select one direction for the first column addition of her pupils and use this direction only for a time?

8. Under what conditions would you use zeros in column addition?

9. What is higher decade addition? What are its two chief uses? Which of these two uses is the more important?

10. How many higher decade addition combinations are there in the teens? The twenties? The thirties?

11. Can we assume that if pupils know the fundamental combinations they will make the transition to higher decade addition without help from the teacher?

12. What is meant by "bridging" in higher decade addition?

13. What is the largest possible carry number which can be obtained if the multiplier is 2? 6? 8? 9?

14. Select from the following list of higher decade addition combinations those which may be used in carrying in multiplication.

14	15	20	21	28	35	38	56	63	68
4	6	5	2	6	7	4	8	7	5

In each case, state the multiplier or multipliers which could be used in examples that would cause the worker to use these higher decade combinations in carrying.

15. Is every two-digit number which is factorable into two one-digit factors a number which may be used in a higher

decade addition combination in carrying in multiplication?

16. Why is higher decade addition sometimes referred to as "adding by endings."

17. Outline the steps you would take in a lesson designed to introduce children to the subject of higher decade addition.

18. Should a pupil learn the higher decade addition combinations one at a time? Discuss.

19. Which method of practice on higher decade addition do you believe is best for training pupils to do column addition? For training pupils to carry in multiplication?

20. Does one carry when he adds a higher decade addition combination? Discuss.

21. If you were to prepare a set of column addition examples which would provide practice on each of the 81 basic addition facts, on each of the 45 higher decade combinations in the teens, and on each of the 45 higher decade combinations which require bridging from the teens to the twenties, how would you proceed? Is it worth while to go to the trouble which the preparation of such a set requires? Why?

22. If pupils have been well trained in column addition and the higher decade addition which is involved, is there need for further training in higher decade addition before taking up carrying in multiplication? Why?

23. Why do pupils who do not count in doing the primary addition combinations sometimes count in adding columns?

24. What explanation of the meaning of carrying do you believe would be the most intelligible to pupils? Would you offer more than one explanation?

25. Is telling ever teaching? Ordinarily, would you say that telling is teaching? Why?

26. Would you teach children in primary grades to write the number carried?

27. Why do pupils have difficulty in adding addends of

unequal length. How would you undertake to dispose of these difficulties?

28. Which is the more important, speed or accuracy? Why? Are both important?

29. What is meant by the statement that "speed is a symptom of mastery"?

30. How should pupils check their answers in addition when they begin to add columns? Later?

CHAPTER TEST

Decide whether each statement is true or false and check your decision by the key on page 405.

1. Addition ability is a single, simple ability.
2. Column addition can be begun before higher decade addition is taught.
3. In column addition, all of the elements of a combination are visible.
4. Three different one-digit numbers permit the formation of six three-digit column addition examples.
5. It has been scientifically determined that it is better to add up than down.
6. Pupils should eventually learn to add both ways with equal facility.
7. In early work in column addition, all adding should be done in one direction.
8. Examples prepared for upward adding will have as great value for training purposes if added downward.
9. One-column addition examples in normal life experience frequently contain zeros.
10. Higher decade addition combinations are always cases of adding a one-figure number to a two-figure number.
11. Higher decade addition requires carrying.
12. There are 45 higher decade addition combinations in the teens.

13. Higher decade addition combinations which require bridging are more difficult than those which do not require bridging.

14. Each higher decade addition combination should be learned as a separate isolated fact.

15. The higher decade combination, 25 + 5, is used in carrying in multiplication.

16. All higher decade combinations which are used in column addition may be used in carrying in multiplication.

17. All higher decade combinations which are used in carrying in multiplication may be used in column addition.

18. The largest carry number which can arise from the use of a one-figure multiplier is one less than the multiplier.

19. In the typical person's experience, the combination, 54 + 3, is more important than the combination, 53 + 3.

20. Higher decade addition combinations resemble the basic addition facts.

21. The higher decade addition combinations in one decade resemble the higher decade addition combinations in another decade.

22. The chief use of higher decade addition lies in carrying in multiplication.

23. Sheets of examples for practice on higher decade addition should have those examples in the equation form.

24. If a pupil is trained to add upward, a higher decade combination should appear in the form, $\begin{array}{r}5\\ \underline{24}\end{array}$.

25. It is possible to prepare a set of 45 one-column addition examples so as to provide practice on each of the 81 primary facts.

26. In preparing sets of column addition examples, the numbers should be chosen at random.

27. If the multiplier is 8, the largest possible carry number is 8.

28. In most instances, telling is not teaching.

29. In adding 14, 18, and 19, pupils should simply be told to carry the 2.

30. Pupils in the primary grades should be told to write down their carry numbers.

31. If addends are of unequal length, the blank spaces should be filled in with zeros.

32. Teaching children to add numbers of unequal length is like teaching them to add zeros.

33. Speed is less important than accuracy.

34. Speed may be looked upon as a symptom of mastery.

35. The pupil's implicit responses are readily apparent from an examination of his test paper.

36. The early development of elaborate habits of language response may have a permanent effect upon the pupil's speed in addition.

37. Ordinarily, the best check is to add again in the opposite direction.

38. Textbooks for third-grade pupils should contain answers.

39. In the pupil's first work in column addition, he should check by adding again in the same direction.

40. Attention span difficulties arise frequently in the primary grades.

SELECTED REFERENCES

1. Brownell, William A. *The Development of Children's Number Ideas in the Primary Grades.* Chicago: The University of Chicago, 1928, pp. 144-190. This chapter of an excellent monograph leads to the conclusion that the teaching of three-digit addition depends upon the teaching of the basic facts and that this, in turn, depends upon an adequate understanding of number.

2. Brueckner, Leo J. *Diagnostic and Remedial Teaching in Arithmetic.* Philadelphia: The John C. Winston Com-

pany, 1930, pp. 110-124. Reports diagnostic studies of the difficulties which pupils experience in adding.

3. Buckingham, B. R. "Adding Up or Down: A Discussion." *Journal of Educational Research,* XII: 251-261, November, 1925. Reports a questionnaire investigation of the direction in which students in teacher-training institutions add and of their preferences. Gives arguments in favor of downward adding.

4. Buckingham, B. R. "Upward versus Downward Addition." *Journal of Educational Research,* XVI: 315-322, December, 1927. Reports an experiment carried on in seven centers. The results favored downward addition.

5. Buswell, G. T. and John, Lenore, *Diagnostic Studies in Arithmetic.* Chicago: The University of Chicago, 1926. 212 pp. Chapter II reports an analysis of column addition made from eye movements. Chapter III gives a time analysis of the four fundamental operations. Chapters IV, V, and VI have to do with diagnostic studies in addition and other operations. Chapter VII contains suggestions for remedial treatment.

6. Glazier, Harriet E. *Arithmetic for Teachers.* New York: McGraw-Hill Book Company, Inc., 1932. 291 pp. Suggestions on the teaching of addition will be found on pages 58-65.

7. Klapper, Paul. *The Teaching of Arithmetic.* New York: D. Appleton-Century Company, 1934. 525 pp. The teaching of addition is treated on pages 259-272.

8. MacLatchy, Josephine. "Reclaiming the 'Counter.'" *Educational Research Bulletin,* XVI: 85-90, April 14, 1937. Indicates that counting in addition is a symptom of inadequate number understanding as well as a bad habit and that the counter can be reclaimed through remedial teaching.

9. Morton, R. L. "Higher-Decade Addition in Some Recent Drill Devices." *Journal of Educational Research,* XV:

104-110, February, 1927. Reports haphazard provision for practice on higher decade combinations in three sets of drill materials.

10. Roantree, William F. and Taylor, Mary S. *An Arithmetic for Teachers.* New York: The Macmillan Company, 1932. 523 pp. Suggestions on teaching addition will be found on pages 41-44 and 53-62.

11. Thorndike, Edward Lee. *The New Methods in Arithmetic.* Chicago: Rand McNally and Company, 1921. 260 pp. Page 92 presents the device given in this chapter for higher decade addition practice preliminary to carrying in multiplication.

CHAPTER 6

ELEMENTARY WORK IN SUBTRACTION

It has been suggested that the addition and the subtraction facts be taught together. Thus, when a pupil discovers that 5 and 7 are 12 and that 7 and 5 are 12, he also discovers that 12 less 7 are 5 and that 12 less 5 are 7. Because of the intimate relationship between the addition and the subtraction facts, teaching them together seems to mean two advantages: (1) less time and energy are required than if the subtraction facts were separated some weeks or months from the corresponding addition facts; (2) since each process reinforces the other, each becomes more meaningful if the two are taught together rather than separately.

After the basic facts have been learned, addition and subtraction can continue to reinforce each other. The two processes should alternate as new stages are reached. Thus, when the pupil has worked on two-digit addends without carrying he can turn to two-digit minuends and subtrahends without borrowing; then, when he has worked on carrying long enough to have this difficulty rather well mastered, he can turn to borrowing in subtraction examples; etc.

Subtraction does not seem to suffer so seriously from time-consuming indirect methods as does addition. Pupils do, indeed, form poor habits in subtraction and, in some cases, invent strange ways for finding differences or remainders. For example, a fourth-grade boy who was very weak in subtraction, particularly subtraction with borrowing and the harder subtraction facts, but who was strong in multiplication subtracted 9 from 65 as follows: "65 is seven 9's and 2 over. One 9 from seven 9's leaves six 9's. Six 9's are 54, and 2 makes 56. So, 9 from 65 must leave 56." But practices of this kind seem to be neither so numerous nor of such frequent occurrence as are indirect methods in addition.

We have said that ability in addition is not a single, simple ability but a complex of several simpler abilities. Subtraction is also complex but it does not seem to be quite as complex as is addition. Let us review the major addition difficulties which were stated in the last chapter and, in each case, look for a corresponding difficulty in subtraction.

First, we have the 81 basic addition facts. Likewise, we have 81 basic facts in subtraction.

Second, we must provide, sometime, for zeros in addition. These must also be provided for in subtraction.

Third, we must teach carrying in addition. We must also teach borrowing (some prefer to call this operation "carrying" also) in subtraction.

Fourth, we have to face difficulties due to addends of unequal length. In subtraction, also, the subtrahend may be shorter than the minuend, but, since there are only two quantities in a subtraction example, this unequal-length matter does not seem to be quite so serious here as in addition.

Fifth, long columns mean attention span difficulties, particularly in higher grades. Numbers of many digits also bring attention span difficulties in subtraction although here, again, they are less likely to occur and seem to be less serious than in addition. Sixth, column addition soon requires the use of higher decade combinations. There is nothing which corresponds to this difficulty in ordinary subtraction.

Finally, higher decade addition is required in carrying in multiplication. Higher decade subtraction is also required in short division but, as we shall see in Chapter 9, short division can be avoided altogether and certainly it should not be taught in the primary grades.

Summarizing, we may say that the problems pertaining to the teaching of subtraction are fewer and simpler than those incident to the teaching of addition.

Subtraction examples without borrowing. The first work in subtraction, beyond the primary facts, should be simple subtraction without borrowing. At first, the examples should include only those facts whose minuends are less than 10 and the examples should be made up of two-digit numbers only. These 36 facts can easily be incorporated in 18 examples each of which requires two subtractions. Set 1 accomplishes this purpose.

Practice Examples in Subtraction. Set 1

Minuends Not Exceeding 9

78	93	69	58	49	86	92	69	59
46	71	43	25	35	71	21	51	46
47	77	58	97	46	68	73	59	98
13	62	31	85	22	34	12	14	23

The same 36 facts may easily be incorporated in examples having three-digit numbers. The 18 examples in Set 2 provide for 54 subtractions. Each of these 36 facts is practised and the more difficult 18 are included twice.

PRACTICE EXAMPLES IN SUBTRACTION. SET 2

Three-Digit Numbers

849	798	596	687	683	885
526	335	471	422	272	362
799	989	795	976	897	489
347	662	651	563	442	123
747	947	689	856	387	792
534	214	571	132	135	181

At this stage in the pupil's advancement, it seems to be well to introduce the zero facts. There are two groups of these: (1) those in which zero is subtracted from a number, leaving the number; and (2) those in which a number is subtracted from itself, leaving zero. When the meaning of the statement that *if zero is subtracted from a number, the number remains* is understood all of the facts in which this principle is involved may be presented as a group. They are:

9	8	7	6	5	4	3	2	1	0
–0	–0	–0	–0	–0	–0	–0	–0	–0	–0
9	8	7	6	5	4	3	2	1	0

Likewise, when the pupils understand the statement that *if a number is subtracted from itself, the remainder is zero,* the second group of zero facts may be presented. They are:

9	8	7	6	5	4	3	2	1
–9	–8	–7	–6	–5	–4	–3	–2	–1
0	0	0	0	0	0	0	0	0

These zero facts can be put to use at once in sets of practice examples. There should be no particular difficulty except, perhaps, in the case of $\begin{array}{r}0\\ -0\\ \hline\end{array}$. This has less meaning in a concrete sense than have the other zero facts. It probably should be postponed for special attention when the others have been mastered.

Zero facts are incorporated in the third set of practice examples. This set, made up of four-digit numbers, includes each of the same 36 primary facts, each of the 19 zero facts, and includes five of these 55 facts twice each.

Practice Examples in Fractions. Set 3

Zero Facts Included

6958	7948	8793	2851	5967
4621	6903	2480	1631	4023
9483	4079	3986	7285	9746
3401	1021	2580	5045	4721
8617	9365	8256	7498	9718
5600	2331	7205	1375	2403

The teacher may easily prepare sets of practice exercises which distribute the drill over these combinations. Many such sets should be prepared and should be available for use. The practice should be distributed rather evenly over the facts included, giving, however, somewhat more practice to the more difficult than to the easier. The few sets which are presented here have been prepared for illustrative purposes. These three sets of examples are not intended to supply sufficient practice on the types of subtraction which they include. Each may be used more than once, to be sure, but it is better for the teacher to prepare other sets, similar to these, that a rich variety of practice material may be at hand. Four-digit minuends and subtrahends without the zero difficulties may constitute a set. The zero difficulties in Set 3 will need much more practice than is afforded by doing the examples of this set. Of course, not all of a set need be used in a single drill period.

In the next stage of the pupil's progress, examples similar to those in the sets given will be used, but in the last subtraction in an example, a single-digit number may be subtracted from a two-digit number. This will give practice on the remaining 45 subtraction facts, and will be a good approach to subtraction examples involving borrowing. As an indication of the kind of subtraction examples which may be used to give practice on these 45 facts, Set 4 has been prepared. In the 45 examples of Set 4, each of the 45 facts referred to occurs once.

It will be noted that in each of the examples in this set the minuend has four digits and the subtrahend, three. Thus, each example gives practice on two facts, in addition to that for which the example is specifically prepared. Each of the 55 subtraction facts whose minuend is not greater than 9 occurs once, but the 35 most difficult of these occur twice.

These 45 harder subtraction facts appear for the first time in Set 4 and they appear only once each. They require much more practice than this. Additional sets, such as Set 4, can be prepared but it is easier to concentrate attention on these harder facts after the borrowing process has been taught.

Practice Examples in Subtraction. Set 4

No Borrowing Required

1389	1097	1426	1184	1659	1257	1513	1087	1256
562	465	904	851	720	834	703	903	352
1189	1078	1775	1124	1496	1097	1383	1162	1548
904	638	870	521	780	192	940	212	903
1218	1097	1849	1368	1083	1493	1179	1068	1516
517	240	947	402	812	611	306	320	806
1390	1258	1648	1274	1489	1197	1326	1089	1127
850	927	935	620	532	756	704	763	415
1457	1236	1769	1196	1295	1623	1074	1585	1376
806	413	917	603	731	810	512	624	645

Methods of subtraction. Before we can consider the subject of borrowing in subtraction, we must examine the various subtraction methods which have been advocated. There are four of these which have been in the limelight for many years. They have been called by various names but they may be indicated by the following descriptive titles:

1. Take-away-borrow.
2. Take-away-carry.
3. Addition-borrow.
4. Addition-carry.

The take-away-borrow method. According to this method, the accompanying example is solved as follows: 8 from 15, 7; 7 from 13, 6; 4 from 9, 5; 9 from 15, 6; 2 from 3, 1. Since 8 is larger than 5, one of the 4 tens in the minuend is "bor-

```
 46045
 29478
 -----
 16567
```

rowed," changed to units, making 15 units and then 8 units are subtracted from 15 units. There are then 3 tens left in the tens' place. Since there are no hundreds in the minuend in this example, one of the 6 thousands is "borrowed," changed to 10 hundreds, one of these hundreds is changed to 10 tens, making 13 tens, and 7 tens are subtracted from 13 tens. Then, 4 hundreds are subtracted from 9 hundreds, and the work is continued in this manner until the example is finished. Because a ten is changed to 10 units, it is thought of as broken up, or decomposed. Hence, this method is often called the *method of decomposition.*

Some object to the use of the word "borrow" in describing what takes place when an example is solved by this method. True, one does not borrow. He simply uses a ten in a manner which suits his convenience and which permits him to see how he can obtain the correct remainder. This is one of many instances in which we are careless in the use of words, but since the word is widely used in this way and since no serious harm seems to be done, it seems best not to push the objection very far. If, on the other hand, one chooses to say "change" a ten to ten units, there can be no objection. Probably, it is best not to use the word "borrow" in early lessons on this subject with the pupils but the method doubtless will continue to be referred to by teachers as a borrow method.

This method is an old method. It came to Europe from India. It seems to be the most commonly used method in the United States at the present time.

The take-away-carry method. If the same example is solved by the take-away-carry method, the process is as follows: 8 from 15, 7; 8 from 14, 6; 5 from 10, 5; 10 from 16, 6; 3 from 4, 1. It will be seen that this method is identical with the take-away-borrow method when the number represented by the minuend figure is no smaller than the number represented by the subtrahend figure. In the example shown, however, 10 units are added to the 5 units so that 8 units may be subtracted and, to compensate for this increase of ten in the minuend, a ten is added to the 7 tens in the subtrahend. Thus, this method is often called the *method of equal additions.*

```
 46045
 29478
 -----
 16567
```

According to this method, the 10 units which are added to the 5 units in the minuend are not obtained by using one of the 4 tens in the tens' place. We simply add 10 to the minuend and then we add 10 to the subtrahend. In a similar way, we add equal amounts to the minuend and the subtrahend as often as necessary in completing the solution.

The take-away-carry method is often called the *borrow-and-repay* method. This seems to be a very unfortunate name for if one does think of himself as repaying what he has borrowed, he does not repay it where it was borrowed. The author has listened to teachers as they explained this method and has heard them emphasize the fact that one must always pay back that which he has borrowed and then proceed to develop a dubious moral lesson by paying the obligation where it was not due. Some one has facetiously remarked that this should be called the rob-Peter-to-pay-Paul method. In actual work with this method, the pupil is usually taught to carry 1 to the number represented by the next figure in the subtrahend.

This method is also an old method. It is said to have been the only method in use in this country in 1820.

The addition-borrow method. Solving the same example by the addition-borrow method, we proceed as follows: 8 and 7 are 15; 7 and 6 are 13; 4 and 5 are 9; 9 and 6 are 15; 2 and 1 are 3. The outstanding feature of this method and of the addition-carry method is that instead of subtracting we *add* to the subtrahend a number sufficient to make the minuend. One thinks at first, "8 and what make 15; 7," and proceeds to write the 7. Later, he cuts down the language response to the form given above. Note that the second figure named in each step is the answer figure.

$$\begin{array}{r} 46045 \\ \underline{29478} \\ 16567 \end{array}$$

This method is seen to resemble the take-away-borrow method in that a decomposition process is employed. It differs from that method only in that it employs an additive process while the other method employs a subtractive process.

The addition-borrow method is very seldom found in the schools of this country or in the subtraction habits of the people. Those who use an addition method nearly always use the addition-carry method.

The addition-carry method. The addition-carry method resembles the addition-borrow method in that it is an additive method and it resembles the take-away-carry method in that it is also a method of equal additions. If this example is solved by this method, one proceeds as follows: 8 and 7 are 15; 8 and 6 are 14; 5 and 5 are 10; 10 and 6 are 16; 3 and 1 are 4.

$$\begin{array}{r} 46045 \\ \underline{29478} \\ 16567 \end{array}$$

This method was known as early as the sixteenth century in Italy. It is often called the *Austrian method* from the fact that it appeared in Austrian Arithmetics nearly a century ago and was picked up from this source by German writers. The term *Austrian* is applied to either of the two additive methods but in this country when one speaks of the Austrian method he usually refers to the addition-carry method.

The interrelationships of these four methods may be indicated diagrammatically as follows. Relationships are seen to exist between the two take-away methods, the two addition methods, the two borrow methods, and the two carry methods.

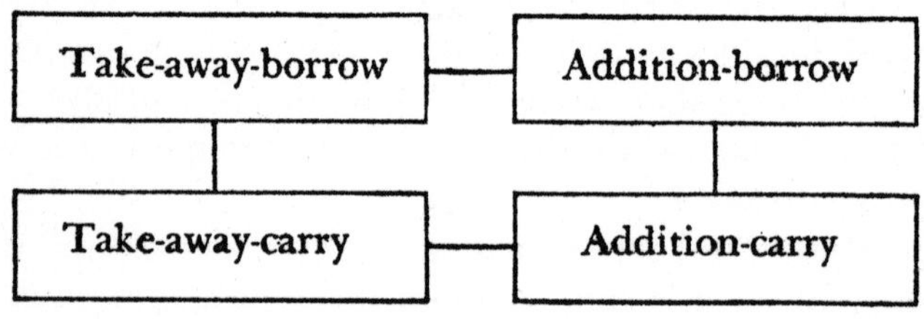

The complementary method. The complementary method is one of the oldest of the subtraction methods. It is seldom encountered today but was popularized in this country by the well-known Pike arithmetics of 1788. The complementary method is a subtractive method but according to this method one does not subtract 8 from 15 but instead takes 8 from 10 and then adds 5 to the result. In this method, the worker first finds the complement of the number represented by the subtrahend figure (the

$$\begin{array}{r} 46045 \\ 29478 \\ \hline 16567 \end{array}$$

difference between that number and 10) and then adds the number represented by the minuend figure to this complement.

The complementary method can be used with either a borrow or a carry process. Using the borrow process, one would solve the accompanying example as follows: 8 from 10, 2, and 5 are 7; 7 from 10, 3, and 3 are 6; 4 from 9, 5; 9 from 10, 1, and 5 are 6; 2 from 3, 1. If the carry process is used, the example would be solved in this manner: 8 from 10, 2, and 5 are 7; 8 from 10, 2, and 4 are 6; 5 from 10, 5; 10 from 10, 0, and 6 are 6; 3 from 4, 1. The carry process, rather than the borrow process, was commonly used with the complementary method although both were found. Although the complementary method is seldom found today, Stone[1] reports one principal in a large system who required that this method and this method only be taught.

Borrowing versus carrying. Concerning the four methods first enumerated, there are two principal disputes. The first of these disputes has to do with the relative merits of decomposition and equal additions. This dispute evidently applies to methods 1 and 3 as opposed to methods 2 and 4. The second dispute has to do with the relative merits of teaching subtraction as a "take-away" process and as an addition process. In this dispute, methods 1 and 2 are allied against methods 3 and 4.

Although in the first dispute methods 1 and 3 are opposed to methods 2 and 4, the dispute over decomposition versus equal additions waxed strong in many

---

[1] Stone, John C. *How We Subtract.* Chicago: Benj. H. Sanborn and Company, 1926, p. 19.

communities in this country before either of the addition methods became well known. For many years, there were ardent advocates of subtraction by a borrowing process and equally ardent supporters of subtraction by a carrying process. Several investigators have undertaken to determine experimentally whether pupils learn better if taught by a take-away-borrow process or a take-away-carry process.

Ballard,[2] an English investigator, found that children who had been taught the equal-additions method could subtract more rapidly and with fewer errors than could children who had been taught the method of decomposition. McClelland,[3] another English investigator, also reported that the method of equal additions appeared to be superior for quick learning of subtraction but that the method of decomposition resulted in greater speed after long practice. Winch,[4] a third Englishman, also claimed some slight superiority for the method of equal additions. Osburn[5] reported the method of equal additions to be slightly superior.

On the whole, the reported investigations seem to

[2] Ballard, P. B. "Norms of Performance in the Fundamental Processes of Arithmetic with Suggestions for Their Improvement." *Journal of Experimental Pedagogy,* II: 396-405 and III: 9-20, December 5, 1914, and March 5, 1915.

[3] McClelland, William W. "An Experimental Study of the Different Methods of Subtraction." *Journal of Experimental Pedagogy,* IV: 293-299, December 5, 1918.

[4] Winch, W. H. "'Equal Additions' versus 'Decomposition' in Teaching Subtraction: an Experimental Research." *Journal of Experimental Pedagogy,* V: 207-220 and 261-270, June 5 and December 6, 1920.

[5] Osburn, W. J. "How Shall We Subtract?" *Journal of Educational Research,* XVI: 237-246, November, 1927.

favor the method of equal additions. However, the differences are not large. The evidence is by no means sufficient to convince us that this method should be uniformly adopted for use in American schools. Ruch and Mead,[6] after reviewing the experimental evidence on this subject suggest that the differences between various methods must be small since controversy and confusion have persisted for so long a time.

At the present time, the method of decomposition seems to be much more extensively used in this country than are all other methods combined. For years, the author has ascertained the methods which his own students used and has found that about 70 per cent of approximately 2000 students normally used the method of decomposition and nearly all of the remaining 30 per cent, the method of equal additions. Some have been taught two methods. Only occasionally is one found who uses the Austrian method. Stone reports that of the students entering the Montclair, New Jersey, State Normal School over a period of years, about 75 per cent used the decomposition method.[7]

Wilson[8] reports the results of a questionnaire study made by Blanche M. Allen in an effort to discover the methods of subtraction in most common use in the

---

[6] Ruch, G. M. and Mead, Cyrus D. "A Review of Experiments on Subtraction." National Society for the Study of Education, *Twenty-Ninth Yearbook*. Bloomington, Illinois: Public School Publishing Company, 1930, pp. 671-678.

[7] Stone, John C., *op. cit.*, p. 16.

[8] Wilson, Guy M. "For 100 Percent Subtraction, What Method? A New Approach." *Journal of Educational Research,* XXVII: 503-508, March, 1934.

United States. The questionnaire was returned by 23 departments of education, 162 cities, and 215 training schools. Of these, 59 per cent reported the use of the method of decomposition, 13 per cent the method of equal additions, 26 per cent the additive methods, and 2 per cent the complementary method. Wilson points out that for the country as a whole, the method of decomposition is probably overwhelmingly prevalent since teacher-training institutions tend to use the additive method more than do city school systems and city schools probably use it more than do schools in small towns and rural areas. Johnson[9] found that 79 per cent of the normal-school students whom he tested used the method of decomposition.

In the Research News and Communications section of the *Journal of Educational Research* there appeared recently a brief account of studies made in Delaware by R. L. Herbst, State Director of Research. One of these had to do with methods used by teachers in 16 schools in teaching subtraction. Of the 21 teachers who taught subtraction without borrowing, 17 used the take-away method and 4 the additive method. Of the 60 teachers who taught subtraction with borrowing, 34 used the take-away-borrow method, 4 the take-away-carry, 3 the addition-borrow, and 19 the addition-carry. In several schools different methods were used by the various teachers.[10]

The decomposition method seems to be easier to rationalize for pupils than is the method of equal addi-

[9] Johnson, J. T. "The Merits of Different Methods of Subtraction." *Journal of Educational Research,* X: 279-290, November, 1924.

[10] *Cf.* Journal of Educational Research, April, 1937, p. 632.

tions. Suppose, for example, that one is to subtract 28 cents from 45 cents. If the coins are used, it is relatively easy for the pupil to see that since 5 cents is less than 8 cents, one of the four dimes can be changed to cents, making 15 cents and that if 8 cents is subtracted from 15 cents, the remainder is 7 cents. It seems to him to be a perfectly natural thing, then, that there are only three dimes left and that if two of these are taken away, one remains. Thus, in a way, he discovers for himself that if he should spend 28 of the 45 cents which he has, he will have 17 cents left. It seems to be considerably more difficult for the young learner to see the reason for what is done if the equal additions method is used in examples in which a borrowing or a carrying process is necessary.

```
45 cents
28 cents
--
17 cents
```

In spite of the evidence which seems to give a slight advantage to the method of equal additions (take-away-carry), then, the author favors the method of decomposition (take-away-borrow). His chief reasons are the two already stated, namely: (1) the take-away-borrow method is already in much more extensive use than is any other method; (2) a more successful explanation of why we do what we do when borrowing (or carrying) is necessary can be made in terms of the method of decomposition.

We know, however, that children learn to subtract by both of these methods. It would be unwise to contend that either method is distinctly superior or inferior to the other. Furthermore, if pupils have already learned one method and can use it, the teacher should by no means ask them to learn another. The teacher should be master of all the methods which pupils use but a pupil is doing well if he masters one.

Subtractive versus additive methods. A second dispute has to do with whether subtraction should be taught as subtraction or as addition. Here, again, we find much argument and often more heat than light. A few investigations have been reported but, like the investigations of decomposition versus equal additions, they are frequently inconclusive. Mead and Sears[11] reported almost no advantage of one method over the other. Taylor[12] found that, although children were taught the additive method, 88 per cent of them had dropped it by the time they reached the sixth grade. Beatty[13] reported results similar to those of Taylor and slight differences between the quality of the work of those using the additive method and those using the borrowing method. Johnson[14] found differences between performances by various methods to be insignificant. Buckingham,[15] experimenting in seven centers found differences which were small but which rather consistently favored those using a take-away method.

Two chief arguments have been advanced in favor of the addition method of subtraction and, until recently,

---

[11] Mead, Cyrus D. and Sears, Isabel. "Additive Subtraction and Multiplicative Division Tested." *Journal of Educational Psychology,* VII: 261-270, May, 1916.

[12] Taylor, Joseph S. "Subtraction by the Addition Process." *Elementary School Journal,* XX: 203-207, November, 1919.

[13] Beatty, Willard W. "The Additive *versus* the Borrowing Method of Subtraction." *Elementary School Journal,* XXI: 198-200, November, 1920.

[14] Johnson, J. T., *op. cit.,* p. 283.

[15] Buckingham, B. R. "The Additive *versus* the Take-Away Method of Teaching the Subtraction Facts." *Educational Research Bulletin,* VI: 265-269, September 28, 1927.

these arguments were sufficiently potent to enable the method to gain ground. The first argument was that the addition method relieved the pupil of the necessity of learning the subtraction facts since he subtracted by using the addition facts. The second argument was that this subtraction method represented the sort of thing that a clerk does when he makes change.

The first argument loses much of its force when the addition and the subtraction facts are taught together. It is little if any more difficult for a pupil to learn the subtraction facts along with the addition facts than to learn the addition facts alone. Furthermore, learning both addition and subtraction facts increases the pupil's understanding of number. Addition and subtraction supplement and reinforce each other; each makes the other more meaningful. This richer meaning seems to be better assured when both processes are taught than when subtraction is taught as only a slight variation of addition.

Furthermore, if pupils are to learn the addition-carry method, they must be familiar with 10 addition combinations in addition to those given in Chapter 4. These are the higher decade combinations in which various one-digit numbers are added to 10. Two of these are needed in the accompanying example. In solving this example by the addition carry method, one thinks "6 and 6 are 12, 10 and 3 are 13, 10 and 4 are 14, 6 and 1 are 7." Such combinations as 10 + 3 and 10 + 4 are not needed if subtraction is taught as a take-away process. These combinations are easy, to be sure, and should be known anyhow, but one should recognize that the statement to the effect that the

$$\begin{array}{r} 7432 \\ \underline{5996} \\ 1436 \end{array}$$

Austrian method requires no new combinations is not quite true.

As to the second argument, in making change one does not ordinarily subtract at all. That is, he neither takes away the amount of the purchase from the amount received from the customer, nor does he add to the amount of the purchase that which will make the amount received from the customer, as in additive subtraction. Rather, he *counts* in terms of our monetary units. Thus, if a clerk is handed a five-dollar bill in payment for goods costing $2.68, he will ordinarily say to himself as he picks the appropriate coins and bills from the till, or as he counts the change out to the customer, "268, 69, 70, 75, 3, 4, 5." Practices followed in making change do not constitute an argument for either method of teaching subtraction.

In the author's opinion, we should cease our efforts to promote the Austrian method of subtraction. It is only slightly known and practiced in this country and to change the practices of the people of a nation is difficult when the reasons are the best. Arguments favoring the Austrian method turn out to have little force. Furthermore, it has been discovered that many children who learn this method drop it for another within a few years.

The type problems of subtraction. Subtraction is a process used to find the answers to three distinct types of problems. One involves the "how-much-more" idea, another requires the finding of a difference, and the third is concerned with what amount is left. Each of these can be illustrated with a problem.

1. Dick wants a bicycle which costs $24.95. He has saved $18.75. *How much more* money does he need?

2. Dick looked at two bicycles. One was priced at $24.95 and the other at $32.45. *What is the difference* in price?

3. Dick has $30. If he buys a bicycle costing $24.95, *how much will he have left?*

It is obvious that all three of these problems are solved by using the process of subtraction but that each represents a different type of problem. It is not necessary that two or more subtraction methods be taught to solve these types of problems for the pupil easily sees that one method will do for all. We do not know the relative frequency of the occurrence of each of these types of problems in ordinary social and business affairs but it seems that the second and the third occur more frequently than does the first. The first seems to lead more naturally to the additive method of subtraction than to a take-away method but the other two seem to suggest the use of a take-away method.

We may say, then, that the take-away method represents what people are more likely to think of when reference is made to subtraction. This is indicated by the etymology of the word. "Subtraction" comes from the Latin, *subtractus,* a participial form of *subtraho,* meaning literally, "withdrawing from under." It clearly represents the take-away idea. The same meaning stands today in many ordinary affairs although the "how-much-more" idea is also occasionally encountered. Depreciation in the value of a house, or a car, is not thought of as an amount to be added to the present sale value. Contemplated expenditures are deducted from what we have, not added to what we shall have left. Reductions in marked-down sales represent what the customer saves out of the original price rather than what should be added to the present price to produce the list price. The take-away method *is* subtraction; the addition method is not subtraction but is a substitute for subtraction.

We may summarize as follows:

1. Experimental evidence seems to give the take-away-carry process a lead over the take-away-borrow process.
2. The take-away-borrow method seem to be used more extensively in this country than are all other methods combined.
3. The take-away-borrow method seems to be the easiest method to rationalize for children.
4. The argument that the Austrian method saves time loses much of its force if the addition and the subtraction facts are taught together and if we recognize that the two operations supplement each other in an important way.
5. The making-change argument is worthless. In making change, clerks do not ordinarily subtract at all.
6. The addition-carry method requires the use of the higher decade combinations involving 10.
7. Most of life's subtraction problems seem to suggest the use of a take-away method.
8. Etymologically, to subtract means to take away.
9. Pupils can learn to subtract by any of the methods discussed in this chapter.
10. Teachers should be masters of all the methods which pupils use. Pupils who have learned a method should not be asked to learn another.
11. We favor the use of the take-away-borrow method for pupils who have not yet learned to subtract.

Teaching the borrowing operation. If the take-away-borrow method of subtraction is taught and if the pupil has been taught the meaning of carrying in addition as was suggested in Chapter 5, it is a rather simple and easy matter to teach borrowing in subtraction. Both coins and splints may be used here as well as in addition. Let us begin with a problem. "Mary has 32 cents. If she spends 18 cents for valentines, how much will she have left?"

32 cents. This is the same as 3 dimes and 2 cents.
18 cents. This is the same as 1 dime and 8 cents.

The coins, 3 dimes and 2 cents, are placed on the table where all can see. The teacher asks, "How can we get 18 cents out of 32 cents?" The pupils are likely to see that one of the dimes must be changed to cents. This is done with the coins, leaving on the table 2 dimes and 12 cents. Then the blackboard statement is changed to read as follows:

32 cents. This is the same as 2 dimes and 12 cents.
18 cents. This is the same as 1 dime and 8 cents.
1 4

First, 8 cents is taken from the 12 cents, both on the table and as an act of subtraction on the blackboard. Then, 1 dime is taken from the 2 dimes both on the table and on the blackboard. There remain on the table 1 dime and 4 cents which the pupils recognize as 14 cents. On the blackboard, the 1 and the 4 appear as shown and then the third line is filled in, making the statement appear as follows:

32 cents. This is the same as 2 dimes and 12 cents.
18 cents. This is the same as 1 dime and 8 cents.
14 cents. This is the same as 1 dime and 4 cents.

A few additional examples should be used in the same way.

If splints are used, the procedure is very similar as may be inferred from the discussion of carrying in Chapter 5 and from the description of the way coins are used there and here.

The pupil should soon become independent of the use of such objective materials as coins and splints and be able to see the borrowing operation in terms of the units and tens of our number system. Then, he should be able to think of 32 as 3 tens and 2 units and of subtracting 8 units from 12 units after 1 ten had been thought of as 10 units and the 2 units increased to 12 units.

$$\begin{array}{r} 32 \\ \underline{18} \\ 14 \end{array}$$

Desirable and undesirable habits in subtraction. Pupils sometimes develop very elaborate habits and involved language responses in doing subtraction examples. These elaborate habits are usually traceable to the early instruction which they received from the teacher and indicate that no successful effort has been made to replace these early elaborate responses with brief and more efficient responses. The language responses are usually implicit, as were those in column addition described in Chapter 5, and are not apparent to the teacher unless she makes individual diagnoses of their methods of work.

Winch gives the detailed responses of several pupils in subtraction examples and notes the extent to which they reproduce in exact detail the steps in the procedure originally taught them. We quote the responses of one pupil on three examples. In the first example, she proceeded as follows:[16]

(1) 9 from 6 you cannot, take 1 from the 7 next door leaves 6, 9 from 10 is 1 and 6 is 7.

[16] Winch, W. H., *op. cit.*, p. 209.

(2) 2 from 6 leaves 4.

(3) 8 from 5 you cannot, take 1 next door, leaves 3, 8 from 10 leaves 2 and 5 are 7.

(4) 9 from 3 you cannot, go next door, take 1 leaves 1, 9 from 10 is 1 and 3 makes 4.

(5) 3 from 1 you cannot, go next door, take 1 from the 6 leaves 5, 3 from 10 is 7 and 1 makes 8.

(6) 1 from 5 leaves 4.

```
 624,576
 139,829
 -------
 484,747
```

It will be seen that this English pupil used the complementary method which has been described and accompanied it with borrowing rather than with carrying.

After listening to this pupil's very elaborate responses on this subtraction example, the examiner told her, when she reached the next example to "work the next sum very quickly." She proceeded as follows:[17]

(1) 7 from 11 is 4.
(2) 8 from 12 is 4.
(3) 9 from 10 is 1.
(4) 0 from 1 is 1.

```
 2131
  987
 ----
 1144
```

The pupil's elaborate language responses apparently were not necessary. When urged to greater speed, she dropped them. Note also that the complementary method has disappeared. It would seem that this pupil has been taught more than one method by her various teachers but it is a safe guess that she was taught the complementary method and the elaborate phraseology first.

It required an example having several zeros in the minuend to reveal in full the complex responses of which this pupil was capable. The example is shown. She proceeded as follows:[18]

---

[17] *Idem.*

[18] Winch, W. H., *op. cit.*, p. 213.

$$\begin{array}{r} 400{,}000 \\ 59 \\ \hline 399{,}941 \end{array}$$

(1) 9 from 0 I can't, go next door I can't, go next door I can't, go next door I can't, go next door I can't, go next door, take 1, leaves 3, and that makes that (pointing to the 0 immediately to the right of the 4 in the minuend) 10, 9 from 0 I can't, go next door I can't, go next door I can't, go next door I can't, go next door, take 1 from the 10 leaves 9, and makes that one (pointing to the 0 in the second place from the 4) 10.9 from 0 I can't, go next door I can't, go next door I can't, go next door, take 1 from the 10 leaves 9 and makes that (pointing to the third 0) a ten. 9 from 0 I can't, go next door I can't, go next door, take 1, leaves 9 and makes that (pointing to the fourth 0) a ten. 9 from 0 I can't, go next door, take 1, leaves that a 9 and makes this a 10, 9 from 10 leaves 1.

(2) 5 from 9 leaves 4.
(3) 0 from 9 leaves 9.
(4) 0 from 9 leaves 9.
(5) 0 from 9 leaves 9.
(6) 0 from 3 leaves 3.

After quoting the cases which we have just examined, Buswell and Judd comment as follows:[19]

Such cases as the foregoing furnish convincing evidence of the need for more frequent analyses of the actual mental operations of pupils in working with subtraction. Pupils can not reach the desired goals of speed and accuracy while such roundabout methods of procedure persist. In many cases these wasteful and uneconomical methods continue to be employed through the upper grades and, in all prob-

[19] Buswell, Guy Thomas and Judd, Charles Hubbard. *Summary of Educational Investigations Relating to Arithmetic.* Chicago: The University of Chicago, 1925, p. 73.

ability, through adult experience. In order to correct adequately these wasteful processes of the pupil, detailed analyses of the type described should constantly be made by the teacher.

The pupil responses which have been described are probably worse than those usually found among elementary school pupils but roundabout responses of this general kind are very common. It is truly remarkable that the pupil whom Winch describes made no errors in the solutions reported for the more elaborate the pupil's reactions to a subtraction situation, other things being equal, the greater the chances of errors.

Pupils who are very slow in doing subtraction examples will usually be found to be following roundabout procedures. Such procedures consume time and, as has been suggested, are often responsible for errors. If a teacher in the intermediate or upper grades will sit down with a pupil and ask him to say aloud what he thinks when he subtracts, she will often be surprised at the persistence of time-consuming habits which were established in learning subtraction with borrowing in the primary grades and which have never given way to more efficient practices. It is the responsibility of the primary teacher to help a pupil form subtraction habits which will be effective and economical.

As soon as the meaning of the borrowing operation has been made clear and the pupil has gained some competence in the process, he should be shown how to shorten the process by abbreviating his implicit responses. He will have to be coached in this. The teacher should spend much time working with the pupils individually to discover how they subtract and to help them establish good habits. In the example shown, for instance, the pupil should think merely, "7 from 14, 7; 6 from 11, 5; 3 from 4, 1," as he writes the digits of the answer from right to left. Of course, this high level of competence is attained only after considerable time but it will be attained if the teaching is well done.

$$\begin{array}{r} 524 \\ \underline{367} \\ 157 \end{array}$$

Types of examples. The pupil's first examples with borrowing should be made up of two-digit minuends and two-digit subtrahends chosen at first so that there are two digits in the remainder and later so that there is but one digit in the remainder. It is assumed that the zero facts have been taught by this time.

$$\begin{array}{r} 46 \\ \underline{28} \\ 18 \end{array} \qquad \begin{array}{r} 46 \\ \underline{38} \\ 8 \end{array}$$

Then the pupils should move on to examples made up of three-digit numbers. These may be chosen first so that borrowing is required in only one step and this step may be either the first step or the second step as shown by these two examples. Then the pupil may undertake examples in which borrowing is required in two steps as indicated in the accompanying example. The various types may then be mixed in a single drill lesson and some examples included in which no borrowing at all is required.

$$\begin{array}{r} 543 \\ \underline{216} \end{array} \qquad \begin{array}{r} 543 \\ \underline{251} \end{array}$$

$$\begin{array}{r} 543 \\ \underline{256} \end{array}$$

Zero facts may also be introduced here as in examples made up of two-digit numbers. Three-digit numbers may be subtracted so as to leave a two-digit remainder or a one-

$$\begin{array}{r} 543 \\ \underline{465} \\ 78 \end{array} \qquad \begin{array}{r} 543 \\ \underline{537} \\ 6 \end{array}$$

digit remainder as shown. Of course, the other kind of zero facts—that in which zero is subtracted from a number—should also be included in practice examples.

It is sometimes said that the most difficult subtraction examples are those having zeros in the minuends. It is well, then, to postpone work on this type until other subtraction difficulties have been mastered. Then pupils should be taught to handle the zero difficulties and should be given intensive practice on examples of this kind.

Start with a simple example such as is supplied by this problem: Clifford made 60 cents last Saturday and spent 28 cents for a kite that evening. How much did he have left?

60 cents. This is the same as 6 dimes and 0 cents.
28 cents. This is the same as 2 dimes and 8 cents.

"We can't subtract 8 cents from 0 cents, of course, so we think of one of the dimes as changed to 10 cents. This leaves 5 dimes." Then the blackboard statement is changed to read as follows:

60 cents. This is the same as 5 dimes and 10 cents.
28 cents. This is the same as 2 dimes and 8 cents.
32 cents. This is the same as 3 dimes and 2 cents.

Then the solution is completed as were the first examples with borrowing. It should not be necessary to use the coins.

Other examples containing forms of this zero difficulty may be presented as indicated in the following paragraphs.

John had \$2.04 and spent 28 cents for a kite. How much did *he* have left? This time there are no dimes so we think of a dollar as changed to 10 dimes, leaving 1 dollar, think of a dime as changed to 10 cents, leaving 9 dimes and making 14 cents. Then 8 from 14 is 6, 2 from 9 is 7, and there is 1 dollar left. So John had \$1.76 left.

```
$2.04
  .28
-----
$1.76
```

Howard had exactly two dollars and he, too bought a kite for 28 cents. How much money did *he* have left? This time we change 1 dollar to 10 dimes again, leaving 1 dollar, change 1 dime to 10 cents, leaving 9 dimes and subtract thus: 8 from 10, 2; 2 from 9, 7; and there is 1 dollar left. So Howard had \$1.72 left.

```
$2.00
  .28
-----
$1.72
```

When we have two zeros together in the upper number, then, we think of the first zero as 10, of the other zero as 9, and take 1 from the third figure. Here is another problem: Mr. Simpson bought 300 pounds of fertilizer for his garden and used 162 pounds. How much did he have left? Think of the first 0 as 10, of the next 0 as 9, and of the 3 as 2. Then 2 from 10, 8; 6 from 9, 3; 1 from 2, 1. So Mr. Simpson had 138 pounds of fertilizer left.

```
300
162
---
138
```

Sometimes, we have more than two zeros together in the upper number, as in this problem: The Smith family started to drive to California, 3000 miles away. When they had driven 1435 miles, how far did they still have to go? We think of the first 0 as 10, of the other 0's as 9's, and of the 3 as 2. Then 5 from 10, 5; 3 from 9, 6; 4 from 9, 5; 1 from 2, 1. So they still had 1565 miles to go.

```
3000
1435
----
1565
```

The preceding paragraphs will not be given as one continuous explanation, but after each new type of example is illustrated the pupils will be given practice on examples in that group. They will gradually learn to solve the more difficult examples and will finally have the most difficult which the course of study in the primary grades supplies.

The use of crutches. Many teachers try to facilitate the pupil's understanding of the borrowing process by writing a small 1 before the first minuend figure and crossing out the adjacent minuend figure from which the 1 was borrowed and writing the next smaller number in its place. The work may then resemble the example shown.

$$\begin{array}{r} 3\,{}_{1} \\ \not{4}6 \\ \underline{28} \\ 18 \end{array}$$

This device may make it easier for the pupil to see what takes place when he borrows and, perhaps, may do more good than harm as a means of explaining the meaning of subtraction in examples of this kind. If full use has been made of the kind of explanation of the meaning of borrowing which we have suggested, however, there seems to be little to be gained from the use of such a crutch. Could we guarantee that its use would stop here, no one would seriously object to it. But children tend to lean on crutches whether we wish them to do so or not. Having discovered an easier way to do subtraction examples in which borrowing is required, they quite naturally choose that method rather than a harder one and use it until it becomes habitual. Since no one would endorse this crutch for permanent use, then, it seems best not to endorse it at all.

Other things being equal, or nearly equal, teachers should not teach pupils procedures which are soon to be forbidden, but should employ approved methods from the beginning. Primary teachers are particularly liable to this sort of error. They permit pupils to use questionable methods because, for a time, they seem to yield results as good as or better than those secured from the use of better methods, forgetting that in later grades, the pupil will be seriously hampered by the habits thus acquired.

Additional sets of practice examples. The teacher should have at hand several sets of practice examples in subtraction providing drill on the various subtraction difficulties which have been discussed. These should be carefully prepared so as to provide practice on each of the types of difficulty and on each of the 100 subtraction facts (including the 19 zero facts). Set 5 contains 25 examples, each of which requires four subtractions, making 100 subtractions in all. The examples have been so constructed that, if the take-away-borrow method is used, each of the 100 subtraction facts occurs once. The set requires borrowing and incorporates the more serious zero difficulties.

PRACTICE EXAMPLES IN SUBTRACTION. SET 5

The 100 Subtraction Facts

6418	3581	7094	4752	9530	3008	6347	8743	2657
1376	2611	2397	3523	3975	1462	5068	7408	743
5041	7761	5930	8522	7155	5123	8461	7380	6000
4052	2484	5041	4039	3457	1064	8298	6717	2179
8754	8720	7852	9870	4002	6402	6200		
5016	6892	988	5798	1966	3985	523		

In the preceding pages, we have indicated several types

of subtraction examples to be used while teaching subtraction with borrowing. We have spoken of varying the length of the minuends and the subtrahends; of examples in which there is borrowing in one step, two steps, etc.; and of all of these with and without the various forms of zero difficulties. There should be at least one set of practice examples prepared for each of these types. Their preparation is left to the teacher. Set 5, above, is a summary set and is intended to be used after practice on the various sets which have been suggested. Preparing such sets is a rather tedious and exacting task but it is worth the effort which it costs. Of course, the examples can be saved and used with succeeding classes.

Checking solutions. To insure accurate results, checking is indispensable. In all written work in subtraction, pupils should habitually check their answers. If the habit of checking is formed in the primary grades, we may hope that it will persist through the intermediate and upper grades.

Adding the remainder or difference to the subtrahend to get the minuend is the easiest and perhaps the best check to use. The sum so secured may be written as shown, or the adding may be done without writing the sum. It is probably best to write the sum in checking the first examples of a new type and later to check without writing the sum. Writing the sum should not become a habit.

```
4629
3874
----
 755
----
4629
```

Some teachers direct pupils to check their answers by copying the subtrahend beneath the remainder and then adding, as shown. This adds somewhat to the labor involved but avoids the difficulty of adding across the line, a feature which seems to disturb pupils who are not accustomed to it. The chief disadvantage in this method, however, is the fact that pupils who have used it do not readily make the transition to checking without writing the sum, since the operation of checking without writing the sum is considerably different from the checking method which they have been using. Neither of these two devices should be used long enough to permit them to become well established habits with pupils.

$$\begin{array}{r} 4629 \\ 3874 \\ \hline 755 \\ 3874 \\ \hline 4629 \end{array}$$

The use of problems. Problems involving the operation of subtraction should occur frequently in the experiences of the pupils. The only purpose in learning subtraction is to develop the technique and skill which are necessary to enable the pupils to solve the problems which involve this operation. There is danger that the drill work will become uninteresting to the pupils if they do not have frequent occasions to apply to problems the skills developed. So far as possible, let the problems come out of the pupils' activities at home, in school, and elsewhere. Those which the teacher chooses or formulates should be realistic, they should make a strong appeal to the imaginations of the pupils, and they should be worded in language which the children can readily understand.

Higher decade subtraction. It is sometimes suggested that after pupils have learned the subtraction facts and before they are taught to do other subtraction examples, they should be instructed in higher decade subtraction. Higher decade subtraction is analogous to higher decade addition. Just as the pupils have extended their knowledge of and skill with the addition facts to higher decades, with and without bridging, now they may similarly extend their knowledge of the subtraction facts.

But the case of higher decade subtraction is quite different from that of higher decade addition. Higher decade addition, as we have seen, is used in column addition and also in carrying in multiplication. Higher decade subtraction, on the other hand, has no use like that of column addition for higher decade addition but it does have a use in short division which is similar to that of higher decade addition in carrying in multiplication. If we multiply 436 by 6, for example, we make use of the two higher decade addition combinations, 18 + 3 = 21 and 24 + 2 = 26. Then, if we divide this product, 2616, by 6 by short division, we make use of the two higher decade subtraction combinations, 26 — 24 = 2 and 21 — 18 = 3. It will be seen that these two higher decade subtraction combinations are closely related to the two higher decade addition combinations which have been used in the multiplication example.

$$\begin{array}{r} 436 \\ 6 \\ \hline 2616 \end{array} \qquad \begin{array}{r} 6\overline{)2616} \\ 436 \end{array}$$

$$\begin{array}{r} 18 \\ 3 \\ \hline 21 \end{array} \qquad \begin{array}{r} 24 \\ 2 \\ \hline 26 \end{array} \qquad \begin{array}{r} 26 \\ 24 \\ \hline 2 \end{array} \qquad \begin{array}{r} 21 \\ 18 \\ \hline 3 \end{array}$$

It will not be necessary to teach higher decade subtraction, however, until the pupil begins his study of short division. In Chapter 9, we recommend that the first work in division with one-digit divisors be done by the long division process and that short division be postponed until grade 4A, at least. But if long division is used in the above example, the pupil need not subtract 24 from 26 or 18 from 21 as a single act of thought but, with all of the numbers before him, he can simply subtract 4 from 6 and 2 from 2 or 8 from 11 and 1 from 1. Thus, higher decade subtraction as such is not needed. Hence, it is not necessary for the primary teacher to be concerned about higher decade subtraction.

Cardinal points in subtraction. In elementary work in subtraction, primary teachers should strive to develop in pupils the ability to find differences and remainders with fair speed and with a high degree of accuracy. With it all, they should lead pupils to an understanding of the processes which they employ and should enable them to gain a better appreciation of number and the number system. We may conclude the discussion with the following summary statements.

1. Recognize the various difficulties in subtraction examples and attack these difficulties one at a time. More and more, primary teachers are realizing the importance of making a detailed analysis of the materials of the curriculum and the necessity of arranging a graded list of exercises through the use of which the pupils may gain a thorough knowledge of the subject-matter and acquire the desired habits.

2. In developing new procedures and new operations, see that the pupils understand them. So far as possible, help the pupils to make discoveries for themselves. Some teachers make their explanations so brief and so abstract that what the pupils learn, they learn by rote. Others go into such detail that the pupil has little opportunity to think for himself. Naturally, the amount of explanation, the number of illustrations necessary, and the rate of progress will depend upon the ability of the pupils and the adequacy of their previous training.

3. Give an abundance of practice material in the form of problems and examples. Keep in mind the old Law of Ex-

ercise which says that, other things being equal, use strengthens and disuse weakens mental connections. The amount of practice on a new type of examples should be rather large at the time of the first presentation and immediately thereafter, but may then gradually become less and less. The intervals between practice periods should be brief at first and then gradually become greater. In other words, pupils need practice if they are to learn satisfactorily and additional practice if they are to maintain their skills at a desirable level.

4. In providing for practice, see that no important elements are neglected. Ordinarily, the more recently presented and the more difficult items of subject matter will receive the major emphasis in sets of practice exercises, but sometimes it is well to arrange a summary or review practice set in which all of the skills so far taught in a given operation are reviewed. Set 5, in this chapter, is an example. The haphazard methods of many teachers who provide just any examples for practice purposes should be displaced by more careful methods which guarantee that no important elements of skill are neglected.

5. The close relationship of interest to effort should be recognized. The Law of Effect which states that the progress which pupils make depends upon the extent to which they enjoy their work is an important guide to good teaching. See to it, then, that the pupils' introduction to a new difficulty is accompanied by a situation which appeals to them. A problem, arising out of a situation in which the pupils are interested, should precede actual instruction on a new type of example. The game element should often be prominent in the drill devices used. Occasional progress tests to show the pupils where they stand are helpful.[20]

---

[20] *Cf.* Panlasigui, Isodoro and Knight, F. B. "The Effect of Awareness of Success or Failure." National Society for the Study of Education, *Twenty-Ninth Yearbook*. Bloomington, Illinois: Public School Publishing Company, 1930, pp. 611-619.

6. Let the program be adapted to the pupils' level of development. The Law of Readiness demands that work shall not be undertaken which is beyond the pupils' understanding or which is ahead of their current needs. On the other hand, to delay instruction on a topic which pupils can understand and put to use is to neglect an educational opportunity and to shirk a responsibility.

If pupils see good reasons for mastering their subject-matter difficulties, if they enjoy their lessons and their practice exercises, and if these lessons are properly organized and well taught, progress will be rapid and sure.

QUESTIONS AND REVIEW EXERCISES

1. How do addition and subtraction reinforce each other? Do you believe that a pupil who learns both of these processes understands number better than the pupil who learns only one?

2. Which has the greater degree of complexity, addition or subtraction? What elements of one do we fail to find in the other?

3. If you were to prepare a set of examples containing all of the subtraction facts but no borrowing, what is the least number of examples that the set would contain?

4. It is quite often true that a person will express himself in favor of the subtraction method which he himself learned when a pupil in the grades. How do you account for this? Is this a sound basis for choosing a subtraction method?

5. Try this example by each of the four subtraction methods. Why should a teacher be proficient in all of the subtraction methods which pupils use?

$$\begin{array}{r} 609004 \\ \underline{298095} \end{array}$$

6. Why is the take-away-borrow method called the *method of decomposition?* Does decomposition take place in the addition-borrow method also?

7. Why is the take-away-carry method called the *method*

of equal additions? Do we make equal additions in the addition-carry method also?

8. Which of these subtraction methods is most prevalent in your home community?

9. How do you account for the prevalence of such expressions as "borrow" and "borrow and pay back" when we don't actually do either of these things in a subtraction example?

10. Each of these four methods is related to two of the remaining three. For each, indicate the two to which it is related.

11. Some writers express regret that the complementary method does not have its supporters. Do you see any reason why it should or should not be as acceptable as the others?

12. Is it any more logical to borrow than to carry in a subtraction example? To carry than to borrow? Should the choice of a method be made primarily on the basis of the logic of the methods?

13. What reasons are given in the chapter for the recommendation that the method of decomposition be taught?

14. If you were teaching the method of equal additions, how would you rationalize it for the pupils?

15. What advantage is there in having pupils see why they do what they do in an arithmetic process?

16. When a clerk makes change, does he subtract? Does he add? What does he do?

17. If a pupil learns to subtract by the Austrian method, what economy is effected in the learning of the primary facts? Do you believe that this economy is offset by any losses to the pupil? If so, what?

18. State and illustrate the three type problems of subtraction. Do you believe that a pupil needs to learn more than one method if he is to handle all three of these types?

19. If all of your pupils knew and used one subtraction method and a pupil entered from another school after hav-

ing learned a different subtraction method, would you expect him to learn the method which your other pupils used?

20. Look up the word "subtraction" in a dictionary. What is its fundamental meaning?

21. Explain in detail how you would use coins in an early lesson in borrowing. How long would you continue the use of coins, splints, or other objective materials?

22. How do you account for the very involved responses which pupils sometimes make in solving subtraction examples? Can these responses be detected by examining the pupil's written work?

23. How can the teacher learn what a pupil's implicit responses are?

24. Is it a safe conclusion that pupils who are slow in subtraction have developed undesirable habits?

25. Can examples whose minuends contain zeros be given before borrowing has been taught?

26. What crutches have you seen pupils use in subtraction? What use, if any, would you make of these crutches?

27. What procedure do you recommend for checking subtraction examples?

28. What is higher decade subtraction? Under what conditions is it used? Should it be taught in the primary grades?

29. State the Law of Exercise. The Law of Effect. The Law of Readiness. Discuss the application of these laws to the teaching and learning of subtraction.

30. How should the practice on a new type of example be distributed? What is the place of drills for maintenance?

CHAPTER TEST

For each of these statements, select the best answer. A scoring key will be found on page 405.

1. One of the facts to be taught with $6 + 5 = 11$ is (1) $11 - 6 = 5$ (2) $21 - 6 = 15$ (3) $6 - 5 = 1$.

2. Compared with addition subtraction is (1) more complex (2) equally complex (3) less complex.

3. Success in ordinary subtraction depends largely upon (1) knowledge of the subtraction facts (2) knowledge of higher decade subtraction (3) attention span.

4. Exclusive of zeros the number of subtraction facts in which two one-figure numbers appear is (1) 36 (2) 45 (3) 81.

5. To provide practice on each of the 100 subtraction facts without borrowing requires that a set of at least (1) 100; (2) 45; (3) 81 examples be prepared.

6. The decomposition method is the (1) take-away borrow (2) take-away carry (3) Austrian method.

7. The method of equal additions is the (1) take-away-borrow (2) take-away-carry (3) Austrian method.

8. It has been argued that those who make change use the (1) take-away-borrow (2) take-away-carry (3) Austrian method.

9. Higher decade addition combinations are used if subtraction is done by the (1) take-away-borrow (2) addition-borrow (3) addition-carry method.

10. The term "borrow and pay back" is applied to the (1) take-away-borrow (2) take-away carry (3) addition-borrow method.

11. In solving the accompanying example by the take-away-borrow method, one thinks in the second step (1) 9 from 9, 0 (2) 10 from 10, 0 (3) 9 and 0 are 9.

$$\begin{array}{r} 4208 \\ \underline{3699} \end{array}$$

12. In doing the same example by the method of equal additions, one thinks in the second step, (1) 10 and 0 are 10 (2) 10 from 10, 0 (3) 9 and 0 are 9.

13. In solving the same example by the addition-borrow method, one thinks in the third step (1) 5 and 6 are 11 (2) 6 and 5 are 11 (3) 6 from 11, 5.

14. In the same example, if the addition-carry method is used, one thinks in the fourth step (1) 0 and 4 are 4 (2) 4 and 0 are 4 (3) 4 from 4, 0.

15. If the same example is solved by the complementary method one thinks in the first step (1) 9 and 9 are 18 (2) 8 and 1 are 9 (3) 9 from 10, 1, and 8 are 9.

16. The take-away borrow method is not related to the (1) take-away-carry method (2) addition-borrow method (3) addition-carry method.

17. The method which seems easier to rationalize is the (1) take-away-borrow (2) take-away-carry (3) Austrian method.

18. On the whole, the method which came out best in the investigations was the (1) decomposition (2) Austrian (3) equal additions.

19. The most extensively used method seems to be the (1) decomposition (2) equal additions (3) Austrian.

20. The method recommended for use is the (1) decomposition (2) equal additions (3) Austrian.

21. The number of type problems in subtraction is (1) 2 (2) 3 (3) 4.

22. If coins are used to illustrate the subtraction of 25 cents from 43 cents, the coins put on the table at first should be (1) 3 dimes and 13 cents (2) 4 dimes and 3 cents (3) 4 dimes and 3 cents in one group and 2 dimes and 5 cents in another group.

23. Roundabout implicit responses are usually (1) the pupil's inventions (2) caused by the textbook (3) taught by the teacher.

24. Speed is (1) a symptom of mastery (2) a guarantee of mastery (3) a guarantee of mistakes.

25. When compared with the method of decomposition, the complementary method requires (1) more subtraction facts (2) the same number of subtraction facts (3) fewer subtraction facts.

26. It is suggested in the chapter that crutches should be used (1) temporarily (2) permanently (3) not at all.

27. In checking subtraction examples, the sum of the

difference and the subtrahend should be written beneath the subtrahend (1) permanently (2) temporarily (3) not at all.

28. Higher decade subtraction is used in (1) short division (2) long division (3) ordinary subtraction.

29. If pupils are taught subtraction before they have a need for it, there is a violation of the (1) Law of Exercise (2) Law of Effect (3) Law of Readiness.

30. The intervals between practice periods should (1) gradually become shorter (2) gradually become longer (3) remain approximately constant.

SELECTED REFERENCES

1. Beatty, Willard W. "The Additive *versus* the Borrowing Method of Subtraction." *Elementary School Journal,* XXI: 198-200, November, 1920. This is a report of one of the early experimental studies.

2. Buckingham, B. R. "The Additive *versus* the Take-Away Method of Teaching the Subtraction Facts." *Educational Research Bulletin,* VI: 265-269, September 28, 1927. A report of an experimental study in seven centers.

3. Buswell, Guy Thomas and Judd, Charles Hubbard. *Summary of Educational Investigations Relating to Arithmetic.* Chicago: The University of Chicago, 1925, pp. 70-78. Summarizes investigations of subtraction prior to 1925.

4. Johnson, J. T. "The Merits of Different Methods of Subtraction." *Journal of Educational Research,* X: 279-290, November, 1924. Describes the test performances of those who had learned various subtraction methods.

5. Klapper, Paul. *The Teaching of Arithmetic.* New York: D. Appleton- Century Company, 1934, pp. 278-290. Discusses various subtraction methods and gives suggestions for teaching.

6. Mead, Cyrus D. and Sears, Isabel. "Additive Subtraction and Multiplicative Division Tested." *Journal of Educational Psychology,* VII: 261-270, May, 1916. One of the first experi-

mental studies. Results indicated very little advantage in one method over another.

7. Osburn, W. J. "How Shall We Subtract?" *Journal of Educational Research,* XVI: 237-246, November, 1927. Reviews other studies and presents evidence in favor of the method of equal additions.

8. Ruch, G. M. and Mead, Cyrus D. "A Review of Methods in Subtraction." National Society for the Study of Education, *Twenty-Ninth Yearbook.* Bloomington, Illinois: Public School Publishing Company, 1930, pp. 671-678. Presents a summary of investigations made up to 1930.

9. Stone, John C. *How We Subtract.* Chicago: Benj. H. Sanborn and Company, 1926. 98 pp. Gives a historical account of subtraction methods and argues for the use of the additive method.

10. Taylor, Joseph S. "Subtraction by the Addition Process." *Elementary School Journal,* XX: 203-207, November, 1919. Children who had been taught the additive method were soon using a method outlawed in the school system.

11. Wilson, Guy M. "For 100 Percent Subtraction, What Method?" *Journal of Educational Research,* XXVII: 503-508, March, 1934. A questionnaire study showed many methods in use but the most frequent of these was the method of decomposition.

12. Winch, W. M. " 'Equal Additions' *versus* 'Decomposition' in Teaching Subtraction: An Experimental Research." *Journal of Experimental Pedagogy,* V: 207-220 and 261-270, June 5 and December 6, 1920. Report of an investigation in English schools. Gives accounts of interesting cases.

CHAPTER 7

TEACHING THE FUNDAMENTAL COMBINATIONS OF MULTIPLICATION AND DIVISION

The reader will note a number of points of similarity between the plans for teaching the multiplication and division combinations as given in this chapter and the plans outlined in Chapter 4 for teaching the fundamental combinations of addition and subtraction. In each case we recommend that the facts of the two processes be organized into teaching units and be taught together. This procedure seems to facilitate learning and to be the economical one to follow. Other points of similarity will appear as the topics of the chapter are developed.

The use of terms. We use the terms *multiplication combination, multiplication fact, division combination, division fact,* and *teaching unit* in this chapter in the same manner as that in which we used similar terms with reference to addition and subtraction. For example, two one-digit numbers such as 4 and 6, give us a teaching unit composed of a multiplication combination and a division combination. For the multiplication combination, there are the two multiplication facts, $4 \times 6 = 24$ and $6 \times 4 = 24$; for the division combination, there are the two division facts, $24 \div 4 = 6$ and $24 \div 6 = 4$. Thus, for each teaching unit there are four primary facts, except when the two digits are the same, as 5 and 5, in which case there are but two facts—the multiplication fact, $5 \times 5 = 25$, and the corresponding division fact, $25 \div 5 = 5$.

The zero combinations. It is widely reported that the zero facts in multiplication cause much trouble. Pupils taking tests in which isolated zero combinations occur, as $\begin{array}{r}0\\ \underline{6}\end{array}$ or $\begin{array}{r}6\\ \underline{0}\end{array}$, are quite likely to write 6 instead of 0 as the product. This is probably due in part to a carry over from the use of zeros in addition and the emphasis which has been placed on the point that zero plus any number or any number plus zero gives us the number itself. It is also due, no doubt, to the lack of adequate instruction as to what is meant by multiplying 0 by a number or a number by 0. The form in which we write zero combinations in many of our tests, as $\begin{array}{r}0\\ \underline{6}\end{array}$ or $\begin{array}{r}6\\ \underline{0}\end{array}$ in isolation, is bad in that it is a form which arithmetic users never meet, except in schoolrooms.

We did not include the zero combinations with the other addition and subtraction combinations. We left them for later treatment for two reasons: (1) the zero combinations as separate combinations do not occur in the pupils real number experiences; and (2) learning the zero combinations is not closely analogous to learning the other combinations. For the same two reasons, we shall not include the zero combinations with the other combinations in multiplication and division. Pupils do have occasion to find the cost of 3 toy balloons at 5 cents each but they do not have occasion to find the cost of 0 toy balloons at that price. Likewise, 3 boys who have been nutting may have occasion to divide 15 capfuls of nuts by 3, but if the quest for nuts was unsuccessful, they do not have occasion to ponder over the amount which each would receive if 0 capfuls were divided among 3 boys. Efforts to formulate problems involving the zero combinations in multiplication and division are likely to result in verbal statements which confuse children or constitute an insult to their intelligence.

The zero combinations should be taught in connection with the situations in which they occur, in examples like $\begin{array}{r}20\\ \underline{3}\end{array}$ or $2\overline{)40}$. That is, they will be taught when pupils are learning to solve examples in multiplication and division and some time after the primary facts have been learned. Then we shall teach all zero combinations in multiplication as a group by teaching the principles that *any number multiplied by zero gives zero as a product* and *zero multiplied by any number gives zero as a product.* Likewise, the principle that *zero divided by any number gives zero as a quotient* will cover all the cases of dividing zero by a number. Later, when the need for it arises if it ever does, pupils will be told that it is impossible to divide a number by zero.

There is some evidence to the effect that with proper methods of teaching, the zero combinations are no more difficult than are the other combinations. Indeed, they should be much easier. Fowlkes reports that there is reason to doubt the validity of the emphasis which has been placed upon the difficulty of the combinations involving zero.[1] It may quite well be that the many errors which pupils make when operating with zeros are due to insufficient opportunity to learn the meaning of such op-

[1] Fowlkes, John Guy. "A Report of a Controlled Study of the Learning of Multiplication by Third-Grade Children." *Journal of Educational Research,* XV: 181-189, March, 1927.

erations, to premature instruction, to the unreal form in which practice is given and the pupils are tested, and to the lack of adequate practice under proper learning conditions.

Writing and speaking the combinations. In some schools, practically every occurrence of the multiplication and division combinations in the experiences of the pupils is in the equation form. Thus, the pupils always see $4 \times 6 = 24$ and $6 \times 4 = 24$ rather than $\begin{array}{r}6\\ \underline{4}\\ 24\end{array}$ and $\begin{array}{r}4\\ \underline{6}\\ 24\end{array}$.

Likewise, they see $24 \div 6 = 4$ and $24 \div 4 = 6$ rather than $6\overline{)24}$ with quotient 4 and $4\overline{)24}$ with quotient 6.

The equation is an important and valuable means of expression but it seems better to have the pupils' first acquaintance with the multiplication and the division facts come in the form which will later be of most frequent occurrence. Multiplication and division examples are not ordinarily expressed in the form of equations, but in such form as is indicated by these examples:

$$\begin{array}{r}76\\ \underline{5}\end{array} \qquad 5\overline{)85}$$

Later, the signs, $\times$ and $\div$, may be taught and multiplication and division facts may be expressed as equations. It will be recalled that a similar suggestion was offered for the addition and subtraction facts.

If 8 is to be multiplied by 6, the expression which indicates this fact is $\begin{array}{r}8\\ \underline{6}\end{array}$, or 6×8. Note that the multiplier is written beneath the multiplicand if the example is written vertically and at the left of the multiplicand if it is written horizontally. In either form, this should be read "six 8's," rather than "six times eight." Many teachers make entirely too much use of the word "times" and not enough use of the former form of expression.

There is nothing inherently wrong with "six times eight" but "six 8's" is much more expressive of what takes place when we multiply. Eventually, pupils should learn to use the word "times" in such situations but at the beginning they will understand multiplication better if this expression is avoided and the other is used. Some teachers seem to be unable to talk about multiplication without using the word "times." They speak of the "times tables." A few even use "times" as a transitive verb. One teacher said that to find the cost of six tickets at 35 cents each, "you write down 35 cents and times it by 6."

The division fact, $\begin{array}{r}7\\4\overline{)28}\end{array}$, should be read in some such form as "4's in 28, 7." The pupil should think of $4\overline{)28}$ as asking the question, "How many 4's in 28?" Such expressions as "28 divided by 4 equals 7," or "$28 \div 4 = 7$," or "4 is contained 7 times in 28" are satisfactory when the pupils are ready for them. Avoid "4 *goes into* 28 how many times?" The 4 does not go into the 28 at all. One boy, when asked what he was doing in arithmetic, replied: "We are having guzinto problems." It is a safe guess that he did not think that one up, himself.

The number of combinations. We have seen that there are 45 addition and 45 subtraction combinations if the zeros are not counted and 55 of each if the zeros are included. We have also seen that the number of facts in each case is 81 without the zeros and 100 with the zeros. In multiplication, we have exactly the same number if we go only as far as 9×9; that is, from 1×1 to 9×9 there are 45 multiplication combinations and 81 multiplication facts. If the zeros are included the number of combinations is 55 and the number of facts is 100 as in the case of addition and subtraction. In division, however, the numbers are different when zeros are included, for, as we have seen, division by zero is impossible. The number of division combinations, including the zeros, is 54 and the number of facts is 90.

But in some schools the pupils are expected to learn the multiplication combinations to 12×12 and division combinations equally far. This means 78 combinations and 144 facts without the zeros and 91 combinations and 169 facts including the zeros. Obviously, going to 12×12 means an added load of considerable proportions in spite of the fact that the 10's are easy and that most of the 11's are not at all difficult.

It seems strange that the practice of requiring third-grade pupils to learn multiplication tables to 12×12 should have persisted for so long a time in this country. How is such a practice defended? As a matter of fact, many of those who follow this practice do not defend it at all; they have given the matter little, if any, thought. However, there are those who argue that the practice of learning the tables to 12×12 saves the pupil much time for, they say, he multiplies by 11 or 12 as a single operation instead of writing out two partial products and then adding them, and he uses short division when dividing by 11 or 12. On the other hand, the great majority of adults who have been so trained actually use the longer form when multiplying by 11 or 12 and employ the long division form when dividing by 11 or 12. This argument, when offered, is usually a weak defense for a custom which came about for quite a different reason.

The real reason lies in the history of the subject. Smith states that the custom of extending the tables to 12 × 12 can be traced to the early influence of English educational practices.[2] In that country the fact that there are 12 pence in a shilling made it seem advisable to teach the 12's. The 11's were put in for mere logical reasons—to make the system complete. The first arithmetic texts used in this country were English texts and the first texts printed in this country were, to a considerable extent, imitations of English books. Hence, we have had for a long time, and still have in places, a practice which is largely useless simply because we were unwilling to change a well-established custom.

Later, the pupil should learn a few 12's, not for use in our money system which is a decimal system, but for use in connection with things in a dozen, inches in a foot, and months in a year. He should eventually know the 12's up to about 6 × 12. He should also learn a few 15's for we have many articles which sell at 15 cents each, 15 cents a pound, 15 cents a dozen, 15 cents a can, 15 cents a box, etc. But the pupil's first work in multiplication should be limited to 9 × 9 with later provision for zero difficulties. At this time he should not be burdened with 12's or 15's. At no time should he be burdened with 11's. Of course the 10's to 100 will be learned before the serious study of multiplication is undertaken; they will

[2] Smith, David Eugene. *The Progress of Arithmetic in the Last Quarter of a Century*. Boston: Ginn and Company, 1923, pp. 43-44.

be learned while the pupil is gaining an understanding of our number system.

The effect of going beyond 9 × 9. It is a common observation that the multiplication and division facts are not well learned in the grade or grades where they are seriously studied. Most of this work is usually assigned to grade three. Some schools undertake to teach some of it in grade two. There is a current tendency, however, to postpone serious work on the multiplication and division facts until grade four is reached. The author's extended observation in these grades and the many tests which he has given to pupils in grades three and four force him to believe that, in general, the teachers in these grades are falling far short of what they are supposed to accomplish in teaching the primary facts of multiplication and division. An important reason for this condition lies in the fact that an effort is made to push the mastery of combinations through the 12's. The pupil's energy is dissipated on material which is difficult and largely useless. He learns less than he would probably learn if he did not undertake to learn so much.

Serial memorizing of tables. There are other reasons why pupils do not learn their multiplication combinations well. One of these reasons lies in the fact that the tables are often taken up in strict numerical order—the 1's, then the 2's, then the 3's, etc.—and the facts of each table are memorized in serial order. Years ago, such tables were memorized for each of the four fundamental operations—addition, subtraction, multiplication, and division. Even today, the author learns occasionally of a school where addition tables are memorized in this manner. But at the present time very few American schools have pupils memorize tables in addition, subtraction or division. However, the practice of committing to memory the multiplication tables in serial order is still quite common. And then the pupils are called upon to recite their ones, their twos, their threes, and so on to the twelves.

This procedure is gradually being abandoned or modified. Teachers are recognizing that when a pupil has learned the 6's for example, he can not answer such a question as "How many are five 6's?" without at least implicitly reciting, "one 6 is 6, two 6's are 12, three 6's are 18, four 6's are 24, five 6's are 30." This delayed response is not adequate for such uses of 6's as one has in ordinary multiplication examples. It seems at times that pupils who have worked long and hard at memorizing tables must learn the multiplication facts anew before they can put them to use in ordinary examples.

Memorizing tables need not be all wasted effort as we shall see in a later section. If a pupil is to see five 6's in relation to four 6's and three 6's on one hand and six 6's and seven 6's on the other hand, he must appreciate the orderly arrangement of 6's in a table; he must be able to count by 6's. But the mere rote memorization of the tables as is the practice in many schools may have little educational benefit. It is likely to be uninteresting because of its abstractness and discouraging because of its difficulty.

The order of teaching the combinations. Reciting tables to find a given product in multiplication is analogous to counting to find a sum in addition. Indeed, reciting multiplication tables *is* counting. The pupil who runs through the table of 8's to find how many six 8's are, actually counts by 8's to 48.

We have already seen that counting is the fundamental

number experience and that counting is a valuable aid to the pupil in learning the addition combinations. In like manner counting by 2's, 3's, 4's, etc. is a valuable aid in learning the multiplication combinations. But this does not mean that the multiplication combinations should be learned as tables any more than that the use of counting in learning addition means that the addition facts should be learned as tables. In general, the multiplication and division teaching units should be taken up one at a time just as the addition and subtraction teaching units are taken up one at a time and the order in which they are taken up should be approximately the order of their difficulty.

In general, the larger a product the more difficult a combination, but there are exceptions to this statement. For example, the 2's are so much like the doubles in addition that they are just another way of expressing facts which are already known. The pupil who knows that 8 and 8 are 16 has little difficulty in understanding that since there are two 8's there, two 8's must be 16. This product is larger than the product of 4 and 3 but 2×8 is probably easier for the pupil to learn than is 4×3. The 5's and the 1's are also comparatively easy but aside from such exceptions, the combinations having larger numbers as products are more difficult than the combinations having smaller numbers as products.

It is suggested that the multiplication combinations be taught in approximately the order of their difficulty. Let us begin with the 2's which, as we have said, simply represent another way of expressing the doubles in addition. Since these doubles are already known as addition combinations, the pupil's task here is to get acquainted with a new form of expression for already familiar facts rather than to learn new facts. Hence, it is not necessary to take up the 2's in table order. We may follow two 2's with two 5's and this with two 8's, etc. referring back to the doubles in addition in each instance.

Let this be followed by a mixture of 3's, 4's, and 5's taking first those in each group which have the smaller multiplicands. Rather late in the list should come the 1's. When they are understood, the 1's are among the very easiest combinations in the list but at first it is hard for a pupil to understand what is meant by multiplying by 1. In a way, multiplying by 1 is not multiplying at all although the reverse form in which 1 is multiplied by a number is a clear case of multiplying. Finally, the list of 45 combinations may be concluded with a group in which there are no 1's, 2's, 3's, 4's, or 5's and the products of which are all comparatively large numbers.

With these points in mind, we can arrange the 45 combinations in a desirable teaching order. Obviously, there are many such orders which will conform to these suggestions. The following arrangement is only one such order but it is believed to be as good as any, and better than many.

2	5	8	4	6	3	7	9	1
2	2	2	2	2	2	2	2	2
3	4	5	4	5	5	6	6	7
3	4	5	3	3	4	3	4	5
6	8	7	7	8	8	9	9	9
5	5	3	4	3	4	3	4	5

5	7	4	8	3	6	9	1	6
1	1	1	1	1	1	1	1	6

7	7	8	8	9	9	8	9	9
6	7	6	7	6	7	8	8	9

The relation of multiplication to addition. Multiplication is a short method for addition. If 37 is to be multiplied by 4 for example, 37 is taken 4 times and this fact may be expressed either in the addition form or in the multiplication form, as shown. If the addition form is used, we *see* four 7's and four 3's whereas in the multiplication form, we do not see four 7's and four 3's but we think, as we multiply "four 7's" in the first step and "four 3's" in the second step. Thus, multiplication is a short method for addition *if the addends are equal.* We use multiplication rather than addition in such cases to save time and to decrease the probability of errors. The economy in the example shown is not so great as it would be if the multiplier were a larger number. Thus, if 37 were to be multiplied by 62, the task would be very laborious if done by the method of addition.

```
      37
      37
 37   37
  4   37
---  ---
148  148
```

It is well that pupils learn multiplication as a short method for addition. There are two reasons: first, it helps to show the pupil the *meaning* of multiplication; second, it gives him a *motive* for learning multiplication. If multiplication as a process is presented independent of its uses and without making clear to the pupil the advantage which will accrue to him from learning it, there is danger that his progress in learning will be slow and unsatisfactory.

Our arrangement of the combinations makes it possible to take excellent advantage of this relationship to addition. We have used the smaller numbers as multipliers, have in general given the smaller multipliers first, and have begun the list with the 2's. Using the smaller number of a combination as the multiplier makes it easier to develop a combination by addition; it is easier, for example, to show by addition $\begin{array}{r}9\\ \underline{2}\\ 18\end{array}$ than to show $\begin{array}{r}2\\ \underline{9}\\ 18\end{array}$. Of course, a combination should be presented in both addition forms often enough for the pupils to see that the product is the same regardless of which of the two numbers is used as the multiplier. Thus, a pupil should see four 2's in a column as well as two 4's in a column when he is learning $\begin{array}{r}4\\ \underline{2}\\ 8\end{array}$ and $\begin{array}{r}2\\ \underline{4}\\ 8\end{array}$.

There are two reasons why we begin with the 2's. In the first place, the various studies of the difficulty of the combinations show that the 2's are among the easiest. This is clearly indicated by the findings of Clapp,[3] of Fowlkes,[4] and of Norem and Knight.[5] In the second

[3] Clapp, Frank L. *The Number Combinations: Their Relative Difficulty and the Frequency of Their Appearance in Text-Books*. Madison, Wisconsin: University of Wisconsin, 1924, pp. 26-27.

[4] Fowlkes, John Guy, *op. cit.*, pp. 186-188.

[5] Norem, G. M. and Knight, F. B. "The Learning of the One Hundred Multiplication Combinations." National Society for the Study of Education, *Twenty-Ninth Yearbook,* 1930, pp. 551-568.

place, the relationship to addition is so close that the 2's are quite easy to teach. If the pupil has learned that 5 and 5 are 10, he has learned that two 5's are 10, but he has not yet learned to state the fact in that manner. If we begin with the 2's it is relatively easy for the pupil to see the relationship of multiplication to addition.

Some will contend that we should carry this argument still further and begin with the 1's. If we begin with the 1's, however, it is difficult for the pupil to learn the meaning of multiplication. As we have said, he is not really multiplying at all when he multiplies by 1. To ask a child "How much is one 6?" is likely either to baffle him or to insult his intelligence. One might as well ask "How many is one dog?" If we postpone the 1's until the pupil has learned the meaning of multiplication and has acquired a fair degree of competence in the use of other easy combinations, we can then take them up as a group and dispose of them in rapid fashion. We merely need to lead the pupil to see that one 4 and four 1's have the same value and to give sufficient practice to enable the pupil to handle with confidence any of the 1's when he meets them.

After all, the pupil has very little, if any, use for 1's before he begins to use multiplication in examples having two-digit numbers. If 21 is to be multiplied by 6, the pupil must know the meaning of six 1's. Such examples can be solved before the pupil has learned all 45 of the combinations, as will be indicated in the next chapter, but even then he will not have use for 1 as a multiplier. When two-digit multipliers are introduced and the pupil has such multiplication examples as $\begin{array}{r}43\\ \underline{31}\end{array}$, he will need to know the meaning of 1 as a multiplier but not until he reaches this stage in his progress will there be need for concern over his use of 1 as a multiplier.

It seems best, then, to begin with the 2's if we would teach effectively the meaning of multiplication and show the relationship between multiplication and addition.

Teaching the 2's. As has already been stated, the 2's are easy because of their intimate relationship to the doubles in addition. Pupils who are proficient in their addition combinations—and many pupils are proficient in the doubles who do not know all of the other combinations well—already know the 2's in multiplication and need, merely, to learn the *meaning* of multiplication and to become accustomed to the *language* of multiplication.

For the first two combinations, $\begin{array}{r}2\\ \underline{2}\end{array}$ and $\begin{array}{r}5\\ \underline{2}\end{array}$, the lesson may proceed in some such manner as the following:

TEACHER. Let us go back to some of our numbers in addition. How many are 2 and 2?

PUPIL. Four.

TEACHER. (*Writing on the blackboard:* $\begin{array}{r}2\\ \underline{2}\end{array}$). Yes. Two and two are four. How many 2's did I write?

PUPIL. Two.

TEACHER. Then we can say that in another way. Instead of saying, "two and two are four," we can say, "two 2's are four." Now, let us take another example. How many are 5 and 5?

PUPIL. Ten.

TEACHER (*Writing* $\begin{array}{r}5\\ \underline{5}\\ 10\end{array}$). Yes. Five and five are ten. How many 5's did I write?

PUPIL. Two.

Teacher. In what other way can I say that five and five are ten?

Pupil. You can say, "two 5's are ten.

Teacher. When we want to say, "two 5's are ten," instead of writing it as I have written it here, we write it this way, $\begin{array}{r}5\\ \times 2\\ \hline 10\end{array}$. That means, two 5's are 10. The sign in front of the 2, (×) tells that we mean, two 5's are 10. When we write this, $\begin{array}{r}2\\ \times 2\\ \hline 4\end{array}$, we mean, two 2's are 4.

It may be necessary to repeat the explanations once or twice, particularly for the slower pupils. While the explanation is being made, one pupil after another is given the opportunity to think and say "two 2's are 4" and "two 5's are 10." One or two other combinations may then be introduced, such as $\begin{array}{r}8\\ 2\\ \hline\end{array}$ and $\begin{array}{r}4\\ 2\\ \hline\end{array}$, and the appropriate responses secured from the pupils. The teacher should remember that the purpose here is not to give new arithmetical facts but to give old facts in new form and to acquaint the pupils in a limited way with the language and meaning of multiplication.

In two or three periods, the whole story of the 2's can become known to the pupils. Once they grasp the idea, they can go as far as their knowledge of doubles in addition permits. This means that a good start is made toward the learning of multiplication without the necessity of presenting any new facts.

Developing the related facts. After a few of the 2's have been presented in this manner, the teacher may proceed to the related multiplication facts. Of course, there is no related fact for the combination $\begin{array}{r}2\\ \underline{2}\end{array}$, but the pupil should discover now that not only two 5's but also five 2's are 10 and that eight 2's as well as two 8's are 16. Taking the former as a specific example, the teacher writes on the blackboard both two 5's and five 2's as shown.

$$\begin{array}{rr} & 2\\ & 2\\ & 2\\ 5 & 2\\ \underline{5} & \underline{2}\\ 10 & 10 \end{array}$$

Then the pupils find by actual addition that each has a sum of 10. Two 8's and eight 2's are similarly treated. Having discovered that two 5's is equal to five 2's and that two 8's is equal to eight 2's, the pupil generalizes to the effect that no no matter whether he writes $\begin{array}{r}5\\ \underline{\times 2}\end{array}$ or $\begin{array}{r}2\\ \underline{\times 5}\end{array}$, the same answer is obtained in either case, that is, no matter which of the two numbers is written below with the sign $\times$ before it, he gets the same answer. This generalization will be reinforced and strengthened by presenting several later combinations in the two addition forms, but it will not be necessary to use the two forms in presenting the entire 45. However, we should present the two forms until three or four different multipliers have been used and for enough combinations to permit the generalization to become well established.

Other combinations should be presented in both forms. Thus, when the combination $\begin{array}{r}4\\ \underline{3}\end{array}$ is reached, it should be presented by addition both as three 4's and as four 3's. Such dual presentation is not necessary for the entire 36 combinations which are not doubles, however. Certainly, by the time that the fifth and last group of nine teaching units is reached, everyone should be ready to assume that the product is the same for the two multiplication facts of

$$\begin{array}{r} \\ 4 \\ 4 \\ \underline{4} \\ 12 \end{array} \qquad \begin{array}{r} 3 \\ 3 \\ 3 \\ \underline{3} \\ 12 \end{array}$$

a combination. Such a combination as $\begin{array}{r}7\\ \underline{6}\end{array}$, then may be presented as six 7's and the pupils may take it for granted that seven 6's are also 42

Many of the later combinations should be seen in their relationship to other combinations which have been learned previously. Thus, when the pupil comes to $\begin{array}{r}8\\ \underline{6}\end{array}$, he should recall that five 8's are 40, add 8 to 40 since six 8's is 8 more than five 8's, and arrive at the new product in this manner. This is somewhat similar to learning the combinations in table form. There are two main differences, however. First, we learn not more than one new combination a day, instead of trying in vain to learn the whole table of 8's in a day. And second, the product of 6 and 8 is discovered from the known product of 5 and 8 instead of being memorized as a totally new fact, unrelated to facts which have been learned before.

Teaching the corresponding division facts. After a few multiplication combinations have been studied, enough to permit the pupil to get an idea as to what multiplication is, attention should be directed to the corresponding division facts. Thereafter, when a new combination is taken up, all four facts (two in the case of the doubles) should be studied and practised together.[6] If the pupil has seen that there are two 2's in 4, two 5's in 10, and five 2's in 10, his attention may be directed to these same facts from the point of view indicated by the questions: How many 2's in 4? How many 5's in 10? How many 2's in 10? This becomes for him simply another way of stating the facts which he has just discovered. He has discovered that two 5's are 10, for example; we ask him how many 5's there are in 10, and he answers, "Two."

We have indicated that it is better not to use the word "times" until the pupils understand well the meaning of multiplication when expressed in the other form. After a time however, the alternative expression should be introduced and the pupils should learn to say "2 times 5 are 10" as well as "two 5's are 10." Probably, this word "times" should not be used until the pupils have learned a majority of the multiplication and the division facts. But when the word "times" has been introduced in multiplication, it should be used at once in division and the pupils will learn to think and say, "2 in 10, how many times?"

We have said that the division facts are not new facts but slightly different ways of looking at the multiplication facts. The written form for division facts is new, however. After several multiplication facts have been turned into the division fact form, they should be writ-

---

[6] A note in the *Journal of Educational Research,* Vol. XXX, page 731 (May, 1937), indicates that a study made in Phoenix, Arizona, yielded results uniformly in favor of teaching the multiplication and the division facts together rather than separately.

ten in the conventional manner. Thus, the pupils see and then write $\begin{array}{r}2\\5\overline{)10}\end{array}$ and $\begin{array}{r}5\\2\overline{)10}\end{array}$ along with $\begin{array}{r}5\\\underline{\times 2}\\10\end{array}$ and $\begin{array}{r}2\\\underline{\times 5}\\10\end{array}$. Pupils should have practice in reading such expressions as $\begin{array}{r}5\\\underline{\times 2}\end{array}$ and $\begin{array}{r}2\\\underline{\times 5}\end{array}$ and thinking of them as asking the questions, "Two 5's are how many?" "Five 2's are how many?" Also, they should have practice in reading such expressions as $5\overline{)10}$ and $2\overline{)10}$ and thinking of them as asking the questions, "How many 5's in 10?" and "How many 2's in 10?"

It may be added that the sign, "$\times$" before the multiplier is put there temporarily to help the pupils remember that they are multiplying and not adding or subtracting. Its use should soon be discontinued. Later, as a means of adding variety to the drill exercises, and of enabling the pupils to learn the signs better, the equation forms, such as $2 \times 5 = 10$ and $10 \div 5 = 2$, will be used. As was pointed out in a previous page, however, the early emphasis should be upon the written forms which have been recommended.

The need for higher decade addition. If multiplication combinations are taught through the medium of column addition, there will be much use of higher decade addition combinations. When the larger combinations are developed, higher decade combinations will be encountered which the pupils have seldom if ever experienced. Seldom will they have gone beyond the thirties or the forties in their column addition up to this time.

If the pupils have been well taught in column addition they should experience no difficulty at this time. The fact that some of the higher decade addition combinations which are to be used are in the fifties, the sixties, and the seventies, should not make the work difficult, for these combinations are very similar to others in lower decades with which the pupils presumably have been having much practice. In Chapter 5, we emphasized the importance of teaching these higher decade addition combinations in family groups and leading the pupils to see how they resemble each other and also how they resemble primary addition facts.

But the teacher who is about to undertake the teaching of the multiplication combinations can not take it for granted that the pupils are proficient in column addition. Tests should be given and additional practice should be provided if it is needed. These tests may well include the very combinations which will be used in developing the multiplication combinations by higher decade addition. The entire list is given in Table 2.

It will be seen that there are 50 higher decade addition combinations in the list and that bridging is required in 28 of these. Special emphasis should be placed upon these 28 in tests and practice exercises.

If the combinations whose products are the larger numbers are developed in one form only by column addition, some of these higher decade combinations will not be needed. If, for example, the combination, $\begin{array}{r}7\\ \underline{6}\end{array}$, is presented as six 7's by column addition but not as seven 6's, as has already been suggested, the combination $\begin{array}{r}36\\ \underline{6}\end{array}$, in this list would not be needed. If this prac-

Table 2. Higher Decade Addition Combinations Used in Learning Multiplication Facts by Column Addition

Multiplier	Higher Decade Addition							Total Number	Number with Bridging
2	10 2	12 2	14 2	16 2				4	0
3	12 3	15 3	18 3	21 3	24 3			5	1
4	12 4	16 4	20 4	24 4	28 4	32 4		6	2
5	10 5	15 5	20 5	25 5	30 5	35 5	40 5	7	3
6	12 6	18 6	24 6	30 6	36 6	42 6	48 6	7	4
7	14 7	21 7	28 7	35 7	42 7	49 7	56 7	7	5
8	16 8	24 8	32 8	40 8	48 8	56 8	64 8	7	6
9	18 9	27 9	36 9	45 9	54 9	63 9	72 9	7	7
Total								50	28

tice is followed for all of those combinations whose products are greater than 40, there are just seven higher decade combinations in the list which are not needed. They are:

40	36	42	48	49	56	64
5	6	6	6	7	7	8

But the pupil who knows higher decade addition will have no more difficulty with these combinations than with others. Hence, there is no good reason why the teacher should delete them from tests and practice exercises.

Rate of progress. In teaching the multiplication and the division facts, the teacher should go slowly. One of the major difficulties with the older method was that a single assignment would often include an entire table. Thus, the pupils would be expected to memorize all of the 4's, from 1×4 to 12×4, in a single lesson. Rarely were they able to do so. Those who succeeded usually learned by rote only. Those who failed, and they were numerous, usually became discouraged and developed a dislike for the subject.

With the exception of the 2's, the 1's, and the 0's, a day's lesson should not include more than one teaching unit. Even one teaching unit a day will mean too fast a schedule when the more difficult combinations are reached. Here, one every other day will be enough. New combinations should not be added to the list faster than the pupils can assimilate them. Assimilation requires much use of the combinations, much practice.

After all, there are not very many of these combinations which can reasonably cause difficulty. We have commented on the fact that the 1's and the 2's are easy. It is generally conceded that the 5's are also easy since children learn to count by 5's and to buy various numbers of articles at 5 cents each before they reach the subject of multiplication in school. Removing the 1's, the 2's, and the 5's from the list, we have only 21 of the 45 combinations left. They are:

3 3	4 3	6 3	7 3	8 3	9 3	4 4
6 4	7 4	8 4	9 4	6 6	7 6	8 6
9 6	7 7	8 7	9 7	8 8	9 8	9 9

Surely, there is no need for haste when there are only 21 combinations which may be expected to cause difficulty. At the rate of two per week, these can be learned in less than three months. But in many schools, the pupils spend the major portion of their arithmetic time for a year on the multiplication combinations and then they do not know them even fairly well.

Games and practice exercises. Most of what was said about games and drill devices in connection with the discussion of the addition and subtraction facts (Chapter 4) applies equally well to the teaching units of multiplication and division. In general, the teacher must go slowly and make provision for an abundance of practice on the facts of a teaching unit immediately after it is presented, if she expects to have these facts well learned. Continued practice must then be provided if the facts are to be retained but the amount of practice at successive repetitions may gradually become less and the intervals between practice periods may gradually become greater.

A great many games and devices have been prepared for drill on the fundamental facts of multiplication and division, particularly multiplication. Some of these are good, some are of doubtful value, and others are poor. To rate high, a drill device must possess the following characteristics.

First, it must be interesting to the pupils for whom it is prepared. One of the most discouraging sights in a primary classroom is that of an unenthusiastic teacher conducting, in a wooden way, a drill lesson with a group of equally unenthusiastic pupils. The author has seen such a lesson dragged out through a period of 20 minutes, while the pupils shifted restlessly in their seats, looked at each other and out the window, and sometimes had to be called upon twice before they would give attention to the part which had been assigned them. We must have repetition but it must be attentive repetition. A good drill lesson is brief and vigorous and the participants are eager and alert. The teacher must take these facts into serious consideration in selecting games and other drill devices.

Second, the game or device must provide much practice on the facts which are in need of drill. There are games which children enjoy playing and which are quite harmless as games, but which are nearly worthless as a means of teaching. Consider, for example, the following game.

Ring Toss Game

A board 20 inches square, made of soft wood, is ruled into 25 smaller squares. Into each smaller square a small cup hook is screwed. Numbers, cut from the calendar, are pasted below the hooks. The pupils, one at a time, toss rubber rings (ordinary fruit jar rings) at the board. If the ring becomes caught on a hook, the pupil must give the product of the number of the hook by some number previously agreed upon or a number which the teacher, at that instant, calls. Each gets four tosses and scores one for each combination successfully answered.

In this game, only one pupil participates at a time, and the period of his participation is so long that only a small group can take part in a single period. Also, success depends too much upon deftness in tossing rings or upon chance, for it is probable that none of the children will be able to throw a ring on a selected hook very often. There is no assurance that the facts on which a pupil needs practice will be those on which he gets practice. Pupils scoring low may make low scores because of inadequate skill in ring tossing or bad luck rather than because of insufficient knowledge of the combinations. This game, like many others, is a peculiar combination of two types of activity quite different, the sort of combination which is not likely to occur, except in a schoolroom. When people play tossing games, they add points to find their scores; they do not recite multiplication combinations.

In the third place, devices should provide for the active participation of a number of pupils, the more the better. If but one pupil can actively participate at a time, his period should be brief, and the active part should be passed on to others in rapid succession. As already indicated, the Ring Toss Game violates this principle.

Fourth, the device should provide for a desirable amount and distribution of practice. Furthermore, the device should enable the teacher to tell how well the pupils know what they seem to know. If pupils have to count, or run through a table, or otherwise figure out an answer, the teacher should have at least a good chance to discover this. Consider this game:

Cat and Mouse

The mice form a circle with the cat outside. Each mouse holds a card containing a combination. The cat taps a mouse on the head and the mouse gives his combination. If he makes a mistake he is caught and must give his place to the cat.

Here each pupil has but one combination to concern him. The teacher has no way of determining whether he knows this combination or takes a great deal of time to find the answer. Games should place a premium upon prompt answers and should not leave the teacher in doubt as to how these answers were obtained.

Flash Cards. Here, as in addition and subtraction, flash cards are of considerable value. To cover all of the facts, will require 81 multiplication cards and 81 division cards. It seems better however, to eliminate the 1's and reduce the number of cards to 64. Those who give drill on the 1's usually find that the pupils have trouble with them but their trouble seems to be due to the fact that they do not see how these operations are carried out with 1's rather than to any inherent arithmetical difficulty.

The 1's should not be drilled on separately because they are not useful in this separate form. Neither children nor adults multiply numbers by 1 and divide numbers by 1 in socially useful situations. Nor do they consciously multiply 1 by a number or divide a number by itself. A child in the primary grades knows that 3 one-cent stamps will cost 3 cents and he does not multiply 1 by 3 to find the cost. He also knows that the number of ice cream cones he can buy for 5 cents at 5 cents each is 1 and he does not divide 5 by 5 to determine the number. Special attention may be given to the 1's in situations which will arise in later work in multiplication and division and the flash card drills may be limited to the remaining 64 facts in each of the two operations.

As in addition and subtraction, the cards should show the facts without products or quotients on one side and the facts with products or quotients on the other side. Thus, one side of a multiplication card may show $\begin{array}{r}9\\ \underline{4}\end{array}$ and the other side, $\begin{array}{r}9\\ \underline{4}\\ 36\end{array}$. The division card may show $9\overline{)36}$ on one side and $\begin{array}{r}4\\ 9\overline{)36}\end{array}$ on the other.

Sample games and devices. A great many games are available for practice on the multiplication and division facts. Lack of space prohibits the description of many here but a few, selected from a variety of sources, are given.

Winging Wild Geese

Arrange the nine digits on the blackboard in an angle representing a number of wild geese in characteristic flight formation.

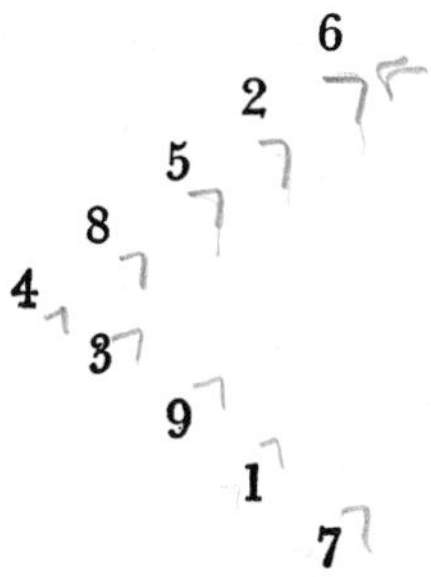

Let the digits occur in random order and let the order be changed occasionaly. As a bullet, use any number from 2 to 9. If the bullet is 7, the pupil wings the geese by naming, in rapid succession, the products, 42, 14, 35, 56, 28, 21, 63, 7, 49. The order in which the products are named may be changed at will; the pupil may begin with 49 and end with 42.

Winging Wild Geese provides an interesting means of getting rapid spirited drills on the multiplication combinations. Many pupils can take part, for the time required for one pupil to wing his geese is very brief. This game may be used when only a portion of the combinations have been presented if care is taken to limit it to those which have been taught. To make the flock of geese larger, some of the digits may be repeated.

As the pupils recall the products more and more easily, greater emphasis may be placed upon the time required to give the products. Pupils may have contests to see who can give the products in the least time. They may also be encouraged to strive to lower their own records.

Winging Wild Geese can also be used for division combination drill. Let the the dividends be the geese while the divisor serves as a bullet. The flock of geese will appear as shown.

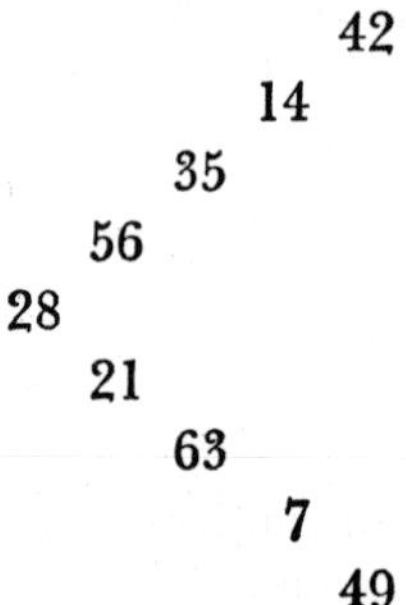

42
14
35
56
28
21
63
7
49

In later work the same scheme may be used for the practice on expressing quotients and remainders. That is, the flock of geese may appear in the following form and the pupil, dividing by 7, will say, "5 and 2 left, 3 and 5 left," etc.

37
26
19
51
60
34
12
43
66

Telling the Whole Story

In this game, the teacher says: "Tell me the whole story of 4 and 6." The pupil responds: "Four 6's are 24; six 4's are 24; 6's in 24, 4; 4's in 24, 6." Of course, the language may be changed to suit that which the pupils have been taught to use with such combinations. This game may be used for written drills, also, the teacher dictating the combination and the pupils writing the four forms $\begin{array}{r}6\\ \underline{4,}\\ 24\end{array}$. $\begin{array}{r}4\\ \underline{6,}\\ 24\end{array}$ $\begin{array}{r}4\\ 6\overline{)24},\end{array}$ and $\begin{array}{r}6\\ 4\overline{)24}.\end{array}$ After a number of combinations have been given, they may check each other's work.

Naming Factors

The teacher chooses a multiple, as 24, and asks: "What numbers make 24?" The pupils respond, orally or in writing, "Four 6's are 24; six 4's are 24; eight 3's are 24; three 8's are 24." Of course, the words, "Factor" and "Multiple," are not used with the pupils.

Supplying Missing Numbers

This drill device affords variety in stating the various facts of multiplication and division. It gives practice in the equation form of statement and in the reading of signs. Mimeographed sheets of exercises can be used for written drill or, if necessary, examples can be written on the blackboard for the pupils to copy, putting in the missing numbers as they copy the examples, or for the pupils to give orally. Teams of pupils may be chosen, the one team setting examples for the other team. For 4 and 9, we may have:

$4 \times 9 = —$	$— \div 9 = 4$	$4 \times — = 36$	$— \div 4 = 9$
$36 \div — = 4$	— = nine 4's	$36 \div — = 9$	$9 \times 4 = —$
36 = — 4's	$9 \times — = 36$	— = four 9's	36 = — 9's
$— \times 4 = 36$	$36 \div 4 = —$	$36 \div 9 = —$	$— \times 9 = 36$

Similar lists may be made for other teaching units. Rather than have all of the statements in a list pertain to a single teaching unit, the teacher may have statements from several teaching units mixed in one list. Both forms should be used.

A Home Run

Draw on the blackboard a figure representing a baseball diamond. Write three numbers at each corner, or base,

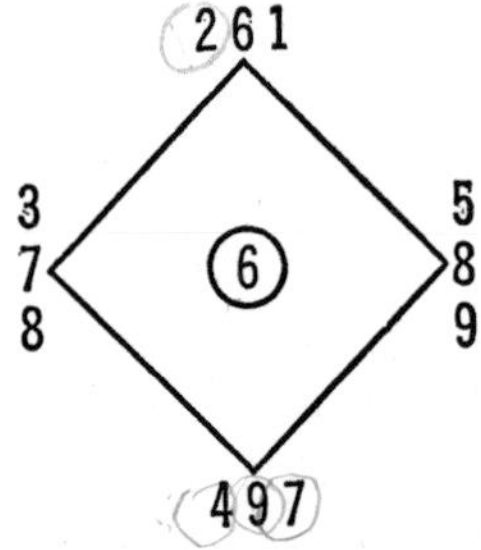

allowing some of the larger numbers to be repeated. Write the multiplier in the pitcher's box. The pupil makes a home run by naming the products of the number in the pitcher's box by the numbers at the bases to which the teacher or another pupil points. For example, the teacher, starting at the home plate, may point to the numbers 2, 7, 4, 9. The pupil responds 12, 42, 24, 54. If he makes a mistake, he is called out at that base, as "out at third." Scores may be kept for individuals and for teams which have been chosen.

Number Wheel

Draw a number wheel on the blackboard as shown. The nine one-digit numbers are written in random order in the outer ring and the multiplier in the center. Both the outer digits and the multiplier can easily be changed. The teacher, or another pupil, points to the digits in the order given, going around the wheel in either direction, and a pupil gives the products. To use this device for division, simply place the products in the outer ring to serve as dividends.

This device is often called "Race Track"; the pupils are urged to race around the circular track.

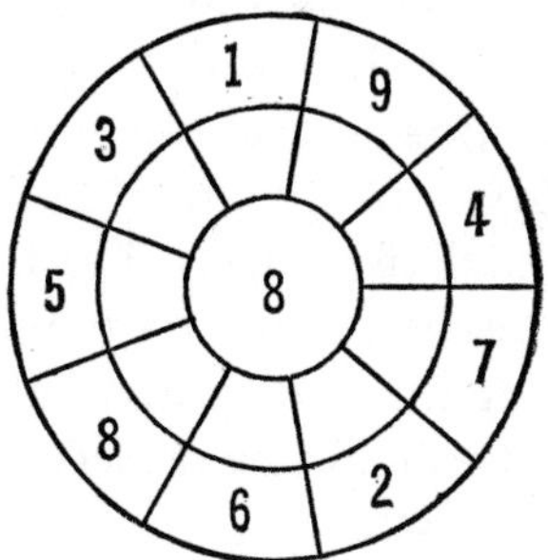

As an interesting variation, the products can be written in the outer ring, the multiplicands in the second ring, and the multiplier in the center. The teacher points to a multiplicand, as 4, and two pupils see who can first point to the product 32. In using the device in this manner, choose two

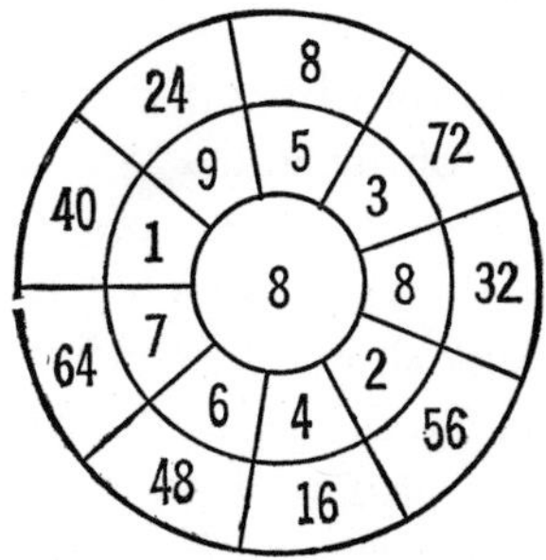

pupils who are nearly equal in ability. The class may be divided into two teams and contest in pairs until all have participated, scores being kept to determine the winning side.

To drill on the division facts, the teacher will point to a

number in the outer ring and the pupil first finding the corresponding number in the second ring (the quotient) will win a point for his team.

There are many forms of the racing game, which is an old favorite. Some, described in Chapter 4, can be used for practice on the multiplication and division facts as well as on the addition and subtraction facts.

Other games given in Chapter 4 can be used for the multiplication and division facts. The teacher can devise still others. The teacher should try to select games which provide for a maximum of educative value. Those which give the best results should be preserved in the teacher's note book for later use.

Solving problems. While the multiplication and division facts are being learned, the teacher should select or formulate problems for each of the teaching units, except those in which the number 1 is involved. Efforts to frame problems for the 1's are likely to result in unreal or fantastic statements of little value for teaching purposes.

We have pointed out, in connection with our discussion of the teaching of the addition and subtraction facts, the importance of the frequent use of problems whose solutions involve the skills which have been acquired. The use of problems should be continuous. The teacher should not try to hold the pupils to drills on the abstract number facts day after day without interesting, realistic, and concrete applications. Each day that multiplication and division facts are on the program, there should be games and other drills on these facts as abstractions and there should also be problems to solve that the pupils may see these facts used in interesting and worth-while ways. Pupils in the primary grades like to solve problems if they possess the necessary knowledge and skill and if the problems are interesting.

There are 64 multiplication facts and 64 division facts if the l's are not included. To cover these facts just once, then, will require 128 problems. Many hundreds of problems should be available during the weeks and months that the pupils devote their attention to learning the primary facts of multiplication and division. Some of these will be furnished by textbooks which are placed in the hands of the pupils but many must be furnished by the teacher. Many should be given orally as the facts of a new teaching unit are being studied and, of course, many should be available in written form.

We do not have space here for many problems. The 16 problems which are given are merely offered as suggestions of the kind the teacher will wish to use. Eight of these involve multiplication and eight, division. For each of the operations, we have used each of the one-figure numbers, except 1, as multiplier and as divisor. Each of these numbers also occurs as multiplicand and as quotient.

1. John makes 2 cents on each *Saturday Evening Post* he sells. Yesterday he sold 6. How much did he make?

2. At the 9-cent sale, mother bought 8 pans. How much did they cost?

3. William's birthday comes 4 weeks from today. How many days until William's birthday?

4. Mildred's mother gives her 3 cents each time she does the dishes all by herself. Last week, she did them 7 times. How much did she earn?

5. The Johnsons live in the country and keep a cow. They

sell the milk in quart bottles. Last evening the cow gave 2 gallons of milk. How many bottles of milk did the Johnsons have to sell?

6. Betty's mother bought a crate of strawberries. When the crate was opened, Betty said: "There are 8 baskets of strawberries in each layer and 3 layers. I can tell how many baskets there are in the crate." Can you?

7. Kenneth's father paid him 5 cents each Saturday for carrying out the ashes. Kenneth saved the money for Christmas. When Christmas came, he had carried the ashes out 9 times. How much money had he earned?

8. Margaret took 5 Christmas packages to the post office to mail them. Each one took 6 cents postage. How much did she have to pay?

9. Richard asked his father how much gasoline their truck used. His father said, "I used 5 gallons to go 45 miles." How far did they go on one gallon?

10. Tom, Jack, Harry, Billy, Dick, and Frank helped Mr. Jones clean up his orchard. When they were through, Mr. Jones said, "Boys, here is a basket of apples that you can divide among you." They counted the apples and found that there were 42. How many did each boy get?

11. Ruth wrote three long letters. When she mailed them she had to pay 18 cents postage. How much postage did each letter take?

12. There were 8 children at Lucile's birthday party. Her mother baked 24 cookies for the party. How many cookies were there for each one?

13. Harry's father pays him 35 cents a week for taking care of the furnace. How much does Harry earn each day?

14. Mother came home from the 9-cent sale and said "I spent 72 cents." How many things did she buy?

15. Tom rode his bicycle over to Jack's house in the morning, rode back home at noon, rode over again in the afternoon and home in the evening. His cyclometer then showed

that he had ridden 8 miles. How far is it from Tom's house to Jack's house.

16. Mary noticed that her mother paid 8 cents for two oranges. How much did each orange cost?

Constructing and using tests. Tests on the multiplication and the division facts should be given frequently. They supply the teacher with information as to what the pupils know and can do and indicate the elements which require additional emphasis. They tell the pupil where he stands and frequently stimulate him to do more and better work.

After a few teaching units have been presented, a test should be arranged so as to include all of the multiplication and division facts so far taught. For example, when the 2's have been learned in multiplication and division form, a test made up of the essential facts may be arranged as follows:

$$\begin{array}{cccccccc} 4 & 6 & 2 & 8 & 2 & 2 & 2 & 7 \\ \underline{2} & \underline{2} & \underline{7} & \underline{2} & \underline{6} & \underline{4} & \underline{2} & \underline{2} \\ 3 & 2 & 2 & 9 & 2 & 2 & 1 & 5 \\ \underline{2} & \underline{5} & \underline{8} & \underline{2} & \underline{3} & \underline{9} & \underline{2} & \underline{2} \end{array}$$

This test includes only multiplication facts, as will be seen. Note that the items are arranged in a miscellaneous order.

Then, a test may be constructed from the division facts of the same teaching units. The division facts corresponding to the multiplication facts above may be arranged in a test as follows:

$$\begin{array}{cccccccc} 7\overline{)14} & 2\overline{)10} & 6\overline{)12} & 2\overline{)8} & 2\overline{)6} & 9\overline{)18} & 2\overline{)12} & 3\overline{)6} \\ 5\overline{)10} & 2\overline{)14} & 2\overline{)2} & 8\overline{)16} & 2\overline{)18} & 4\overline{)8} & 2\overline{)16} & 2\overline{)4} \end{array}$$

Many of the tests which the teacher prepares should include both multiplication and division facts. The next test, for example, includes 18 multiplication facts and 18 division facts. It is based upon the following nine teaching units.

6	8	7	7	8	8	9	9	9
4	5	3	4	3	4	3	4	5

This is the third group of nine teaching units given earlier in the chapter. Since there are no doubles in this list, each teaching unit includes four facts, two in multiplication and two in division.

4)24	4 8	9 5	7)21	9)27	8)24	5 8	9 4	5)45
8 5	7 3	8)32	4 7	4)36	5)40	6 4	7)28	3 8
8 3	3)27	9)45	6)24	9 3	4 6	8)40	3 7	4)28
4)32	7 4	3 9	3)21	9)36	5 9	8 4	3)24	4 9

Similar tests may be prepared for other groups of teaching units. Those most recently taught should be given the greatest emphasis but others should be brought in for periodic review and re-testing.

Brief summary of suggestions for teaching the multiplication and the division facts. Typical results secured from efforts to teach the multiplication and division facts are far from satisfactory. Teachers who desire to do better should keep in mind the following major suggestions:

1. Postpone treatment of zeros until examples in which they normally occur are encountered.

2. Use language which will indicate the fundamental meaning of multiplication and division, such as "Four 7's are how many?" and "How many 7's in 28?" rather than "Four times seven equals what?" and "How many times does 7 go into 28?"

3. Let the major emphasis in writing the combinations be upon the commonly used forms rather than upon the equation form.

4. Limit early work to 9×9 and to $81 \div 9$.

5. Attack the teaching units one at a time rather than a table at a time.

6. Teach multiplication as a case of abbreviated addition. Use counting by multiples of 2, 3, 4, . . . 9, and let the pupils see the relation of a product to related products, but avoid rote memorizing of tables.

7. Teach the easier combinations first. Begin with the 2's and, in general, proceed according to the size of the products but delay the teaching of 1's.

8. Teach the multiplication and the division facts together as teaching units.

9. Be sure that pupils are proficient in column addition before multiplication combinations are taught as abbreviated cases of column addition.

10. Have at hand many and varied games and drill devices. Use those which conform to the standards of good drill materials.

11. Use many problems. See that all of the facts, except the 1's, are incorporated in problems.

12. Make frequent use of carefully constructed tests.

QUESTIONS AND REVIEW EXERCISES

1. For the numbers, 8 and 7, state the multiplication and division facts to be taught.

2. Why should the zero difficulties in multiplication and

division be postponed until the pupils are ready for two-digit multiplicands and two-digit quotients?

3. You will recall the division check, Divisor × quotient = dividend. Now, if it were possible to divide a number by zero, some number would be obtained as a quotient. But, this quotient, multiplied by the divisor, zero, would give zero for the dividend, since any number multiplied by zero gives zero as a product. Does this help you to see that division by zero is impossible?

4. Divide 4 by 4, 2, 1, $\frac{1}{2}$, $\frac{1}{4}$, $\frac{1}{8}$, $\frac{1}{16}$, etc. As the divisor becomes smaller, what happens to the quotient? As the divisor approaches zero, what happens to the quotient? Does this help you to understand the difficulty of deciding upon what the quotient would be if we should undertake to divide by zero?

5. What is the disadvantage of limiting early written work on the multiplication and division facts to the equation form of statement?

6. Why is it better at first to say, "Seven 4's are 28" instead of "Seven times four is 28?"

7. How many multiplication facts are there from 1 × 1 to 9 × 9? If the 1's, 2's, and 5's are eliminated, how many remain?

8. What is gained if the first work in multiplication goes only to 9 × 9 instead of to 12 × 12? What, if anything, is lost?

9. Do you believe that it would be more profitable to learn 15's than to learn 11's? Why?

10. What is the disadvantage in memorizing multiplication tables in serial order?

11. Why is it better to begin with the 2's in multiplication than with the 1's. What would you think of beginning with the 5's since they are considered to be easy?

12. Are there any circumstances which require a pupil in the grades to multiply by 1? If so what? Are there any cir-

cumstances which require him to divide by 1? If so, what? Does a pupil in the grades ever have to divide a number by itself?

13. What is the advantage in teaching multiplication as a case of abbreviated addition?

14. Would there be any advantage in teaching division as abbreviated subtraction?

15. Why should the two facts of a multiplication combination be taught together?

16. Why should the multiplication facts and the division facts of a teaching unit be taught together?

17. Why is it better to have pupils discover for themselves the product of two numbers than to have the teacher tell them the product?

18. How would weakness in higher decade addition make it difficult for pupils to learn multiplication combinations? Is it the responsibility of the teacher who must teach multiplication to make up pupil deficiencies in higher decade addition if this subject was supposed to be taught in the preceding grade?

19. What is the danger in going too rapidly with a program of multiplication?

20. What are the characteristics of a good drill device?

21. What are the more common faults found in games and drill devices designed to give practice on the multiplication and division facts?

22. Collect some drill devices in addition to the few described in this chapter.

23. Is a good drill device one which children enjoy? Is a drill device which children enjoy a good drill device?

24. How many flash cards are needed for practice on the multiplication facts? the division facts? Give instructions for preparing such cards.

25. Can you suggest racing games in addition to those given in this chapter?

26. Which gives pupils more practice per unit of time, abstract drill devices or problems? Why is it desirable to use many problems?

27. Enumerate typical situations in pupil experiences from which teachers may obtain desirable problems which require a knowledge of multiplication and division facts.

28. What instructions would you give a beginning teacher for constructing tests on multiplication and division facts?

CHAPTER TEST

Determine whether each statement is true or false. A scoring key will be found on pages 405-406.

1. Ordinarily, the number of facts in a teaching unit is the same in multiplication and division as in addition and subtraction.

2. The number of multiplication facts from 1×1 to 9×9 is the same as the number of addition facts from $1 + 1$ to $9 + 9$.

3. The number of division facts from $1 \div 1$ to $81 \div 9$ is the same as the number of subtraction facts from $2 - 1$ to $18 - 9$.

4. The quotient of 0 divided by 6 is 0.

5. The equation form of statement is the preferred form for early work on the multiplication and division facts.

6. The expression, "Five 3's," is preferable to "Five times 3" in early work in multiplication.

7. There are 81 multiplication combinations from 1×1 to 9×9.

8. The 15's are more important than the 11's.

9. Most adults, in multiplying by 12, write two lines of partial products and add them.

10. Our custom of going to 12×12 is a purely American custom.

11. Each multiplication table should be memorized in serial order.

12. It is impossible to divide zero by a number.

13. Early learning of multiplication combinations should be rote learning.

14. It was recommended that the 2's be taught before the 1's.

15. It was recommended that multiplication be taught as a short form for addition.

16. It was recommended that division be taught as a short form for subtraction.

17. The division fact, $20 \div 5 = 4$ should be taught with the multiplication fact, $4 \times 5 = 20$.

18. Studies of difficulty of the combinations show that the 2's are among the easiest.

19. It is easier for the pupil to understand the meaning of multiplication if 2 is the multiplier than if 1 is the multiplier.

20. The word "times" should be used as a synonym for the word "multiply."

21. Both facts for each multiplication combination should be presented by column addition.

22. Pupils can learn to discover products for new combinations for themselves.

23. Pupils need skill in higher decade addition in learning multiplication combinations.

24. The best rate of progress in learning the multiplication and division facts is two or three teaching units per day.

25. Exclusive of the 1's, 2's, and 5's, there are only 21 multiplication facts to be taught.

26. The intervals between practice periods should gradually become less.

27. The Ring Toss Game was recommended as a desirable teaching device.

28. It was recommended that 81 flash cards be prepared for the multiplication facts.

29. In the game, Winging Wild Geese, the numbers should be arranged in random order.

30. Pupils can get more drill per unit of time in problems than in examples.

31. Problems should be used for all of the 81 multiplication facts.

32. Problems should be used for all 81 division facts.

33. Teachers should be expected to make their own tests for multiplication and division facts.

34. Multiplication and division facts should be mixed in one test.

35. In general, combinations having the larger products are harder than those having the smaller products.

SELECTED REFERENCES

1. Clapp, Frank L. *The Number Combinations: Their Relative Difficulty and the Frequency of Their Appearance in Text-Books.* Madison, Wisconsin: University of Wisconsin, 1924. 120 pp. The arrangement of multiplication and division facts in the order of their difficulty as determined by tests given to pupils in grades IV-VIII, inclusive, is given on pages 54-57 and 59.

2. Fowlkes, John Guy. "A Report of a Controlled Study of the Learning of Multiplication by Third-Grade Children." *Journal of Educational Research,* XV: 181-189, March, 1927. Reports the results of a study made with 31 pupils in a third-grade class.

3. Kennedy, Agnes. "Making Multiplication Meaningful." *Foundations in Arithmetic.* Washington, D.C.: Association for Childhood Education, 1937, pp. 26-30. Gives specific suggestions for teaching the primary multiplication facts.

4. Klapper, Paul. *The Teaching of Arithmetic.* New York: D. Appleton-Century Company, 1934. 525 pp. Suggestions for teaching the multiplication combinations will be found on pages 292-298.

5. Lockhart, Lovine, Eldridge, A. C., and Brown, J. C. *Number Helps.* Chicago: Rand McNally and Company, 1924. 120 pp. This book contains games, rimes, and songs. Multiplication and division games are given on pages 48-61.

6. Losh, Rosamond, and Weeks, Ruth Mary, *Primary Number Projects.* Boston: Houghton Mifflin Company, 1923. 199 pp. Multiplication projects are described on pp. 113-125.

7. Norem, Grant B. and Knight, F. B. "The Learning of the One Hundred Multiplication Combinations." National Society for the Study of Education, *Twenty-Ninth Yearbook,* 1930, pp. 551-568. Classifies combinations according to learning difficulty. Results differ considerably from Clapp's.

8. Oftedal, Laura. "How Division Is Made Meaningful." *Foundations in Arithmetic.* Washington, D.C.: Association for Childhood Education, 1937, pp. 30-32. Discusses briefly the teaching of the basic facts of division.

9. Ruch, G. M. "Relative Difficulty of the One Hundred Multiplication Combinations with Special Reference to Textbook Construction." *Elementary School Journal,* XXXII: 369-377, January, 1932. Brings together the results of difficulty studies made by Clapp, Norem and Knight, and Fowlkes. Suggests that the so-called zero difficulties disappear with proper teaching.

10. Smith, David Eugene. *The Progress of Arithmetic in the Last Quarter of a Century.* Boston: Ginn and Company, 1923. 78 pp. Suggestions relative to the multiplication facts occur on pages 40-46. Suggests English origin of tables through the 12's.

11. Washburne, Carleton and Vogel, Mabel. "Are Any Number Combinations Inherently Difficult?" *Journal of Educational Research,* XVII: 235-255. Reports a study of the difficulty of combinations. Compares results with those of Clapp.

CHAPTER 8

ELEMENTARY WORK IN MULTIPLICATION

Courses of study differ considerably as to the amount of arithmetic to be included in the program of each of the primary grades. Some barely begin the teaching of the multiplication facts in grade three while others complete the multiplication and division facts and then direct attention to a rather elaborate array of multiplication and division examples. It is the purpose of this chapter to discuss the teaching of multiplication as far as any third-grade classes are likely to undertake it. Chapter 9 will provide a similar discussion of the teaching of division.

Early use of examples. In the grade in which the multiplication combinations are learned, the pupils will almost surely be acquainted with two-digit numbers. It seems desirable, then, that they be given practice in the solution of examples and problems in multiplication in which one-digit multipliers and two-digit multiplicands occur while the facts of the 45 teaching units are being learned. Of course, these early examples will not require carrying. It may be desirable to use three-digit multiplicands at this time.

Such problems and examples should be used at this time to provide the pupils with opportunities to put to very practical use the skills which they are acquiring and to vary what might otherwise become a monotonous program. To teach all of the multiplication and the division facts with no opportunities for application except the simple type of problems suggested in the preceding chapter is likely to result in loss of interest and consequent ineffective learning.

At this point, it may also be said that elementary work in multiplication and division will go hand in hand. The fact that these topics are treated in separate chapters here should not lead the teacher to believe that they are so completely separated in teaching; they are discussed separately merely for the sake of convenience.

Work limited to one-digit multipliers. We shall assume that the multiplication examples are to be limited to one-digit multipliers. This means that the technique of training pupils to write second and later partial products in the proper positions and of adding partial products to obtain the complete product will be left for attention in the intermediate grades. We shall take up multiplication with one-digit multipliers under three major heads: (1) multiplication without carrying; (2) multiplication with carrying; and (3) zero difficulties. The application of each of these types to verbal problems will then be indicated.

Multiplication without carrying. Multiplication examples without carrying may have either two-digit or three-digit multiplicands. It seems better, however, to wait until carrying has been taught to use examples having three-digit multiplicands. If two-digit multiplicands are to be used and there is to be no carrying, certain very obvious limitations are placed upon the second digit of the multiplicand. If the multiplier is 2, the second multiplicand digit may be 1, 2, 3, or 4, (zero difficulties not yet introduced); if the multiplier is 3, the second multiplicand digit may be 1, 2, or 3; if the multiplier is 4, it may be 1 or 2; if the multiplier is 5, 6, 7, 8, or 9, the second multiplicand digit must be 1.

Assume that a class has been taught the 2's, the first group of nine teaching units given in the preceding chapter. The 38 examples of Set 1 can now be used.

PRACTICE EXAMPLES IN MULTIPLICATION. SET 1
The First 9 Teaching Units

11 2	21 2	31 2	41 2	51 2	61 2	71 2	81 2	91 2	12 2
22 2	32 2	42 2	52 2	62 2	72 2	82 2	92 2	13 2	23 2
33 2	43 2	53 2	63 2	73 2	83 2	93 2	14 2	24 2	34 2
44 2	54 2	64 2	74 2	84 2	94 2	22 3	22 4		

These are all of the examples of this kind which can be used at this time. But as the number of combinations taught increases, the number of two-digit multiplicands which can be used becomes considerably greater. When we have taught the entire 45 combinations, we can use a total of 126 multiplicands in examples without carrying. That is, we can multiply any two-digit number ending in 1, 2, 3, or 4 by 2, making 36 examples (these are the first 36 of the list given above); we can multiply any two-digit number ending in 1, 2, or 3, by 3, making 27 examples; when the multiplier is 4, we have 18 examples; for the multipliers 5, 6, 7, 8, and 9, we have 9 examples each. This makes a total of 126 examples.

It does not seem to be desirable to use all of these 126 examples for practice, for doing so means considerable overlearning on the 1's. It seems best for the teacher to select from these 126 examples those which will distribute the practice fairly well over the 72 multiplication facts which remain after we eliminate from the list of 81 those in which 1 is the multiplier. There will still be some overlearning of the easier facts because of their frequent occurrence in the higher decades to avoid carrying. We should include the harder facts at least once each in a set of examples made for practice without carrying. These harder facts can be given greater emphasis after carrying has been taught.

The next set of practice examples in multiplication has been designed to give practice on each of these 72 multiplication facts. To do this in examples having two-digit multiplicands, without carrying, requires a minimum of 58 examples. These examples give more practice than is necessary or desirable on the 1's, as would be expected. After carrying has been taught, a much more desirable distribution of practice can be provided.

PRACTICE EXAMPLES IN MULTIPLICATION. SET 2
The 72 Facts Without Carrying

21	81	42	91	41	81	63	61	51	72
5	7	4	8	6	9	3	7	5	4
51	72	61	81	51	62	41	83	71	61
8	3	9	6	7	4	5	2	8	6
71	82	71	41	81	41	92	71	61	71
5	4	9	7	8	9	2	4	8	7

31	52	61	81	41	52	91	91	31	21
9	4	2	5	8	2	7	3	7	8

82	31	91	91	42	51	51	91	31	71
3	6	5	9	3	9	6	4	5	6

31	32	91	21	21	21	52	61
8	4	6	9	7	6	3	5

The teacher should not forget that it is important to introduce a new type of examples through the medium of real and interesting problems. Rather than start out with such examples as $\begin{array}{r}21\\ \underline{5}\end{array}$ in abstract form it is much better to take up the cost of 5 gallons of gasoline for Dad's car at 21 cents per gallon or some other practical situation which requires the use of this particular example. Problems help to supply the pupils with a motive for learning to solve such examples.

Multiplication with carrying. The teaching of carrying in multiplication is similar to the teaching of carrying in addition. Since carrying in addition has already been taught and, presumably, the pupils have become proficient in it, there should be no serious difficulty in getting them to see the meaning of, and reasons for, carrying in multiplication.

Again, let us begin with a problem. "For her birthday party, Eleanor's mother let her take 4 of her little friends to the movies. Eleanor bought 5 tickets, one for herself and 4 for her friends. Each ticket cost 15 cents. How much did she pay for the 5 tickets?" After the problem is stated, the lesson may proceed as follows:

TEACHER. If 1 ticket costs 15 cents, how shall we find the cost of 5 tickets?

PUPIL. Multiply 15 by 5.

TEACHER. Show us how you would write the example on the blackboard if we are to multiply 15 cents by 5. (*A pupil writes the example as shown.*) You will remember that we can also find the cost of the 5 tickets by adding. (*The addition example is also written as shown.*) What do you get when you add the first column?

```
15 cents        15 cents
 5              15 cents
                15 cents
                15 cents
                15 cents
```

PUPIL. Twenty-five.

TEACHER. What do you do with the 25?

PUPIL. Write the 5 and carry the 2.

TEACHER. Finish adding the example. What do you get?

PUPIL. Seventy-five cents.

TEACHFR. Now let us multiply. Think of the 15 cents as 1 dime and 5 cents. How many cents is 5 times 5 cents?

PUPIL. Twenty-five cents.

TEACHER. But 25 cents is equal to how many dimes and how many cents?

PUPIL. Two dimes and 5 cents.

TEACHER. Now let us carry just as we did in the addition example. What do you write and what do you carry?

PUPIL. Write the 5 and carry the 2.

TEACHER. How many dimes is 5 times 1 dime.

PUPIL. Five dimes.

TEACHER. And the 2 dimes which you carried make how many dimes?

PUPIL. Seven.

TEACHER. Then what answer do you get when you multiply?

PUPIL. Seventy-five cents.

The teacher should stress the close resemblance of the

multiplication example to the addition example with which the pupils are already familiar. In both the addition example and the multiplication example, the pupils first see five 5's; in each, they see that 2 is the number carried; in each they see five 1's; and in each they see the answer, 75 cents.

Other concrete problems will follow. The addition analogy is soon dropped and the solution is rapidly abbreviated. This is indicated in the solution for the next problem.

If I bought 5 gallons of gasoline for my car and paid 19 cents a gallon, how much did it cost? This is the way to find out:

	19 cents
Think, five 9's are 45. Write 5 and carry 4.	5
Think, five 1's are 5. Carry 4 and write 9.	95 cents

Then 5 gallons of gasoline cost 95 cents.

As in carrying in addition, the pupils should rapidly get away from thinking about cents and dimes and think about numbers. They remember that if a product is a two-figure number, they write the right-hand figure, carry the left-hand figure, and add it in after the next multiplication step.

The pupils will then proceed to the solution of examples involving carrying. The work will be limited to two-digit multiplicands until the pupils can solve such examples accurately and easily.

With well planned initial presentation and sufficient practice pupils should soon become proficient in multiplication with carrying. There is one type of error which the teacher should watch for, however. In the example shown, the pupil did his multiplying correctly, but added in the carry number *before* performing the second multiplication. This is a most natural mistake for a pupil to make for in addition he has been taught to add in the carry number before proceeding to the addition of the next column. It is not recommended that the teacher caution pupils about this error for many of them will never think of it unless it is called to their attention; but the teacher should be alert to recognize this error if it occurs and to give the proper instruction. To help a pupil see his mistake if he has been guilty of this error, transform the multiplication example into an addition example as was done in the case of Eleanor's movie tickets.

$$\begin{array}{r}43\\ \underline{6}\\ 308\end{array}$$

When three-digit multiplicands are taken up, four types of examples will be found. These are: (1) those in which there is no carrying, as $\begin{array}{r}232\\ \underline{3}\end{array}$; (2) those in which there is carrying in the first step only, as $\begin{array}{r}224\\ \underline{3}\end{array}$; (3) those in which there is carrying in the second step only, as $\begin{array}{r}263\\ \underline{3}\end{array}$; (4) those in which there is carrying in two steps, as $\begin{array}{r}457\\ \underline{3}\end{array}$. Each of these types should be included in practice exercises. The first type will cause no difficulty and will require but little time. It is recommended that the teacher begin with the second type, then proceed to the third type, and finally the fourth type. Eventually, all four types should be mixed in one practice exercise.

Preparing examples for practice. The two sets of

practice examples which have already been given provided practice on multiplication without carrying. These were arranged so as to provide practice on each of the primary facts except those in which 1 is a multiplier but we found that it was necessary to include 1 in the multiplicand more often than any other digit.

When carrying has been taught, we can distribute the practice over the basic facts much more uniformly. The ideal plan, though, is to include all of the facts but to give special emphasis to those which are the more difficult.

Set 3 is designed for use after the first two groups of nine teaching units each, as given in the preceding chapter, have been taught. All of the facts of these 18 teaching units, except those obtained from $\begin{array}{r}1\\ \underline{2}\end{array}$ have been included in this set. Six of these have been included twice each.

Practice Examples in Multiplication. Set 3

The Facts of 17 Teaching Units

65	46	57	79	63	32	84	45	35
2	3	5	2	4	6	2	4	3
43	32	22	26	27	25	22	43	26
5	2	8	3	5	7	9	6	4

Set 4 is intended to be used after three groups of nine teaching units each have been taught. Again $\begin{array}{r}1\\ \underline{2}\end{array}$ has been omitted; it is included in the next set. The 45 facts obtained from the other 26 teaching units have been included once each.

PRACTICE EXAMPLES IN MULTIPLICATION. SET 4

The Facts of 26 Teaching Units

28	46	47	53	52	96	74	28
3	4	2	5	4	2	3	5
53	45	35	49	28	54	35	37
8	6	3	5	2	7	9	4
23	96	67	42	89	24	53	23
7	3	5	9	4	8	2	6

Set 5 provides practice on all of the 72 facts in which 1 is not a multiplier. Nine of the more difficult of these 72 facts have been used twice each in this set. Obviously, this set is a summary set and is to be used after all of the multiplication combinations have been taught.

PRACTICE EXAMPLES IN MULTIPLICATION. SET 5

Summary of the 72 Facts

37	29	31	28	19	62	46	35
4	7	6	5	3	8	2	9
27	41	62	38	62	46	17	37
3	7	4	2	9	6	8	5
35	18	49	68	59	84	74	57
8	4	5	7	6	3	9	2
87	16	84	49	91	35	19	37
6	5	8	4	9	3	2	7

12	57	59	98	72	69	95	79
2	7	4	9	6	3	5	8

Set 6 is designed for more intensive practice on all the combinations except the 1's, 2's, and 5's—a group of 36 facts. Each of these 36 facts occurs twice in this set.

Practice Examples in Multiplication. Set 6

The 36 Harder Facts

84	68	48	97	79	74	86	79	48
8	6	3	9	7	4	7	6	9

69	93	98	34	73	36	43	63	76
8	3	4	7	8	9	6	4	3

43	39	93	67	74	97	98	73	43
3	8	7	6	7	3	6	4	6

48	73	86	96	49	86	68	48	76
8	9	3	9	4	4	7	9	8

Set 7 contains examples having three-digit multiplicands. Each of the 72 facts in which 1 is not a multiplier occurs once and once only in this set. In addition to giving practice with multiplicands of three digits, this set is another summary and review set for it includes all of the facts, except zero facts, which might reasonably occur in such examples. The set includes examples which require carrying in the first step only, in the second step only, and in both steps. There is also one example which requires no carrying.

Set 8 also contains examples having three-digit multiplicands. This set, like Set 6, is designed to give intensive practice in the 36 facts which remain after the 1's, 2's, and 5's have been eliminated. Each of these 36 facts occurs twice in this set.

Practice Examples in Multiplication. Set 7
Three-Digit Multiplicands, 72 Facts

258	463	632	528	298	261
4	7	3	6	8	5
417	362	364	496	387	147
9	2	8	4	5	3
184	715	397	362	289	579
2	7	6	9	7	2
495	895	371	715	641	958
5	3	4	8	6	9

Practice Examples in Multiplication. Set 8
Three-Digit Multiplicands, the 36 Harder Facts

963	849	389	693	687	674
4	6	7	9	3	8
367	934	389	478	647	374
6	3	8	4	7	6
843	846	368	973	698	697
8	7	9	7	6	8
384	479	486	679	487	397
4	9	3	4	9	3

The teacher can prepare many more sets of practice examples similar to these. A careful record of the facts included should be kept in order that the amount of practice given to each may be known. Only in this way can we be sure that no item is neglected.

The zero difficulties. Since we are concerned here with one-digit multipliers only, the only zeroes with which we need be concerned are those which occur in the multiplicand. Obviously, zero in the multiplicand can be multiplied by any of the one-digit numbers which we are using, namely, those from 2 to 9, inclusive. Zero in the multiplier is meaningless until we have multipliers of two or more digits. Even then the treatment is quite different from the treatment of the multiplication of zero by a number.

Our responsibility now is to lead the pupil to see that if zero is multiplied by any number, the product is zero. This point must be understood by the pupils and if they are to understand it, it must have some sort of concrete representation. The best approach seems to be through addition, the usual approach in teaching the meaning of multiplication.

In addition, the pupils have learned that *any number plus zero equals that number* and as a special case of this *that zero plus zero equals zero*. They may have learned by this time that if any number of zeros in a column is added, the sum is zero, as in the addition example shown. In other words, they may have learned that two 0's are 0, that three 0's are 0, etc. If so, they are ready for the generalization that the sum of any number of 0's is 0, or, stating this fact in the language of multiplication, that if 0 is multiplied by any number, the product is **0**.

$$\begin{array}{r} 430 \\ 260 \\ \underline{170} \\ 860 \end{array}$$

A concrete situation involving 0's alone may be set up in some such form as the following:

Teacher. Dick has 4 pockets in his sweater. In the first pocket there are no apples, in the second pocket there are no apples, in the third pocket there are no apples, and in the fourth pocket there are no apples. How many apples has Dick in his sweater pockets?

Pupil. Not any.

Teacher. We can say it this way. There are zero apples in the first pocket, zero apples in the second pocket, zero apples in the third pocket, and zero apples in the fourth pocket. If we add 4 zeros, what do we get?

$$\begin{array}{r} 0 \\ 0 \\ 0 \\ 0 \\ \hline 0 \end{array}$$

Pupil. We get zero.

Teacher. Then 4 zeros are how many?

Pupil. 4 zeros are zero.

Teacher. If Dick had had five pockets and zero apples in each pocket, how many apples would he have had all together?

Pupil. Zero.

Teacher. Then 5 zeros are how many?

Pupil. 5 zeros are zero.

Teacher. And how many are 6 zeros?

Pupil. 6 zeros are zero.

In this manner, the pupils see again that any number of zeros added together gives zero for a sum and they discover that zero multiplied by any number gives zero for a product.

The teacher then proceeds to a multiplication example in which the last digit of the multiplicand is 0. This first example should arise from a problem. Several examples, illustrating the multiplication of 0 by a number, will be solved on the blackboard as group exercises. These examples will have various multipliers but the 0 will occur in the last place of the multiplicand only until the pupils become proficient in solving examples of this type.

As the next step, the pupils may learn to solve examples in which three-digit multiplicands have 0 in the middle position. This type requires special attention at the beginning because of the fact that the carry number is added to a zero product. This point is not a particularly difficult one but the teacher should not overlook it. Of course, three-digit multiplicands may also contain two zeros.

Immediately after they first encounter zeros in multiplication, the pupils should be given intensive practice on the various types of examples in which this difficulty appears. When this difficulty has been well mastered, zeros may be allowed to occur in multiplicands as often as other digits appear.

The following set of practice examples is typical of the kind which may be used. In this set, each of the eight zero combinations occurs twice and six of them occur three times each. The multiplicands are so selected that no other combination occurs more than once—that is, the set does not include both facts for any combination. Each one-digit number, except 1, occurs twice as a multiplier; 8 and 9 occur three times each.

Practice Examples in Multiplication. Set 9

Zeros in the Multiplicand

420	600	704	410	730	209
5	3	8	6	9	4
400	380	803	806	960	206
7	2	8	5	8	9

300	760	590	205	600	501
4	6	9	7	2	3

Solving problems. Good problems are indispensable. An abundant supply will be needed not only for the benefits which come from the experience of thinking out solutions but also for the interest which they lend to practice on multiplication. If the teacher is alert, she will find them in many of the pupil's experiences and in the experiences of their elders. These problems will be drawn from a wide variety of sources; they will be descriptive of many kinds of situations with which children are acquainted. An effort should be made to find or invent problems which involve the various multiplication skills which have been discussed in this chapter. Those which follow are typical and are offered as suggestions. These produce examples which have various kinds of multiplicands. Each of the multipliers, 2 to 9, inclusive, is used once.

1. Mr. Jones bought 2 bags of fertilizer for his garden. Each bag weighed 150 pounds. How much did the 2 bags weigh?
2. John gets $6.00 per month for taking care of a neighbor lady's furnace. How much does he earn in 5 months?
3. At a sale, Mr. Dixon bought 4 tubes for his radio at $2.48 each. What did the four tubes cost?
4. What does Mrs. Brown have to pay for 3 pounds of steak at 29 cents a pound?
5. The fare to the city is $1.05. What would be the fare for a party of 8 people?
6. Robert delivers 45 papers each evening, except Sunday. How many does he deliver in a week?
7. A group of 9 boys formed a baseball team. What did the suits cost at $2.75 each?

8. Mildred counted up on the calendar the number of weeks until her birthday. She found that it was just 18 weeks. How many days until Mildred's birthday?

Checking results. In their early work in multiplication, pupils should be taught to check results. Neither the answers to problems nor those to examples should be accepted as satisfactory until the pupil has assured himself by proper checking that those answers are correct.

The best check for the pupils in the primary grades to use for multiplication seems to be the reverse of that process, or division. This check can not be used for early work with one-digit multipliers, however, unless the elementary work in multiplication and that in division are presented at the same time. We have indicated in Chapter 7 that we would teach the multiplication and the division facts together and, in the fourth paragraph of this chapter, we have stated that "elementary work in multiplication and division will go hand in hand." As soon as the corresponding type of division examples has been taught, then, the pupils will check their multiplication results by dividing the product by the multiplier and comparing the resulting quotient with the multiplicand.

However, instruction on each type in multiplication will precede instruction on the corresponding type in division. Thus, multiplication without carrying will be taught before division without carrying; zeros in multiplicands will be experienced before zeros are found in quotients; etc. Each of these new types will be checked at first, then, by repeating, carefully, the multiplication steps already taken.

Some teachers use addition as a check for multiplication examples having small multipliers. Thus if 238 has been multiplied by 6, the example is checked by writing 238 six times and adding, as shown. This is a fairly satisfactory check if the pupil in adding thinks, "16, 24, 32, 40, 48." But the training which he has had in multiplication and the similarity of multiplication to addition which has frequently been indicated will probably lead him to think "six 8's" in both the addition example and the multiplication example. After all, that is just what he should do. Under such conditions, the check by addition amounts for all practical purposes to repeating the steps in the multiplication example just as he took them there.

```
          238
          238
          238
          238
 238      238
   6      238
----     ----
1428     1428
```

It is probably best, then, to check multiplication by repeating the multiplication in the same way until the corresponding division type has been taught. Then check multiplication by division.

Which way should we multiply? It is sometimes suggested that multiplication examples be checked by thinking of the combinations in the reverse way when the example is checked. Thus, in checking the example shown, the pupil would think, "six 7's" instead of "seven 6's," "three 7's" instead of "seven 3's," and "four 7's" instead of "seven 4's." This is sometimes referred to as multiplying down in contrast to multiplying up.

```
 436
   7
----
3052
```

As a check, the scheme has something to be said in its favor. Like adding down when one has added up, different facts are encountered and it seems less likely that one will make the same mistake a second time. It is hard to say whether the increased difficulty is sufficient to prohibit the use of such a check. We need experimental evidence on this subject.

The teacher should remember, however, that it is the multiplicand which is multiplied, not the multiplier. Furthermore, the zero difficulties, if any, are different in multiplying down. After the pupil has learned the meaning of multiplication and has become proficient with all kinds of multiplication examples, it matters little in which direction he multiplies, but in the primary grades it seems to be better to multiply in one direction only, namely, up.

QUESTIONS AND REVIEW EXERCISES

1. Why is it advantageous to begin using examples having two-digit multiplicands before the pupils have learned all of the multiplication combinations?

2. Is there anything about the multiplication example, $\begin{array}{r}42\\ \underline{3}\end{array}$ which makes it more difficult than the separate combinations, $\begin{array}{r}4\\ \underline{3}\end{array}$ and $\begin{array}{r}2\\ \underline{3}\end{array}$?

3. What is meant by the statement that "elementary work in multiplication and division will go hand in hand?" Is it possible or desirable to keep the two subjects absolutely abreast? Just how and to what extent would you keep these topics together?

4. What is the advantage in teaching multiplication and division together rather than letting multiplication be finished before division is begun?

5. If there is to be no carrying and we are to use examples having two-digit multiplicands, what may the units figure of the multiplicand be if the multiplier is 2? 4? 7? 9?

6. Look over the examples of Set 1. Can any additional

examples of this type be constructed without going beyond the first group of nine teaching units?

7. Practice exercises which use one-digit multipliers sometimes use 1 as a multiplier. Is this desirable?

8. We have seen that the number of multiplication facts from 1×1 to 9×9 is 81. How many are there if 1 is not used as a multiplier?

9. What advantage is there in introducing a new type of multiplication examples with a problem?

10. We have seen that multiplication is closely related to addition. What use can be made of this relationship in teaching carrying in multiplication?

11. Would you warn pupils not to add in the carry number before the next multiplication? Why? If you found pupils making this mistake, what corrective measures would you employ?

12. Is it worth while to undertake to rationalize the process of carrying in multiplication? Why?

13. What four types of examples do we have with three-digit multiplicands and one-digit multipliers? State these four types in the order in which you would teach them.

14. If you were to prepare a set of multiplication examples which were to include each of the 72 facts in which 1 is not used as a multiplier, how would you proceed so as to assure yourself that each of the 72 facts was included?

15. Is it worth while to spend the time and energy required in the preparation of such sets of practice examples as those given in this chapter? Why?

16. When should zero occur in the multiplicand? In the multiplier? How would you show pupils that if zero is multiplied by any number, the product is zero?

17. Is it any harder to use zero in the tens place in the multiplicand than in the units place? Why?

18. What is the best check for multiplication? What are

the advantages and disadvantages of using addition as a check?

19. Is there anything to be gained in multiplying both upward and downward? Would you teach pupils in the primary grades to multiply downward?

20. From what sources should the pupil's problem material come? Is it permissible to use with pupils in the primary grades problems derived from the experiences of adults?

CHAPTER TEST

Determine whether each statement is true or false. A scoring key will be found on page 406.

1. Examples having two-digit multiplicands should be used before all of the multiplication combinations have been taught.

2. Courses of study differ but little as to the amount of multiplication which should be taught in the third grade.

3. Pupils should complete their work in multiplication before beginning their work in division.

4. If there is to be no carrying and the zero difficulties have not been taught, the last digit of the multiplicand must be 1 if the multiplier is 5.

5. Multiplication examples can not contain facts whose products are more than 9 before carrying has been taught.

6. Each new type of multiplication example should be introduced through the medium of a problem.

7. The teaching of carrying in multiplication is similar to the teaching of carrying in addition.

8. It was recommended that coins be used to teach the meaning of carrying in multiplication.

9. It was recommended that the teacher caution the pupils against adding in the carry number before the next multiplication is performed.

10. If the pupil obtains 548 as the product of 58 and 6, it is probable that he is making a natural mistake.

11. Four types of examples were enumerated for three-digit multiplicands and one-digit multipliers.

12. In using three-digit multiplicands, it was suggested that pupils learn to carry in the first step before they learn to carry in the second step.

13. If zeros are not used and 1 is not used as a multiplier, the number of multiplication facts is 72.

14. Exclusive of the 1's, 2's, and 5's, there are 45 multiplication facts.

15. In multiplication examples, the easier facts should receive as much practice as the harder facts.

16. There are 19 zero facts in multiplication.

17. In the primary grades, 0 should be used in both the multiplicand and the multiplier.

18. The resemblance of multiplication to addition does not help in teaching the zero facts.

19. The best check for multiplication is division.

20. Pupils in the primary grades should be taught to multiply both upward and downward.

SELECTED REFERENCES

1. Karpinski, Louis Charles. *The History of Arithmetic* Chicago: Rand McNally and Company, 1925. 200 pp. An interesting historical account of multiplication is given on pages 106-111.

2. Klapper, Paul. *The Teaching of Arithmetic.* New York: D. Appleton-Century Company, 1934. 525 pp. The teaching of multiplication is discussed on pages 300-303.

3. Lennes, N. J. *The Teaching of Arithmetic.* New York: The Macmillan Company, 1923. 486 pp. There is a brief discussion of multiplication on pages 234-238.

4. Roantree, William F. and Taylor, Mary S. *An Arithmetic for Teachers.* New York: The Macmillan Company, 1932. 523 pp. Factual material pertaining to multiplication

will be found on pages 69-74 and suggestions for teaching on pages 97-100.

5. Thorndike, Edward L. *The Psychology of Arithmetic.* New York: The Macmillan Company, 1922. 314 pp. Interesting graphs showing actual distributions of practice on basic facts are shown on pages 157-167. Some phases of learning are discussed on pages 267-270.

CHAPTER 9

ELEMENTARY WORK IN DIVISION

Division in the primary grades. There is a marked lack of agreement as to the amount of division which should be included in the course of study of the third grade of the elementary school. There are schools which make no provision at all for work in division in the third grade. There are others which not only include all of the basic division facts but also examples having one-digit divisors and three-digit quotients and which undertake to include the essential facts about carrying, remainders, and zeros in the quotient. Schools of this latter classification frequently teach only the short division form and thus make the program one of almost maximum difficulty.

The phases of division which are discussed in this chapter are intended to be sufficient to meet all requirements. This chapter is not a third-grade course of study in division; nor does the chapter contain recommendations as to what should be taught in the third grade and what should be postponed for consideration in grade four. Teachers may use from this chapter those suggestions which apply to their own teaching situations.

Division related to multiplication. In Chapter 7, it was recommended that the primary facts of multiplication and the primary facts of division be taught together. This recommendation was offered for two reasons: (1) each of these two operations supplements the other and each is made more meaningful by virtue of experience in the other; (2) it is more economical to teach the division facts along with the multiplication facts since division merely states what multiplication has already stated in another way. The same two reasons justify the continued teaching of division along with multiplication. As was suggested in Chapter 8, the best time to teach division without carrying seems to be immediately after multiplication without carrying is taught. Likewise, other phases of division may follow the corresponding phases of multiplication. Again, this should mean economy and better learning.

The early use of examples. As in multiplication, it is not necessary to wait until the entire 45 combinations have been taught before introducing examples having two-digit quotients. The use of such examples permits the pupils to put to real use what they are learning in the way of division facts. It is especially desirable to use such examples early if problems leading to the solution of such examples can be found.

Work limited to one-digit divisors. In Chapter 8, we discussed multiplication only so far as the use of one-digit multipliers was concerned. Likewise, our concern with division in this chapter will be limited to the use of one-digit divisors. Surely, the use of two-digit divisors will not be undertaken before grade four or grade five, since the estimation of quotients with two-digit divisors is very much more difficult than the estimation of quotients with one-digit divisors.

Using the fraction form in division. So far we have considered but one meaning of division. When the pupil thinks: "how many 8's in 48?" as the reverse of "six 8's are 48," he is thinking in terms of the *measurement* idea of division. One measures 48 when he finds how many 8's there are in 48. The unit of measure is 8. This is similar to measuring the length of a room by finding how many feet there are in the length; in this case, the unit of measure is one foot.

Another fundamental meaning of division is *partition.* Partition refers to the finding of parts, or in this case, to dividing a number into parts. Thus, since six 8's are 48, one of the six equal parts of 48 is 8. But one of the six equal parts of a number is *one sixth* of the number.

The teacher should be clear in her own thinking as to these two meanings of division. The terms *measurement* and *partition* are technical terms for the teacher's vocabulary, not terms for the pupils. But the pupil may learn both of these meanings of division. He may see several multiplication facts represented in column addition form as follows:

				8				
	3			8				9
	3		6	8	5		4	9
4	3		6	8	5	2	4	9
4	3	7	6	8	5	2	4	9
4	3	7	6	8	5	2	4	9
12	15	14	24	48	20	6	16	45

Since three 4's are 12, 4 is one of the three equal parts of 12, or 4 is one-third of 12; since five 3's are 15, 3 is one of the five equal parts of 15, or 3 is one-fifth of 15; etc. Then such questions as, "What is one-half of 14?",

"What is one-fourth of 24?", "What is one-sixth of 48?", etc., may be asked.

This elementary work in division provides an excellent opportunity to develop the pupils' understanding of fractions as well as another point of view from which to interpret the division facts. In the next chapter, we shall have more to say about the development of a fraction concept among pupils in the primary grades. In this connection, it may be said that this is a phase of arithmetic experience which is often neglected in the primary grades but which the pupils are quite capable of understanding. Polkinghorne[1] tested 266 children in the kindergarten, the first, the second, and the third grades and found that they had already made considerable progress toward an understanding of unit fractions (fractions having 1 as a numerator) and some progress toward an understanding of other fractions. What they had learned had come largely from out-of-school experiences.

Each of the primary division facts, except those having 1 as a divisor, can be expressed in this fraction form. The pupils can learn to think of one-fourth of 4 as 1, of one-fourth of 8 as 2, of one-fourth of 12 as 3, etc., and of other sets of division facts in like manner.

Of course, this meaning of division should be developed concretely. The pupil's first experience in finding one-half of a number should be an experience in which he finds one-half of a group of 4 pencils, one-half of 6 pieces of candy, etc. Not until the meaning of such fractional parts is well developed in this concrete form

---

[1] Polkinghorne, Ada R. "Young Children and Fractions." *Childhood Education,* XI: 354-358, May, 1935.

should the pupil attack the purely abstract forms in which he deals with fractional parts of abstract numbers.

Later, other fractional parts may be learned, as three-fourths of 8, two-thirds of 12, etc.

Short division or long division first? Many teachers use the term "short division" when referring to division examples having one-digit divisors and the term "long division" when referring to examples in which the divisors have two or more digits. The distinction between short division and long division, however, is not one having to do with the number of digits in the divisors but one having to do with the form of the solution. If the writing of the quotient is the only writing which is done in solving a division example, the other operations being done "mentally," the example is solved by short division; but if the work representing the various steps is written out, the example is solved by long division.

More than ten years ago, the author in his *Teaching Arithmetic in the Intermediate Grades* and later in his *Teaching Arithmetic in the Primary Grades* recommended that the pupil's first work in division be done with examples having one-digit divisors and that it be done by long division, contrary to the usual school practice. Since then, several articles have appeared reporting studies on long *versus* short division. Johnson[2] reported that if examples having one-digit divisors are solved by long division, the pupil makes better progress with examples having two-digit divisors.

[2] Johnson, J. T. "Short Division or Long Division First." *Chicago Schools Journal,* XII: 55-56, October, 1929.

John,[3] in the school year 1927-1928, conducted an experiment with two grades of pupils, one of which was taught short division first and the other of which was taught long division first with one-digit divisors. She found that long division was conducive to greater accuracy and suggested that the long form be taught first and applied to examples having divisors of any number of digits and that later the short form be taught *as a short cut.* Buckingham[4] expressed himself as in entire sympathy with the plan which provides that the long form be taught first, the short form to come later as a short cut, and reported that five of the six members of the Committee on Arithmetic of the National Society for the Study of Education were in favor of the long form. The sixth member of this Committee was not against this practice but preferred to see more experimental evidence in its favor.

Ballard[5] "flatly denies" that the "short division road is the easier road." He says that it is wrong to regard short division and long division as two different methods and that there is only one method—long division. Myers[6] suggests that tradition must account for the persistence of short division as the first division procedure.

---

[3] John, Lenore. "The Effect of Using the Long Division Form in Teaching Division by One-Digit Divisors." *Elementary School Journal,* XXX: 675-692, May, 1930.

[4] Buckingham, B. R. "The Training of Teachers of Arithmetic." National Society for the Study of Education, *The Twenty-Ninth Yearbook.* Bloomington, Illinois: Public School Publishing Company, 1930, pp. 317-408.

[5] Ballard, Philip Boswood. *Teaching the Essentials of Arithmetic.* London: University of London Press, 1928, p. 170.

[6] Myers, Garry Cleveland. "Beginning Long Division." *Grade Teacher,* XLVII: 542 and 576-577, 626 and 654, March and April, 1930.

Grossnickle[7] gave tests in each grade from the fifth grade to the junior year in college. All of his subjects had been taught the short form. He found that those who used the long form were more accurate but that those who used the short form were more rapid. However, the difference in speed became insignificant when the more difficult examples were encountered. Grossnickle concluded that the long form was superior to the short form and that it is not worth while to teach the short form at all.

During recent years, the author has interviewed many teachers who have tried teaching long division first, not in a rigidly scientific way, but as a change from the plan which they had been using. These teachers are located in several states. So far, the testimony has been unanimously in favor of the change. However, it is probably true that there are in this country today far more schools in which short division is taught first than schools in which the contrary condition prevails.

For any given example in which carrying is involved, short division is intrinsically more difficult than long division because in short division one must deal with numbers which he can not see while in long division all of the numbers used in the solution are in plain sight. In an example like $4\overline{)84}$, where the divisor has but one digit and the dividend is so constructed that carrying is not necessary, it is probably just as easy to write the solution by short division as by long division, but in most division examples carrying is required and, for this

[7] Grossnickle, Foster E. "An Experiment with a One-Figure Divisor in Short and Long Division." *Elementary School Journal,* XXXIV: 496-514 and 590-599, March and April, 1934.

reason, the example is much more difficult if undertaken by short division.

For instance, if a pupil divides 4173 by 6 and uses short division, he must subtract an invisible 36 from a visible 41, must think of the remainder 5 as prefixed to the 7, must think, "How many 6's in 57?" when the 57 is only partially visible, must subtract an invisible 54 from a partially visible 57, etc. This is difficult, very difficult for children who have not yet learned division in any other form. But if the solution is written out in the customary long division form as shown, the steps in the process are clearly portrayed, and the pupil will master the elements of a difficult process without the unfortunate condition of initial discouragement.

```
   695
6)4173
  36
  --
   57
   54
   --
    33
    30
    --
     3
```

Furthermore, short division requires the use of higher decade subtraction. In the example shown, for instance, the pupil must subtract 36 from 41 and he is supposed to do this as a single act of thought. But in long division, he subtracts 36 from 41 by thinking, "6 from 11," and possibly, "3 from 3." This latter is subtraction as he has learned it. The inclusion of the higher decade subtraction difficulty is another reason why short division is much harder than long division.

Whether short division should ever be taught is a question which is difficult to answer. We have seen that John and Buckingham favor the teaching of short division later as a short cut but that Ballard and Grossnickle deny that it is ever worth while to teach short division. As to short methods in general, it may be said that they are learned and used only if they mean an appreciable saving in time and energy, or an appreciable increase in accuracy, or both. For example, the student of statistics soon discovers that short methods mean a very large saving in time and a greatly increased degree of accuracy. But in division, we have seen that the short method means lesser accuracy and no significant saving of time except with the easier examples. There seems to be serious doubt, then, as to whether the teaching of short division in any grade of the elementary school is worth while.

Certainly short division should not be the first division method to be taught. In no other place in mathematics or statistics, so far as the author can recall, is a long method taught after a short method has been learned. Let us begin with long division and let us make that the one and only form, "the King's Highway," as Ballard expresses it,[8] until the pupil has learned well the fundamentals of this difficult operation. In the junior high school, when the finishing touches are being put on the pupil's skill in division with integers, it may be well to introduce him to the shorter method. This may increase his interest in the subject of division. But if he is below the average of his class in general intelligence and arithmetical ability it will probably be better to let him go on blissfully ignorant that there is such a method as short division.

The major difficulty steps in division. It is important that early work in division be planned so that the pupils will move gradually from one type of example to another a little more difficult. So far as possible, but one difficulty should be introduced at a time. Pupils who are taken rapidly or suddenly into the intricacies and difficulties

---

[8] Ballard, P. B., *op. cit.*, Chapter VI.

of division are overwhelmed by them; they become discouraged. But if but one new phase is presented at a time and this phase is pretty well mastered before the next is presented, interest may be sustained and the subject may be mastered.

The major difficulty steps for examples having one-digit divisors may be stated as follows:

1. The primary division facts, as 8)48.
2. Examples having two-digit and three-digit quotients, no carrying.
   (a) Divisor contained in first digit of dividend, as 3)69, 2)486.
   (b) Divisor contained in first two digits of dividend, as 3)126, 4)2484.
3. The primary facts, with remainders, as 2)17, 6)53.
4. Examples involving carrying, no remainders.
   (a) Two-digit quotients, as 6)84, 4)172.
   (b) Three-digit quotients.
      (1) Carrying in first step only, as 5)3755, 7)3157.
      (2) Carrying in second step only, as 8)1696, 3)1575.
      (3) Carrying in both steps, as 4)2532, 9)3753.
5. Examples involving carrying, with remainders, as 6)86, 4)175, 5)3757, 8)1699, 9)3758, etc.
6. Zeros in quotient, without and with remainders.
   (a) At end of quotient, as 4)40, 5)750, 3)32, 8)2643
   (b) In midst of quotient, as 6)1206, 4)1612, 9)5419, 8)3218.

Division without carrying. While the primary facts of multiplication and division are being learned, pupils may learn to divide with examples having two- and sometimes three-digit quotients, but in which there is no carrying, and which do not have remainders. Such examples, like multiplication examples without carrying, enable the pupils to put their division facts to use and to learn, under the simplest and easiest conditions, the form of division. At first these examples will arise from problems, such as, "John, Dick, and Robert collected old magazines and sold them for 93 cents. How much did each boy get?"

Since there is to be no carrying in these first division examples, the same limitations are placed on the dividends that were imposed upon the multiplicands in multiplication without carrying. If the quotient is a two-digit number, the second digit of the quotient must be 1, if the divisor is 9, 8, 7, 6, or 5; it must be 1 or 2, if the divisor is 4; it must be 1, 2, or 3, if the divisor is 3; it must be 1, 2, 3, or 4, if the divisor is 2. If the quotient is a three-digit number, these statements apply to both the second and the third quotient figures.

The first set of practice examples in division is designed to give practice on all of the primary division facts, except those in which 1 is the divisor. We omit 1 as a divisor for the same reason that we omit 1 as a multiplier. Dividing by 1 is not division at all. This set provides for an excessive amount of practice on those facts in which the quotient is 1 for the reason stated in the preceding paragraph. When division with carrying has been learned, we can equalize better the distribution of practice on these primary facts.

Set 1 contains 58 examples. This is the minimum number of examples having two-digit quotients in which practice can be given on each of these 72 primary division facts (all except the nine in which 1 is the divisor).

Practice Examples in Division. Set 1

The Primary Facts, Without Carrying

7)357	6)486	9)549	3)216	8)408	2)148
4)248	5)205	7)427	5)255	3)189	9)729
6)246	8)728	4)168	7)567	5)105	3)156
5)305	6)126	7)147	9)189	6)546	4)128
8)248	6)426	5)155	4)364	6)306	9)459
3)126	9)819	5)455	6)186	3)246	8)168
7)217	3)273	7)637	2)104	8)328	5)405
2)122	4)208	9)279	7)497	8)488	4)284
2)184	9)369	8)648	7)287	9)639	4)328
5)355	6)366	8)568	2)166		

Such examples as these will normally be solved by the short division form. To write out the long division form for such examples will bring in what will appear to the pupils to be unnecessary work. Since these examples are easy, we need spend but little time on them before going on to examples of the next difficulty level. The quotients should be written above the dividends as they will be written when more elaborate examples are solved.

The primary facts with remainders. The next step toward division with carrying is division in which we use the primary division facts but have remainders. Much practice on examples of this type should be given. Problems of the "How-many-for-each-and-how-many-left-over?" kind will be solved frequently. Such a problem as the following may introduce pupils to examples of this kind.

When the four children came home from school, they were very hungry. "You may have the rest of those cookies in the jar," said their mother. The children ran to the jar and found that there were 11 cookies. How many were there for each, and how many left over?

Pupils will have no difficulty in solving some of the easiest of these examples without writing out the solution, but the more difficult will be hard to do since higher decade subtraction is involved. From the start, such examples should be written out in the usual division form. If the pupils became acquainted with this form while solving the easier examples, they will use it more successfully when the harder examples are reached. Thus, the solution for the cooky problem may appear as shown. It is not hard for most pupils as this stage in their progress is to see that there are two 4's in 11 and that there is a remainder of 3. There is no higher decade subtraction here. But the form of the solution should be learned through the use of such examples.

```
   2
4)11
   8
   3
```

As the examples become harder, the pupil's difficulty lies in the determination of the quotient figure. Thus, if 59 is to be divided by 7, the pupils are likely to have difficulty in seeing that 59 lies between 56, which is eight 7's, and 63, which is nine 7's. This not only requires a thorough knowledge of the division facts but also an acquaintance with numbers which will enable the pupils to see that 59 is between 56 and 63 and that there are no numbers between 56 and 63 which represent a whole number of 7's. Teachers frequently underestimate this difficulty. They seem to assume that because a pupil knows that there are eight 7's in 56 and nine 7's in 63, he must know that there are eight 7's and a remainder in any number between 56 and 63. This represents a decided step forward for the pupil who has learned the division facts, however, and it is a difficult step for many pupils to take.

Here, as with other difficult parts of arithmetic, the teacher should go slowly. The pupils should have much practice on the easier facts with remainders (those in which the smaller numbers are used) before the harder facts are attacked. In general, it seems best to take up the facts with remainders in approximately the order indicated by the size of the dividends.

The older arithmetic textbooks distributed the practice given to the primary facts with remainders very unevenly. Furthermore, immensely more practice was usually given to the primary facts without remainders than to the primary facts with remainders. Thorndike[9] found that a well-known textbook made provision for dividing 24 by 3, 91 times; 24 by 4, 76 times; 24 by 5, 18 times; 24 by 6, 50 times; 24 by 7, 5 times; 24 by 8, 61 times; and 24 by 9, 1 time. Four of these divisions have no remainders; they occurred 278 times, an average of 70 times each. But the three that have remainders occurred a total of 24 times, an average of 8. Note, too, that 24 divided by 5 occurred 18 times, but that 24 divided by 9 occurred but once.

Not only have textbooks given much more practice on divisions without remainders than on divisions with remainders, and on some uneven divisions than on others, but they have also tended to give much more prac-

[9] Thorndike, Edward Lee. *The New Methods in Arithmetic.* Chicago: Rand McNally and Company, 1921, p. 72.

tice on the smaller dividends of the primary facts than on the larger. For example, the book referred to in the preceding paragraph[10] made provision for dividing 48 by 5, 7 times; 48 by 6, 17 times; 48 by 7, 4 times; 48 by 8, 33 times; and 48 by 9, 2 times. Here, for the two divisions which come out even, there were 50 practices, an average of 25. The three divisions which do not come out even occurred a total of 13 times, an average of 4. These figures should be compared with those given in the preceding paragraph.

The authors of modern textbooks have given much more attention to this matter of distribution of practice. But there are many communities which still use old books. Even though recently-published books are in use, the teacher can not be sure that the distribution of practice is a desirable one. It may be necessary to provide additional practice exercises for some of these divisions, particularly for those which are the more difficult.

There are many of these uneven divisions upon which specific practice should be provided in teaching the primary facts with remainders. If 2 is the divisor, the dividend may be 3, 5, 7, 9, 11, 13, 15, 17, or 19; if 3 is the divisor, the dividend may be 4, 5, 7, 8, 10, 11, 13, 14, 16, 17, 19, 20, 22, 23, 25, 26, 28, or 29, etc. Table 3 shows the number of examples to be used and the smallest and largest dividends for each divisor. When the divisor is 6, for example, the smallest dividend used will be 7, and the largest, 59. There will be 45 examples for this divisor. These will have, as dividends, all the numbers from 7 to 59 inclusive, except those which contain 6 without

[10] *Ibid.*, p. 73.

a remainder. It will be seen that there is a total of 324 examples upon which practice may be given. Practice should be distributed rather evenly over these examples, if the primary facts are equally well known, but if the pupils show more hesitation on those in which the larger numbers occur, additional practice may be needed for those examples. However, since the group provides much more practice for the larger divisors than for the smaller, the practice may be very satisfactorily distributed if all of the examples in the group are used.

TABLE 3. DIVISION FACTS WITH REMAINDERS

Divisor	Dividends		
	Smallest	Largest	Number
2	3	19	9
3	4	29	18
4	5	39	27
5	6	49	36
6	7	59	45
7	8	69	54
8	9	79	63
9	10	89	72
Total	3	89	324

We could easily give these 324 examples in a series of sets of practice exercises but they would take up several pages and they would be of little help to the teacher. The teacher should prepare such sets of exercises for herself. To do so, simply write down the 9 numbers which are to be divided by 2, the 18 numbers which are to be divided by 3, the 27 numbers which are to be divided by 4, etc., keeping the numbers for each divisor in a separate group. Then check off these numbers as they are used as dividends in the practice exercises. The various divisors and dividends should be taken in a miscellaneous order.

Division with carrying. The next step beyond that of primary facts with remainders is division with carrying in examples having two-digit quotients. At first, the pupils should have such examples without remainders and with the smaller one-digit numbers as divisors. Some such problem as the following will yield an example of this type. "A group of Boy Scouts rode 84 miles on their bicycles in 3 days. On the average, how far did they ride in a day?"

It is not difficult for the pupils to see that the first step in the solution of this example is just like the work which they have been doing on primary facts with remainders. They write the 2 above the 8, write the 6 below the 8, and subtract. From here on, the example represents new experience for the pupils. They "bring down" the 4, think, "How many 3's in 24?", write the 8 above the 4 and the 24 below the 24. Then they check by multiplying 28 by 3 and comparing the product with the dividend, 84.

```
  28
3)84
  6
  --
  24
  24
  --
```

After a few such examples without remainders, examples with remainders should be introduced and solved. Such a problem as the following may be used. "There are 365 days in a year. How many weeks are there in a year?"

Teacher. How do we find out?

Pupil. Divide 365 by 7.

```
   52
7)365
  35
   15
   14
    1
```

Teacher. Let us write the example as we have been writing our division examples. (*The pupil writes the example, 7)365.*) How many 7's in 36?

Pupil. Five.

Teacher. Where do we write the 5?

Pupil. Above the 6. (*The pupil writes the 5, multiplies, writes the 35 beneath the 36, subtracts, writes the 1, and brings down the 5.*)

Teacher. How many 7's in 15?

Pupil. Two. (*The pupil completes the solution.*)

Teacher. Then, how many weeks are there in a year?

Pupil. Fifty-two.

Teacher. And how many extra days?

Pupil. One.

There should be many examples having two-digit quotients before those having three-digit quotients are undertaken. These examples should gradually increase in difficulty until finally the hardest in this classification are reached. The hardest will probably be those in which the divisor is 8 or 9 and in which the quotients are in the eighties and the nineties. There are literally thousands of examples having one-digit divisors and two-digit quotients, with carrying. We can divide any number from 20 to 199, inclusive, by 2 and get a two-digit quotient; this means 180 examples. But in one-half of these, there is no carrying (those whose dividends are in the twenties, the forties, the sixties, etc.) so we have, when the divisor is 2, 90 examples with two-digit quotients and in which one must carry. Likewise, when the divisor is 3, we can use any number from 30 to 299 as dividend;

this gives us 270 examples in 90 of which there is no carrying, or 180 examples which suit our present purposes. When the divisor is 4, we get 360 examples (using as dividends all numbers from 40 to 399, inclusive) in 270 of which there is carrying. These facts for all divisors from 2 to 9, inclusive, are shown in Table 4. It will be seen that if we wish to give practice on division examples with carrying—examples having two-digit quotients—there are 3240 different examples which may be used.

TABLE 4. EXAMPLES HAVING ONE-DIGIT DIVISORS AND TWO-DIGIT QUOTIENTS

Divisor	Dividends	Number of Examples	
		Total	With Carrying
2	20–199	180	90
3	30–299	270	180
4	40–399	360	270
5	50–499	450	360
6	60–599	540	450
7	70–699	630	540
8	80–799	720	630
9	90–899	810	720
Total	......	3960	3240

To make systematic provision for practice on each of these 3,240 examples is a task which we can hardly expect the teacher or the textbook writer to assume. In situations such as this, we must expect transfer of skill. With proper teaching, there is no doubt that transfer will take place but we have reason to believe that such transfer is more likely to occur if the examples are selected so as to permit each digit to appear in the first place in the quotient, and, so far as possible, in the second place in the quotient, and remainders to occur in more or less chance order.

To illustrate what we have in mind, two sets of practice examples, containing a total of 72 examples, have been prepared. For the most part, the first set contains examples having the smaller one-digit numbers in the first place in the quotient, and the second set, the larger. In the two sets together there are nine examples for each divisor from 2 to 9, inclusive. In each divisor group, the dividends are so chosen that each of the nine digits is used as the first quotient figure, that those which can occur in the second quotient place in examples with carrying are used, and that all possible remainders are found.

Practice Examples in Division. Set 2

Two-Digit Quotients, with Carrying

3)206	7)325	5)172	2)31	6)224	4)312
8)217	4)139	9)716	3)74	6)334	7)133
9)315	5)284	6)114	2)75	3)238	8)412
7)197	3)171	9)832	4)50	5)391	6)279
4)387	5)473	8)306	2)96	7)389	3)40
7)261	9)415	8)395	5)60	6)169	8)128
2)119	4)225	9)732	2)52		

The teacher can prepare additional sets of practice examples similar to these by simply selecting quotients, divisors, and remainders and multiplying the quotient by the divisor in each case and adding in the remainder to get the dividend. The quotients, divisors, and remainders should be selected so that there will be a desirable distribution of practice. Of course, the remainder can never be as large as the divisor. The second quotient figure cannot be 1, except when the divisor is 6, 7, 8, or 9; it cannot be 1 or 2, if the divisor is 2 or 3; it cannot be 1, 2, 3, or 4, if the divisor is 2.

Practice Examples in Division. Set 3

Two-Digit Quotients, with Carrying

3)140	4)93	6)389	8)679	9)223	5)116
4)180	6)584	9)125	3)106	5)228	7)574
2)131	7)453	2)196	8)501	6)438	5)335
4)271	2)175	7)641	9)618	4)358	8)760
3)250	5)447	8)590	6)493	3)289	7)517
2)152	9)515				

In this early work in division, we should give the pupils very specific instructions as to where they should place the figures of the quotient. Each quotient figure should be placed directly above the last figure of the partial dividend which is being used. There are three reasons for this: (1) it will help the pupil later to keep track of the dividend digits which he has brought down; (2) it will help when difficulties arise in connection with the appearance of zeros in the quotient; (3) it will help him later in locating a decimal point in the quotient correctly.

None of these reasons would be understood if given now but we try to get the pupil to form the habit of placing the quotient figures in their proper places since they must get into the habit of placing them somewhere. It is a little like training young children in certain socially approved habits of conduct at the dining table long before they can appreciate reasons for the practices which we urge.

The division examples which arise from life problems usually have remainders. But those given in textbooks are frequently constructed so that there will be no remainders. In the pupil's first experience with a new type of example, it may be better to arrange that the examples should not have remainders for the sake of simplifying the examples and making it easier for the pupil to focus his attention upon the new difficulty; but in ordinary practice exercises, remainders should be allowed to occur as they would in a chance selection of examples.

When the divisor is 2, the possible remainders are 0 and 1. These, in the long run, will occur equally often. But when the remainder is 0, of course, the example comes out even. So, when the divisor is 2, we should expect one-half of our examples to come out even.

When the divisor is 3, the possible remainders are 0, 1, and 2. These, in the long run, will occur equally often. So, when the divisor is 3, we should expect one-third of our examples to come out even.

When the divisor is 4, we should expect each of the remainders, 0, 1, 2, and 3, to occur equally often. So, when the divisor is 4, we should expect one-fourth of our examples to come out even.

Likewise, when the divisor is 5, one-fifth of our examples will, in the long run, have no remainders. When it is 6, one-sixth of them will come out even. When it is 48, one-forty-eighth of them will yield whole number quotients. And so on.

Then, in our early work in division with carrying, if the divisors, 2, 3, 4, 5, 6, 7, 8, and 9, are used equally often, and if dividends are selected at random, we can expect less than one-fourth of our examples to come out even and more than three-fourths of them to have remainders.[11] The teacher of elementary work in division will do well to provide that remainders shall occur frequently in practice exercises and that they shall become more and more frequent as the divisors become larger. In later grades, when pupils are using two-digit and three-digit divisors, examples without remainders should be so rare as to be the occasion for comment.

Some pupils find that their examples have remainders so seldom that when they do get remainders they conclude at once that their solutions are incorrect. Artificialities in textbook materials should not lead pupils to form such conclusions. The pupils should check their solutions to determine whether they are correct.

Turning now to examples having three-digit quotients, we find ten times as many examples as we have with quotients of two-digits. Table 4 shows that there are, in all, 3960 examples having one-digit divisors and two-digit quotients. For one-digit divisors and three-digit quotients, there are 39,600 examples, as shown in Table 5. This table indicates that when the divisor is 2, we can use as dividend any number from 200 to 1999, in-

[11] Under these conditions, the theoretical frequency of examples without remainders will be 22.86%.

clusive, and have three digits in the quotient. This gives us 1800 examples, of which 1350 involve carrying. Of the total number of 39,600 examples, 37,620 involve carrying.

These 37,620 examples include those in which zeros occur in the quotient—a type which is discussed in later pages.

TABLE 5. EXAMPLES HAVING ONE-DIGIT DIVISORS AND THREE-DIGIT QUOTIENTS

Divisor	Dividends	Number of Examples	
		Total	With Carrying
2	200–1999	1800	1350
3	300–2999	2700	2340
4	400–3999	3600	3330
5	500–4999	4500	4320
6	600–5999	5400	5220
7	700–6999	6300	6120
8	800–7999	7200	7020
9	900–8999	8100	7920
Total		39600	37620

We do not expect the primary teacher to be keenly interested in this table. The table is supplied to show the enormity of the task of giving practice on all possible examples having one-digit divisors and three-digit quotients. Only a few of these 37,620 examples will be given to the pupils to solve as a means of gaining facility in dealing with the type of division examples which we are now discussing. However, these few should be selected with care. The impromptu writing of just any examples —a practice which many teachers follow—will not provide adequately for practice on the various elements of difficulty which occur in division examples. Each of the eight divisors from 2 to 9, inclusive, should be used; each of the nine digits should appear about equally often in the quotient; and the various possible remainders should appear about equally often.

In our outline of types of division examples, we indicated that if the quotient had three digits there might be carrying in the first step only, in the second step only, or in both the first and the second steps. It is a little easier for the pupils to become accustomed to three-digit quotients if they have for awhile examples in which there is only one carrying operation before they undertake to solve those which require two carrying operations. Most of the basic difficulties will have been mastered by this time, however, so it does not seem to be necessary for the pupils to spend very much time on these types of examples separately before they have all of them in mixed practice exercises.

Practice Examples in Division, Set 4, indicate how the various divisors may be used in a small number of examples and how the various digits may appear in the quotient. The set contains four examples having 2 as a divisor and three examples with each of the remaining one-digit numbers (except 1) as divisor. It was necessary to include four examples with 2 as the divisor in order that all nine digits might appear in the quotient, for 1, 2, 3, and 4 can appear in the first step only, if there is to be carrying in each step of the example. Each of the digits from 1 to 9, inclusive, appears at least once in the quotient with each of these divisors. Remainders appear in nearly all of these examples, and the same remainder does not appear twice for any one divisor, except 2. Each example requires carrying in both steps.

PRACTICE EXAMPLES IN DIVISION. SET 4

Three-Digit Quotients

$3\overline{)2810}$	$8\overline{)3087}$	$5\overline{)933}$	$2\overline{)972}$	$6\overline{)5591}$
$4\overline{)1077}$	$9\overline{)2550}$	$2\overline{)719}$	$3\overline{)741}$	$7\overline{)4490}$
$9\overline{)6831}$	$6\overline{)1724}$	$4\overline{)734}$	$3\overline{)556}$	$8\overline{)1395}$
$6\overline{)2740}$	$4\overline{)2299}$	$2\overline{)357}$	$7\overline{)1986}$	$5\overline{)2862}$
$7\overline{)6705}$	$9\overline{)5776}$	$2\overline{)592}$	$5\overline{)1974}$	$8\overline{)2156}$

Zeros in the quotient. Zeros in the quotient cause much trouble. In the example, $4\overline{)962}$, pupils tend to write 24 as the quotient, leaving 2 as the remainder. In the example, $7\overline{)4214}$, a very common answer is 62, instead of 602. These errors seem to be less frequent when the examples are solved by long division than when the short division form is used, for we can rather easily emphasize the point that each time we bring down a figure we must write another figure in the quotient. In the former example, we brought down the 2 and must, then, write something in the quotient. Likewise in the latter example, when we bring down the 1 there is nothing left to do but place a 0 in the quotient.

$$\begin{array}{r} 240 \\ 4\overline{)962} \\ \underline{8} \\ 16 \\ \underline{16} \\ 2 \end{array}$$

```
   602
7)4214
  42
  --
    14
    14
    --
```

If this important principle—*every time we bring down a figure we must write something in the quotient*—is emphasized when examples containing zero in the quotient are first presented, if there is then a period of intense practice on examples of this type, and if the pupils are required to check all solutions, this zero difficulty will soon be mastered and will cause little trouble in later lessons. But when examples of this category are first presented, there must be a careful explanation of the difficulty, several illustrative examples must be worked out, and there must then be a period of practice which is closely supervised by the teacher.

```
 $2.05
4)8.20
  8
  -
   20
   20
   --
```

The procedure to be followed when a zero should be placed in the quotient may be rationalized in terms of the number system or, more easily, in terms of dollars and cents. Consider the problem: "Four boys earned $8.20 mowing the neighbors' lawns. They divided the money equally. How much did each boy receive?" The pupils readily see that if a little more than eight dollars is divided among 4 boys, each boy must receive a little more than two dollars. Emphasis may be placed on the fact that $8.20 means 8 dollars, 2 dimes, and 0 cents. Dividing 8 dollars by 4, we get 2 dollars. We can not divide the 2 dimes by 4 but we can think of the 2 dimes as 20 cents and divide 20 cents by 4. We get 5 cents. Then each boy receives two dollars and five cents and the pupils know by this time that two dollars and five cents is written $2.05. Then the teacher calls attention to the fact that the figures in the quotient, 2.05, tell in order the number of dollars, the number of dimes, and the number of cents each boy receives. Since the dollars come out even and there are not enough dimes to go around, the dimes are changed to cents and no boy receives any dimes. We place a 0 in the dime's place in the quotient to show that a boy's share does not include any dimes just as we place a 2 in the dollar's place to show that a boy's share includes 2 dollars. Pupils easily see in such a case as this that it would be absurd to think of each boy's share as being either 25 dollars or 25 cents.

Such an example can also be expressed in terms of the hundreds, the tens, and the units of our number system. If 836 is divided by 4 we may think of dividing 8 hundreds, 3 tens, and 6 units by 4. When we divide 8 hundreds by 4, we get 2 hundreds as the quotient and we place a 2 in the hundreds place in the quotient. There are not enough tens for us to divide them by 4 so we place a 0 in tens place in the quotient to show that the quotient contains no tens. Then we think of the 3 tens as 30 units, combine these 30 units with the 6 units, and divide 36 units by 4, writing 9 in the units place in the quotient.

```
   209
4)836
  8
  --
   36
   36
   --
```

It will be seen that this explanation resembles the explanations of the operation of carrying in addition and the operation of borrowing in subtraction.

If pupils are taught to write their quotient figures in the proper places and to make neat figures of uniform size and with uniform spacing, there is less likelihood of the zero being omitted from the quotient. In the accompanying example the 2 has been placed correctly above the 8 and the 9

```
   2 9
4)836
```

above the 6. The conspicuous gap between the 2 and the 9 may well call the pupil's attention to the fact that he has carelessly omitted the zero.

In this discussion, we are limiting ourselves to examples having quotients of not more than three digits. In our outline of difficulty steps, we distinguish between examples which have a zero at the end of the quotient and examples which have a zero in in the middle quotient position. Zero at the end of the quotient can occur with either two- or three-digit quotients; zero in the middle quotient position, of course, can occur in the three-digit quotients only. We may also have three-digit quotients containing two zeros.

If the divisor is 2, and the quotient is to have two digits, the second of which is 0, the possible quotients, of course, are 10, 20, 30, 40, 50, 60, 70, 80, and 90. Each of these can occur without or with a remainder of 1. So we have, in all, 18 examples having a 0 in the two-digit quotient when the divisor is 2. They are:

$2\overline{)20}$ $2\overline{)21}$ $2\overline{)40}$ $2\overline{)41}$ $2\overline{)60}$ $2\overline{)61}$ $2\overline{)80}$ $2\overline{)81}$ $2\overline{)100}$

$2\overline{)101}$ $2\overline{)120}$ $2\overline{)121}$ $2\overline{)140}$ $2\overline{)141}$ $2\overline{)160}$ $2\overline{)161}$ $2\overline{)180}$ $2\overline{)181}$

If the divisor is 3, we have the same nine quotients, but each can occur with no remainder, a remainder of 1, or a remainder of 2. This gives us 3×9, or 27 examples.

When the divisor is 4, we have the same nine quotients, each occurring with no remainder, a remainder of 1, a remainder of 2, or a remainder of 3. When the divisor is 4, then we have 4×9, or 36 examples.

Likewise, when the divisor is 5, we have 45 examples; when the divisor is 6, we have 54 examples; and so on.

These facts are summarized in Table 6. The table shows that when the divisor is 2, there are 18 examples having quotients of two digits, one of which is 0. The total number of such examples is 396.

Table 6 also shows the number of examples having zeros in three-digit quotients. When the zero is at the end of the quotient, as in the example, $4\overline{)2522}$ with quotient 630–2, there are 3960 examples, ten times the number in the preceding column. For zeros in the midst of the quotient, as in the example, $5\overline{)3528}$ with quotient 705–3, there are 3564 examples. Quotients like 100, 200, 300, etc., containing two zeros, are included in the numbers in the third column, but not in the fourth. If they were included in both, the total of each column would be 3960.

The reader may satisfy himself that the numbers in the third and fourth columns of the table are correct by a line of reasoning similar to that employed for two-digit quotients ending in 0. Thus, if the divisor is 2, and the quotient is to have three digits, the last of which is 0, the possible quotients are 100, 110, 120, 130, 140, and so on to and including 990. This is a total of 90 quotients. Each may occur with no remainder or with a remainder of 1. Hence there are, in all, 2×90, or 180 examples in this class and for this divisor.

Again, it is obvious that there are more examples having zeros in the quotient than we can hope to use. It is our responsibility to select from these 7920 examples

TABLE 6. ZEROS IN QUOTIENTS WITH ONE-DIGIT DIVISORS

Divisor	Number of Examples Having Zeros in the Quotient		
	Two-Digit Quotients	Three-Digit Quotients	
		Zero at End of Quotient	Zero in Midst of Quotient
2	18	180	162
3	27	270	243
4	36	360	324
5	45	450	405
6	54	540	486
7	63	630	567
8	72	720	648
9	81	810	729
Total	396	3960	3564

those which will develop the ability to deal with zeros in the quotients and which will give an otherwise desirable distribution of practice.

The fifth set of practice examples in division contains 34 examples having 0 as the second digit of a two-digit quotient. The divisor 2 is used twice; 3, three times, 4, four times; 5, 6, 7, 8, and 9, five times each. No remainder occurs twice for any one divisor. Each of the digits 2 to 7, inclusive, occurs four times in quotients; 8 and 9 occur five times each.[12]

[12] The reader will appreciate better these sets of examples if he will check them to see that they conform to the descriptions.

Practice Examples in Division. Set 5

Zeros at End of Two-Digit Quotients

4)163	7)421	8)242	5)350	3)272
6)125	2)160	9)456	4)281	8)647
3)61	5)453	7)286	9)544	2)101
6)182	8)725	5)154	7)490	3)180
4)322	5)202	6)304	9)187	4)80
6)483	9)360	7)634	8)481	7)212
8)403	6)541	9)638	5)401	

Set 6 contains 20 examples. Each example has a quotient of three digits, the last of which is 0. Practice is distributed over the remaining digits in divisors and quotients in much the same manner as in Set 5.

Practice Examples in Division. Set 6

Zeros at End of Three-Digit Quotients

6)4324	8)5044	5)4703	9)7291	7)5950
4)3883	7)1123	3)1680	8)3841	6)5583
5)3600	9)5760	2)1741	4)1401	7)6444
9)3334	5)901	8)2003	3)572	6)2762

Set 7 includes 40 examples. Each has a three-digit quotient with a 0 in the second place. The quotients include the digits 2 to 9, inclusive, nine times each, and 1, eight times. The larger divisors are given more intensive practice than the smaller, 2 being used twice and 9, eight times. Each of the possible remainders occurs approximately as frequently as it would in a chance selection of examples.

Practice Examples in Division. Set 7

Zeros in Middle Quotient Position

7)2849	5)4033	9)2724	8)876	6)3617
9)4557	4)3231	7)6308	6)2434	3)2124
8)2422	9)6316	5)2049	4)1220	7)4261
6)5419	8)3261	2)1004	5)1505	3)1216
9)3686	7)1424	8)4866	6)4209	9)7240
4)2410	6)4830	9)2763	7)3546	5)1036
8)4011	9)8137	4)3605	7)6358	6)1838
9)1856	3)9029	8)3217	2)1417	5)2507

The amount of practice to be provided for each of the kinds of examples will vary from pupil to pupil and from class to class. It will depend upon the rate at which the pupils learn. What we wish to do is to make the pupils proficient in the technique of division, using the long division form, and to enable them to master the zero difficulties, limiting our examples to those having one-digit divisors and three-digit quotients. This will ordinarily require considerably more practice than that provided by the examples in our sets of practice exercises. These sets of exercises will suggest how additional practice materials may be prepared.

In discussing division difficulties, we have recognized zero difficulties only so far as they appear in the quotient. Undoubtedly, zeros in the quotient represent the most serious of the zero difficulties which pupils encounter in division. But zeros may also appear in the divisor and in the dividend. Zeros in the divisor will not concern us at this point since we are not considering divisors of more than one digit. However, zeros in the dividend sometimes cause trouble. In examples like $8\overline{)408}$, the zero should cause little trouble for it is combined with the 4 when dividing, and the pupil thinks, "How many 8's in 40?" But in the example, $7\overline{)2807}$, the pupil must actually think of dividing 0 by 7. In examples such as this we have the zero facts concretely applied. Here we need to teach the fundamental principle that *zero divided by any number equals zero,* and apply this principle in a brief period of intensive practice. If the work so far has been skilfully developed, the pupil should not find it difficult to see that there are no 7's in 0. It may be necessary to prepare a set of practice examples giving specific training on this form of zero difficulties. Set 7 contains several examples of this kind.

Checking results. Every division example should be checked. From the time of his introduction to the subject, the pupil should learn to apply the important principle that *divisor times quotient plus remainder equals dividend.* Or, when he has learned the signs, it may be written in equation form, thus:

Divisor × quotient + Remainder = Dividend.

We have seen that the first multiplication examples of any type which the pupil solves can not be checked by division for he has not learned at that time to solve the corresponding type of division example. But all division examples can be checked by multiplication. It seems best, then, to teach the multiplication check for division examples from the first. In the primary grades, it will not be advisable to teach any other division checks.

In solving a division example, the pupil divides, multiplies, and subtracts; in checking the example, he multiplies and, if there is a remainder, he adds. Thus all four of the fundamental operations are practised with emphasis upon the two most recently learned.

The use of problems. It is as important to supply an abundance of problems in division as in the other fundamental operations, but, unfortunately, problems which require the use of division occur much less frequently in the affairs of most people than do problems which require the use of addition, subtraction, or multiplication. Such problems can be found, however, and it behooves the teacher to be on the alert for occurrences of them. Unless practical problems are supplied from time to time, the pupils may conclude that division is not a very useful process. Division is hard enough at the best and if it appears to the pupil to be not only difficult but useless, interest is almost certain to subside.

The activities of the pupils will lead to occasional problems which require division. If the teacher exercises some direction over these activities, they may yield more division situations than would otherwise be the case. Problems requiring division may also be taken from the affairs of others, hypothetical problems from the experiences of other children as well as problems from the experiences of older people. If the teacher will watch for opportunities for the use of division and make notes of these when they occur, she will be able to supplement the textbook and the course of study in a very worth-while manner.

QUESTIONS AND REVIEW EXERCISES

1. Examine your local course of study to determine how much division is to be given in the third grade and in the fourth grade. Criticize the recommendations which you find. What, if any, division would you have given in the third grade?

2. Why is it recommended that each phase of multiplication be followed by the corresponding phase of division? Do you think that it would be desirable to have all of the multiplication which is to be offered in a given grade before any of the division for that grade is taken up?

3. How early should the pupil have examples with one-digit divisors and two-digit quotients?

4. What is meant by division as measurement? By division as partition? What use should be made of these two meanings of division in teaching pupils to divide?

5. What is a unit fraction? What unit fractions can be used in connection with practice on the division facts?

6. Which did you learn first, short division or long division? Do you agree with the chapter recommendation that the long form should be taught before the short form?

7. How do you account for the general practice of teaching short division before long division?

8. In general, are short cuts taught before or after the corresponding long processes?

9. Is short division more difficult than long division for all division examples?

10. What is higher decade subtraction? Is it related to higher decade addition? Is it used in short division? In long division?

11. If long division is taught first, would you teach short division later? If so, would you teach it to all pupils?

12. Check over the outline of major difficulty steps for examples having one-digit divisors. Can you suggest addi-

tional classes or sub-classes of examples?

13. Why is it true that you can not construct an example having 8 as the divisor and having a two-digit quotient ending with 2, if the example has no carrying?

14. Is it worth while to make the effort required in the preparation of sets of practice examples such as those given in this chapter? What is the disadvantage of setting down numbers at random in the preparation of division examples?

15. Why is it best to introduce the long division form with primary facts with remainders.

16. Should a pupil have as much practice in dividing 55 by 8 as in dividing 56 by 8? Why?

17. Would it be reasonable to expect the use of all of the 324 examples indicated in Table 3? The 3960 examples indicated in Table 4? The 39,600 examples indicated in Table 5? If selections are to be made from these large groups, how should these selections be made?

18. Where should the quotient be written in solving a division example? Where should the first figure of the quotient be written? Have you seen the quotient written at the right of the dividend? Is there any advantage in writing it in this position?

19. In ordinary life situations, what proportion of division examples should have no remainders if the divisor is 2? If the divisor is 7? If the divisor is 43? If the divisor is *n*?

20. If a pupil wrote 8 as the quotient of 645 divided by 8 and showed a remainder of 5, what would you do if you were the teacher? What would you do if he gave 23 as the quotient of 1218 divided by 6?

21. Under what conditions may a pupil have to divide zero by a number?

22. What is the best check for division? Would you teach more than one check for this process?

23. Collect a set of life-like problems which require the use of division with one-digit divisors.

CHAPTER TEST

For each of these items, select the best answer. A scoring key will be found on page 406.

1. Concerning the place of division in the primary grades, there is (1) marked uniformity of opinion (2) marked disagreement (3) slight disagreement.

2. Division is least related to (1) addition (2) subtraction (3) multiplication.

3. Division without carrying should be taught (1) before multiplication without carrying (2) with multiplication without carrying (3) just after multiplication without carrying.

4. Partition refers to (1) the use of the fraction form in division (2) division as a short cut for subtraction (3) division as measurement.

5. A unit fraction is a fraction which (1) is equal to 1, (2) has 1 for a numerator (3) has 1 for a denominator.

6. Short division is very generally taught before long division because (1) it is easier (2) it is harder (3) of the influence of tradition.

7. Higher decade subtraction is required in (1) short division (2) long division (3) neither short division nor long division.

8. In general, short methods are taught (1) before long methods (2) with long methods (3) after long methods.

9. We recommended that division by one-digit divisors without carrying (1) be taught by short division (2) be taught by long division (3) not be taught at all.

10. Of examples having three-digit quotients we recognized (1) 2 (2) 3 (3) 4 classes.

11. If the divisor is 4 and there is to be no carrying, the second quotient figure can not be (1) 1 (2) 2 (3) 3.

12. We recommended that in working with the primary division facts with remainders the pupils should (1) use the

short division form (2) use the long division form (3) do the work in their heads.

13. Of the following combinations the typical textbook gives the most practice to (1) 54 ÷ 7 (2) 55 ÷ 7 (3) 56 ÷ 7.

14. If the divisor is 6 and the quotient is a one-digit number with a remainder, the total number of examples is (1) 6 (2) 45 (3) 81.

15. If the divisor is 6 and the quotient is a two-digit number, the largest possible dividend is (1) 594 (2) 599 (3) 600.

16. If the divisor is 3 and the quotient is a two-digit number, the proportion of the examples which have carrying is (1) one-half (2) one-third (3) two-thirds.

17. The best place for the first quotient figure is (1) above the first figure of the dividend (2) above the second figure of the dividend (3) above the last figure of the partial dividend which is being used.

18. About one-fifth of our examples should have no remainders if the divisor is (1) 5 (2) 10 (3) 25.

19. In miscellaneous lists of practice examples in division, the proportion of examples without remainders should be (1) less than half (2) half (3) more than half.

20. Zeros cause the most trouble when they are found in (1) the divisor (2) the dividend (3) the quotient.

21. If the divisor is 6 and the quotient is a two-digit number ending in 0, the total number of examples is (1) 45 (2) 54 (3) 180.

22. The best check in division consists of (1) multiplication (2) repeating the work (3) subtraction.

SELECTED REFERENCES

1. Ballard, Philip Boswood. *Teaching the Essentials of Arithmetic.* London: University of London Press, 1928. 260 pp. Chapter VI entitled "The King's Highway" suggests that the teacher should make the pupils familiar with the highways "before they begin to explore the byways." Chapter

XVI indicates that long division is the important method.

2. Buckingham, B. R. "The Training of Teachers of Arithmetic." National Society for the Study of Education, *The Twenty-Ninth Yearbook*. Bloomington, Illinois: Public School Publishing Company, 1930, pp. 317-408. The entire reference is well worth reading. Pages 376-378 discuss dividing by a one-digit number.

3. Grossnickle, Foster E. "An Experiment with a One-Figure Divisor in Short and Long Division." *Elementary School Journal,* XXXIV: 496-514 and 590-599, March and April, 1934. Reports the extent to which persons who have left the primary grades are successful with short division. Recommends that short division not be taught at all.

4. John, Lenore. "The Effect of Using the Long Division Form in Teaching Division by One-Digit Divisors." *Elementary School Journal,* XXX: 675-692, May, 1930. Reports the results of an experimental attack upon the subject of short *versus* long division. Found that those who used long division were the more accurate.

5. Klapper, Paul. *The Teaching of Arithmetic.* New York: D. Appleton-Century Company, 1934. 525 pp. On pp. 309-313 is a brief discussion of division with one-figure divisors.

6. Myers, Garry Cleveland. "Beginning Long Division." *The Grade Teacher,* XLVII: 542 and 576-577, 626 and 654, March and April, 1930. Suggests the long form for elementary work in division and points out that tradition accounts for the continued use of the short form.

7. Polkinghorne, Ada R. "Young Children and Fractions." *Childhood Education,* XI: 354-358, May, 1935. Tests given to children in lower grades revealed a sufficient acquaintance with fractions to justify our suggestion as to the use of the fraction form with the division facts.

8. Thorndike, Edward Lee. *The New Methods in Arithmetic.* Chicago: Rand McNally and Company, 1921. 260 pp. Interesting results found by analyzing textbook drill materials are reported in Chapter IV.

CHAPTER 10

ROMAN NUMERALS, MEASURES, FRACTIONS

The broad base of number experience. The teacher in the primary grades finds many and varied opportunities for developing an understanding and an appreciation of number. We have indicated that counting is the fundamental number experience. But in addition to counting, pupils have many other opportunities to gain an appreciation of number. These have to do with comparisons of objects, groups of objects, distances, sizes, and the like, and a determination of which is the larger, the more, the greater, etc.

Pupils in the primary grades learn to count, to read numbers, to write numbers, to add, to subtract, and possibly to multiply and to divide. They also gain some understanding of the number system and its usefulness in social affairs, and some appreciation in an elementary way of the meaning of fractions. They learn to apply their skills in the solution of problems and to check their solutions as a means of assuring themselves that these solutions are correct. They learn to think in numerical and quantitative terms. But in addition to all of this, they have further experiences which are quantitative in character or which have quantitative aspects.

Children have quantitative experiences in many kinds of situations. For example, the readers which they use contain many words having to do with arithmetical concepts. In Chapter 2 we referred to Gunderson's study.[1]

[1] Gunderson, Agnes G. "Nature and Amount of Arithmetic in Readers

She analyzed the primers, the first readers, and the second readers in ten recently published sets of readers. A list of 416 different items having to do with arithmetic or quantitative concepts was found. The total number of occurrences of these items was 22,916. Her results are summarized briefly in Table 7.

According to this table, 18 different items were found which had to do with size. This was 4.3 per cent of the total of 416 items. These 18 items occurred so frequently that they were found, in all, 5113 times in the ten sets of readers examined.

The 18 items having to do with size are: *big, deep, great, huge, large, little, long, middle-sized, narrow, short, size, small, tall, thick, thin, tiny, wee,* and *wide.*

The most frequently mentioned items in the group referring to quantity are: *some, all* (every one), *no* (not any), *other, many, every,* and *another.* Of the 113 items referring to time, those most frequently mentioned are: *soon, now, day, winter, morning, night, today,* and *summer.* Others had to do with seasons, duration of time, before and after certain times and events, and the like.

The numbers expressed in words included: *one, two, three, four, five, six, seven, eight, nine, ten, twelve, fifteen, twenty, twenty-five, thirty, fifty, hundred, thousand,* and *million.* The Arabic numerals used were all of the numerals from 1 to 41, inclusive, and 300. The ordinals were *first, second, third,* and *fourth.* The Roman numerals found were: I, II, III, IV, V, VI, and VII.

Gunderson raises the question as to whether there should be a closer integration of reading and arithmetic.

---

for Grades I and II." *Elementary School Journal,* XXXVI: 527-540, March, 1936.

Table 7. DISTRIBUTION OF ARITHMETIC OR QUANTITATIVE TERMS IN TEN SERIES OF READERS (AFTER GUNDERSON).

Classes of Terms	Items Found		Frequency of Items	
	Number	Per Cent	Number	Per Cent
Terms referring to size	18	4.3	5,113	22.3
Terms referring to quantity	30	7.2	3,619	15.8
Terms referring to time	113	27.2	3,104	13.6
Terms referring to location	34	8.2	2,760	12.0
Numbers expressed in words	19	4.6	2,142	9.4
Arabic numerals	42	10.1	1,886	8.2
Miscellaneous arithmetical concepts	21	5.0	1,540	6.7
Terms referring to money	32	7.7	1,071	4.7
Miscellaneous arithmetical terms	25	6.0	641	2.8
Terms of Comparison	39	9.4	558	2.4
Ordinals	4	1.0	181	0.8
Terms referring to groups	16	3.8	126	0.6
Miscellaneous measures	16	3.8	100	0.4
Roman numerals	7	1.7	75	0.3
Total	416	100.0	22,916	100.0

She suggests that readers are already rather well integrated with the social studies and that perhaps the amount of integration between reading and arithmetic should be increased.

This chapter will be devoted to a discussion of some miscellaneous number experiences. We are particularly concerned with Roman numerals, the matter of comparisons, measurement, the more common denominate measures and their uses, and the development of an elementary understanding of fractions. Roman numerals suggest the clock face and telling time; the calendar becomes an object of interest; objects are compared as to size, weight, and number; experiences in stores lead to money and the recognition and value of the more common coins; fractions and measures of quantity and volume are used in recipes, in painting and in constructions; distances are appreciated through walking to school, through riding buses and street cars, and through trips taken in the family car, on boats, on trains, and in airplanes; and many other aspects of the pupil's life have quantitative phases and require number appreciation and quantitative thinking.

Roman numerals. Many of the older courses of study provided very definitely for systematic instruction in Roman numerals in the first grade and for a more extended acquaintance with this subject in grades two and three. There were marked variations, to be sure. Some courses went as far as XX in the first grade and L or LX in the second grade. Courses have been found which provided that this subject be taught as far as M in grade three. Other courses neglected the subject entirely in the first and second grades and went only as far as V in the third grade.

Various arguments have been advanced for early instruction in Roman notation. The chief of these has had to do with telling time. It was taken for granted that first grade children should learn to read the time from the face of a clock or a watch and that this could not be done unless Roman numerals were known. However, it has become apparent that telling time in anything like a precise and accurate way is difficult for young children, too difficult for most of those in grade one. Furthermore, it seems finally to have dawned upon students of primary education that no watches and very few clocks of recent manufacture have Roman numerals on their faces. Arabic numerals have very generally taken their place. Consequently, both the extent and the intensity of instruction in Roman notation in the first grade, and also in the second grade, have been considerably reduced. Other reasons for knowing Roman numerals exist. We find them in the front matter of books where they are used to number pages. Chapters are often numbered in Roman. Other reasons for studying Roman notation could be stated but they do not seem to be very potent reasons for studying the subject in the earliest grades. It is doubtful whether the subject should be considered at all in the first grade and in the second and third grades it should receive much less attention than it has had in many schools.

No fixed rule can be stated as to when the subject of Roman notation should be begun. The time when this subject should first be taught will depend upon the pupils, their intelligence, their experiences, and their interests. As is the case with all school topics, some pupils are ready at much earlier ages than are others. Some children ask questions about Roman numerals when in the

letters. Other uses may be found or improvised by the teacher.

The next numeral to be learned is V. There is no particular reason apparent to the pupil why 5 should be represented by V any more than by some other letter of the alphabet. But if he sees this letter associated with 5 and if he finds it in situations where a 5 might have been used, he soon comes to think of five when he sees V in a situation which suggests numbering.

It is now time to develop the subtractive and additive principles in Roman notation. The pupils review the fact that I means 1 and that V means 5. The teacher writes IV on the blackboard and simply tells the pupils that this means 4 and that we get 4 from this statement by subtracting I (1) from V (5). Then VI appears and the pupils learn that this means V and I added. These new numerals are then put to use along with a review of those already learned and the pupils practice on situations in which the numerals I to VI are used.

The teacher then calls attention to the fact that when a letter representing a smaller number is placed *before* a letter representing a larger number, the value of the smaller is *subtracted* from the value of the larger. Thus IV means I subtracted from V. Also when a letter representing a smaller number is placed *after* a letter representing a larger number, the value of the smaller is *added* to the value of the larger. Thus VI means I added to V. Then the teacher writes VII on the blackboard and asks the pupils what they think it means. After they have discovered the meaning of this number, they also discover the meaning of VIII. There should be considerable emphasis upon these additive and subtractive principles.

When these eight numerals have been learned, they may be reviewed in association with the Arabic numerals by having them appear on the blackboard,

I	II	III	IV	V	VI	VII	VIII
1	2	3	4	5	6	7	8

What we have sketched so far will require several lesson periods with intervening opportunities for practice. Teachers sometimes ruin their chances to have this subject well learned by moving too rapidly and taking up a new phase of the subject before that which has already been presented has been sufficiently well learned.

Note that after teaching I, II, and III, we jumped to V and then returned to IV. The reason for this will be apparent; IV can not be meaningful unless V is known if the subtractive principle is to be recognized. In like manner, we jump from VIII to X and then return to IX. In X, the pupil has a new numeral to learn. Here, again, he will see no reason why 10 should be represented by X. The procedure in teaching IX, XI, XII, and XIII will be similar to that followed in teaching IV, VI, VII, and VIII, except that with IX, XI, XII, and XIII, the pupil will put to use what he already knows about the subtractive and additive principles and will discover the meaning of these new numerals for himself. This is an important point. If the pupils have learned the Roman numerals to VIII and have learned the subtractive and additive principles, they should by all means put this knowledge and this skill to use in learning IX, XI, XII, and XIII, after X has been learned. For the teacher to present these latter numerals as something new and unrelated to what the pupil already knows is to miss a golden opportunity to develop in the pupils that independence and ability to think for themselves which we desire.

These three numerals (I, V, and X) and these two principles (additive and subtractive) will care for all of the Roman numerals which children in the lower grades will need to learn. Through the teens, the pupil sees a repetition of what he has already learned below ten but with X prefixed. When he gets to XX, he needs a slight modification or extension of the additive principle which he has learned. He needs to learn that the additive principle applies not only when a letter representing smaller number is written after letter representing a larger but also when the same letter is repeated. Thus XX, means 10 + 10, or 20. He has already seen this principle, probably without recognizing it, in II (1 + 1) and III (1 + 1 + 1). He moves rapidly through the twenties as he did through the teens, learns that XXX means X + X + X, or 30, and recognizes further numbers in the thirties.

This will be sufficient for the needs of the pupils under ordinary conditions. The teacher's knowledge should go farther. She should be able to answer the occasional questions of bright pupils. She should know L (50), C (100), D (500), and M (1000), and the application of the subtractive and additive principles in writing numbers, such as dates, to 2000.

Comparisons. An appreciation of size and quantity is often developed through the making of comparisons. Opportunities for this will be very numerous. Such questions as the following will suggest what can be done.

Who has more marbles, John or Dick?
Who is taller, Helen or Eleanor?
Which of these tables is larger?
Which of these two bowls has the more goldfish in it?
Which pencil is longer?
Which book is thicker?
Which sheet of paper is thinner?
Which coin is smaller?
Which way to school is shorter?
Which paper has fewer mistakes?
Which stone is heavier?
Which balloon is lighter?
Which picture is cheaper?
Which pair of skates costs more?
Which hill is higher?
Which book do we have more copies of?

These are just random suggestions. If the teacher is alert, she will find many others.

So far, we have considered comparison in the comparative degree. The superlative degree may also be used if three or more objects are compared. Of course, the comparative degree will come first and there will be considerable practice with two objects before the superlative is introduced. Each of the situations suggested by the above questions can be used for the superlative degree also.

Measurement. Elementary experience with measurement will come early in the child's school program. Measurement, in a simple way, is often found in the kindergarten where the children talk about the long and the short, the big and the little, the wide and the narrow, the thick and the thin, etc. More serious measurement with a foot rule may be demanded by the activities of the first grade, where the child may make a two-inch square, cut a strip six inches long, etc.

There have been those who looked upon measurement as an experience of such fundamental importance that it ranked equal to or above counting. Smith's study to which we referred in Chapter 2, however, showed that "counting plays a very large part and that spatial measurement plays a very small part in the ordinary uses of number made by first-grade pupils."[2] Nevertheless, spatial measurement can be brought into a prominent place in connection with many of the experiences of first- and second-grade pupils, it is usually interesting to them, and it contributes in no small way to their growing understanding of number meanings.

Additional opportunities for the use and understanding of measurement will arise in connection with denominate measures other than those of length.

Denominate measures. A few of the denominate measures occur frequently enough in the experiences of young children in school and at home to justify their deliberate inclusion in an arithmetic program. This is particularly true of measures of length, time, and capacity (liquid). There is also use for such special collective terms as *pair* and *dozen*.

Measures of length and distance. We have referred to the foot rule in connection with a brief discussion of measurement in the preceding section. As the pupils use the foot rule, they become acquainted with inches and note that there are 12 inches in a foot. Later, they

---

[2] Smith, Nila B. "An Investigation of the Uses of Arithmetic in the Out-of-School Life of First-Grade Children." *Elementary School Journal,* XXIV: 621-626, April, 1924.

have experiences with the yard stick, measuring and discussing lengths of articles and short distances in terms of yards, and discover that a yard contains three feet, or 36 inches. This latter fact is incorporated in a problem when the first work with two-digit multiplicands and one-digit multipliers is undertaken and the pupil discovers it anew by multiplying 12 by 3.

These facts—12 inches in a foot, 3 feet in a yard, and 36 inches in a yard—are not to be given as facts of a table to be memorized and drilled upon, as is so often the case when work in denominate measures is first seriously undertaken in a later grade, but are facts which the pupil discovers in his own activities as he makes use of measurement. They will be learned, to be sure, if they are used often enough, but they will be learned as such facts ought to be learned, namely, through use.

There will be other items of distance measure before the pupils leave the primary grades. In cities, distances to the school, to the post office, to the theater, etc., will be expressed in terms of *blocks* or *squares*. Both city and rural children will learn something of the *mile* in connection with travel by automobile and distances to neighboring towns and cities will be expressed in terms of miles.

Measures of time. We have referred to the fact that precise and accurate telling of time is too difficult for first-grade pupils. It is also too difficult for many if not most of those in the second grade. But some acquaintance with the clock face and some understanding of time as revealed by the clock is quite possible in both the first and the second grades.

For example, children learn how the clock looks when

it is time to go to school, when it is lunch time, when it is bed time, etc. These rudimentary beginnings of telling time do very well until greater skill is developed. They hear talk about the time the stores open, the time the stores close, the time the train leaves in the morning and arrives in the evening if members of the family commute, the time a certain radio program comes on, the time the school bus arrives, etc. They learn of time duration from the time they practice music, the time required to get to school, time limits for parking automobiles, etc.

They learn the number of days in a week, and their names, and the number of days in the school week. They study the calendar page and learn to tell which day is today, when birthdays, holidays and other special days come, the name of this month, the name of last month, the name of next month, the name of the first and last months of the year, the months in which dates of interest and importance come, the number of days in this month, the number of days in last month, etc. Eventually, they know the names of all of the months and finally know them in their proper serial order. They learn the number of months in a year and they may learn the number of days in a year.

After a time the number of hours from noon to midnight and midnight to noon is discovered and from this the number of hours in a day, as from noon today until noon tomorrow or yesterday. The number of minutes in an hour may also be observed.

Again, the table is not memorized and the facts learned do not come in the order in which they occur in the table but in an order which conforms to the developing interests of the pupils and which satisfies their growing needs.

Measures of capacity and weight. Pints and quarts soon come to occupy a fairly prominent place in the lives of many pupils in the primary grades. Milk bottles of both these sizes are frequently seen and handled and the pupils learn that one holds half as much as the other, or that one holds twice as much as the other.

Half-pint bottles will probably be known also. Pupils learn better the meaning of *one-half* by discovering that a half-pint bottle holds one-half as much as a pint bottle. They learn that a half-pint makes a glassful or a cupful and from this that two glassfuls or two cupfuls make a pint.

Children see measuring cups used at home and, from this source, may learn that if the recipe calls for two cups of milk, a pint is required. At school, also, there may frequently be opportunities for the use of measures in their activities. Six quarts of water may be required to fill the goldfish bowl. If we must use a pint cup or bottle, how many will be required?

There will be other needs and opportunities for the use of capacity measures. For example, the discussion of pints and quarts may lead to a consideration of the gallon and the half-gallon. This brief discussion gives only a few hints. What is actually done will depend very much upon the children's out-of-school experiences and upon the activities in which they engage at school.

As to measures of weight, the pound probably will receive some consideration. Children first compare objects by lifting them to determine which is the heavier or which is the lighter. They are interested in their own weights, which are stated in pounds. They hear the pound mentioned in connection with purchases of many household necessities.

Collective terms. We have indicated that such common collective terms as *pair* and *dozen* will provide further opportunities for number experience and for making other number experiences meaningful. The word *pair* soon comes to be associated with *two* as it is used to refer to a pair of mittens, a pair of gloves, a pair of skates, etc. Other terms, such as *couple* and *twins* will also be associated with *two*.

The terms *dozen* and *half-dozen* will be heard early and frequently. References are made to a dozen eggs, a dozen oranges, a dozen pencils, etc., and to a half-dozen of each of these. When a dozen is learned to be 12 and a half-dozen, 6, new meaning is put in the addition double, $6 + 6 = 12$.

Young children sometimes associate definite numerical values with such indefinite collective terms as *few* and *several*. One child insisted that a few was three and that several was five. She even went so far as to say that a *very few* was two. This was probably due to some early accidental association of these numbers with these terms. The primary teacher may find it necessary to give some help to pupils with these terms. Of course, all that she can do is to indicate that these terms have no definite numerical meanings, that both mean an indefinite number but not many, and that *several* usually indicates a greater number than *few* when applied to the same things and at the same time.

Developing an understanding of fractions. So far as the author knows, the best study which has been made of the knowledge which young children have of frac tions is that reported by Polkinghorne,[3] a study to which reference has already been made in Chapters 2 and 9. Miss Polkinghorne's results indicate very clearly that even with no planned teaching of the subject in the primary grades, the pupils had gained a very considerable understanding of the more common fractions.

Miss Polkinghorne's subjects were given 42 test items. On these tests they were asked to give the examiner one-half of 2 pencils, to draw a line half as long as another line, to tell whether a little stick of candy was one-half, one-third, or one-fourth as long as a big one, to draw a picture containing one-half as many apples as another which contained four apples, to color a glass so as to show that it was three-fourths full of orange juice, to color three-fourths of a group of marbles, to tell what is the same as three-halves, as four-thirds, as four halves, as five-fourths, as seven fifths, and in other ways to show their understanding of fractions. Every one of the pupils tested gave evidence that he knew something about fractions. None gave correct responses to all 42 test items but one was correct on 41, two on 40, three on 38, etc., the average number of correct responses being 11.

These children were located in the kindergarten, the first, the second, and the third grades. The average number of correct responses was about 4 in the kindergarten, about 6 in the first grade, about 12 in the second grade, and about 18 in the third grade. It was found that the fractions which they knew best were the unit fractions and that other proper fractions came next. They knew

[3] Polkinghorne, Ada R. "Young Children and Fractions." *Childhood Education,* XI: 354-358, May, 1935.

little about improper fractions or equivalent fractions and were not very successful on the identification of fractions. But enough was known to indicate that these pupils often had experiences which involved fractions and that quite independent of the school program they acquired some very definite fraction concepts.

However, there was marked variation among the pupils tested and with many of them a lack of satisfactory responses on very simple and elementary test items. Tests given in the intermediate grades often show that the pupils have a very unsatisfactory understanding of what fractions are and what they mean. Hence, it seems desirable that teachers in the primary grades attempt to fill in some of the obvious gaps in the experiences of pupils whose grasp of fractions is less than their intelligence might lead one to expect.

The first work with fractions should be with concrete and familiar situations such as those used in the Polkinghorne tests. At first, attention should be given to unit fractions only; in fact, it is doubtful whether any but unit fractions should receive attention in the primary grades. The fraction to receive attention first is one-half; this should be followed by one-fourth. Pupils should see these fractions concretely represented and should talk about them but the numerical forms, $1/2$ and $1/4$, should not appear until long after early experiences have developed an understanding of what these fractions mean.

Teaching unit fractions. Those who work with children who are six, seven, and eight years of age often find that they have acquired erroneous notions of what one-half means. Such children have been known to divide a bag of candy among three or more giving *one-half* to each. Also, when some object is divided, as a candy bar or a cooky, they talk about the "biggest half" and the "littlest half," using English which is no better than their arithmetic. These erroneous notions should be corrected.

Polkinghorne[4] found that children know more about a unit fraction as applied to a single object, as one-half of one, than about a unit fraction applied to a group of objects, as one-half of 4. It is best, then, to begin with a concrete representation of the meaning of one-half of a single object.

Let some familiar object, as an apple, be cut into halves. Cut the apple neatly through the core. Through the use of questions, call the attention of the pupils to the fact that there are *just two pieces* and that these pieces are *exactly the same size.* When we have just two pieces and these pieces are exactly the same size, each of them is one-half of the whole apple. Repeat with other familiar objects. Then have two pieces but pieces unequal in size and let the pupils decide whether these are halves and why they are not. Also have more than two pieces (being careful to provide that one of them is not one-half, as a half and two quarters) and let the pupils decide why these are not halves. The development of an adequate concept of what one-half is can very well be accomplished with average first-grade pupils.

Pupils learn that one object is one-half as large as another more easily than they learn that one group of objects is one-half as many as another group of objects. Thus, it is easier for them to understand that a pint of milk is one-half as much as a quart of milk (when the

[4] Polkinghorne, *op. cit.*, p. 357.

pint and the quart are in pint and quart bottles) than to see that 4 pints of milk is one-half as much as 8 pints of milk. If the pupils have experiences with the more common measures, as was suggested in a preceding section, their understanding of the meaning of one-half and other unit fractions can be strengthened thereby.

The fraction, one-fourth, is easily taught with such objects as an apple or an orange, by dividing the halves into halves. The pupils see that if there are four pieces and they are equal in size, each is one-fourth. Pupils frequently see fourths represented, as in the division of waffles and the cutting of pies. After a time, they will learn that a fourth means a quarter, that a quarter of a dollar (usually called simply a *quarter*) is one-fourth of a dollar, that a quarter past six means one-fourth of an hour past six, etc.

Other unit fractions will follow one-half and one-fourth. One-third, one-fifth, and one-eighth are occasionally encountered and at times one meets one-sixth. A candy bar may be conveniently divided into thirds if the markings are right and a foot may be seen as one-third of a yard. A cent may be seen as one-fifth of a nickle and a nickle as one-fifth of a quarter. Pies are very often cut in fifths. Pies are also cut in sixths and eighths, and other objects may be cut into six or eight equal pieces. Of course, one-eighth will also be seen as one-half of one-fourth, when an object is cut into halves, then into fourths, and finally into eighths.

We have already indicated in Chapter 9 that the fraction form may be used as an alternative method of expressing the division facts and that each of the unit fractions from one-half to one-ninth, inclusive, will be used in this manner. This not only helps in the learning of the division facts but also provides a valuable means of gaining an understanding of these unit fractions. We have said that unit fractions used in this manner, as one-sixth of 42, are more difficult for children than when applied to a single object, as one-sixth of a pumpkin pie. But the partition form of division will be introduced considerably later than the unit fraction applied to such objects as pies.

Other proper fractions. If it is desired to go on to two-thirds, two-fourths, three-fourths, and other fractions which are not unit fractions but which are proper fractions, the same objective materials which we have discussed may be used very conveniently. Thus, if a pie is cut in fourths and the pupil sees that one of the pieces is one-fourth of the whole pie, he may also see that two of the pieces are two-fourths of the whole and that three of the pieces are three-fourths. Also, if a pie is cut in fifths, he may see two-fifths, three-fifths, and four-fifths. He may see that if one foot is one-third of a yard, two feet make two-thirds of a yard. Other fractions may be developed in a similar manner.

Some of these fractions which are not unit fractions may be developed in the third grade. Indeed, second-grade pupils are sometimes found to be acquainted with them. But it is probable that many children will not be ready for this kind of experience with fractions before they arrive in the fourth grade.

This introductory work with fractions rounds out the arithmetic program of the primary grades in a very important way. It supplements the out-of-school experiences of the pupils with material which has decided so cial utility, it corrects erroneous impressions which have been gained, it helps pupils to understand numbers, quantities, and magnitudes, and it lays an important foundation for more extensive work with fractions in later grades.

QUESTIONS AND REVIEW EXERCISES

1. What benefit do young children gain from comparing objects as to size and groups of objects as to number? Can the comparing of one object with another to determine which is the larger be called arithmetic?

2. Does the fact that readers designed for use in the primary grades contain many terms drawn from the field of arithmetic constitute an argument for devoting time to the development of arithmetic concepts in the primary grades?

3. Examine a few courses of study to find what Roman notation is to be taught in each of the primary grades. What suggestions for teaching this subject are given? Are the additive and subtractive principles developed?

4. Do you agree that the accurate telling of time is too difficult for pupils in the first grade?

5. Where do you find Roman numerals used? Are the volume numbers of magazines recorded in this way? How high do you find such numbers going? Among other sources, consult again the footnote references in this book.

6. Why should the number V be presented before IV and X before IX?

7. To test and develop your own knowledge of the subject, write a few large numbers in Roman notation. Try a few important dates including the year of your birth and the present year.

8. Which is the more fundamental as a number experience, counting or spatial measurement?

9. Did you learn measures of length by first memorizing

a table and then using what you had learned to solve examples and problems? Do you know schools where this practice is still followed? What advantages are to be gained by the method of development suggested in this chapter?

10. Why does our discussion of measures of length and distance include the inch, the foot, the yard, the mile, but not the rod?

11. What should be the nature of the pupil's first experiences in telling time from a watch or a clock? What use could you as teacher make of a large cardboard clock face with adjustable hands?

12. What would be the nature of the first lessons which you would give pupils on the calendar? With which month would you begin?

13. In teaching the number of days in the various months, would you use the rime,

> "Thirty days hath September,
> April, June, and November," etc.?

Is it desirable than an adult go through this rime when he needs to recall the number of days in a particular month? If not, how would you prevent this method of recall as a habit?

14. The text makes no mention of dry measure. Is it less important than liquid measure in the lives of young children? How does a dry quart differ from a liquid quart?

15. Does the typical course of study with which you are acquainted make provision for the development of an understanding of fractions in the primary grades?

16. Have you known children who had erroneous ideas of the meaning of fractions, such as one-half? How do you account for these erroneous ideas? What can the primary teacher do to correct them?

17. How do you account for the marked variation found among young children as to their knowledge and understanding of fractions?

18. Do all of the unit fractions from one-half to one-ninth occur frequently in the concrete experiences of pupils?

19. If pupils are to be made acquainted with proper fractions other than unit fractions, which of these fractions should be the first to receive attention? What concrete experiences would you suggest for teaching them?

20. Do you think of miscellaneous items other than those mentioned in this chapter which should be included in the arithmetic experiences of children in the primary grades?

CHAPTER TEST

Read these statements and decide whether they are true or false. Check your decisions against the key on page 406.

1. The Gunderson study revealed more terms referring to time than size.

2. The same study revealed that terms referring to time were used more frequently than were terms referring to size.

3. We recommended that Roman notation be taught before pupils are given instruction in telling time.

4. The recent tendency has been to reduce the amount of Roman notation taught in the first and second grades.

5. Most clock faces are now made with Roman numerals.

6. The additive principle in Roman notation applies only to a letter representing a smaller number appearing after a letter representing a larger number.

7. Pupils in the primary grades should learn Roman numerals to C.

8. The year 1938 is written MCMXXXVIII.

9. The comparison of objects as to size tends to lead to quantitative thinking.

10. Counting is more fundamental as a number experience that is spatial measurement.

11. We recommended that third-grade pupils learn the table for measures of length.

12. Precise telling of time is too difficult for first-grade children.

13. Pupils should begin the study of measures of time by learning that there are 60 seconds in a minute.

14. Primary pupils will normally learn that there are two pints in a quart before they learn that there are four quarts in a gallon.

15. We suggested the inclusion of the term *dozen* in the course for the primary grades.

16. Polkinghorne's study indicated that children know more about unit fractions than any other class of fractions.

17. More primary children know *one-half* as applied to a single object than to a group of objects.

18. If John and Joe divide a dollar so that John gets 60 cents and Joe, 40 cents, John gets the larger half.

19. Pupils frequently have occasion to use *one-seventh* with concrete objects.

20. Polkinghorne found that her subjects had no acquaintance with proper fractions which are not unit fractions.

SELECTED REFERENCES

1. Clark, John R., Otis, Arthur S., and Hatton, Caroline. *First Steps in Teaching Number.* Yonkers-on-Hudson; New York: World Book Company, 1929. 225 pp. Measurements are discussed on pages 70-81, the clock on pages 120-124, halves on pages 153-154, and the fractions one-third and one-fourth on pages 183-185.

2. Gunderson, Agnes G. "Nature and Amount of Arithmetic in Readers for Grades I and II." *Elementary School Journal,* XXXVI: 527-540, March, 1936. Gives in detail an account of quantitative terms found in ten sets of primary readers.

3. Polkinghorne, Ada R. "Young Children and Fractions." *Childhood Education,* XI: 354-358, May, 1935. Reports an investigation of what pupils in the kindergarten, the first, the second, and the third grades know about fractions.

4. Smith, Nila B. "An Investigation of the Uses of Arithmetic in the Out-of-School Life of First-Grade Children." *Elementary School Journal,* XXIV: 621-626, April, 1924. Reports the kind of arithmetic which first-grade pupils use. Indicates that spatial measurement is used less than counting.

5. Roantree, William F. and Taylor, Mary S. *An Arithmetic for Teachers.* New York: The Macmillan Company, 1932. 523 pp. See pages 9-10 and 22 for Roman numerals, pages 277-303 for denominate numbers, and portions of chapter IV for elementary work in common fractions.

CHAPTER 11

PROBLEM SOLVING

In connection with our discussion of the teaching of addition, subtraction, multiplication, and division, we have made frequent reference to the importance of problem solving. We have indicated that each new phase of a process should be introduced through the medium of a problem and that the skills which pupils acquire should be put to use promptly in solving problems. The four fundamental operations are not ends in themselves but only means to an end; the end is problem solving.

Distinction between problems and examples. In the preceding chapters, we have observed carefully a distinction between problems and examples. An example is an arithmetical situation in which the operation to be performed is indicated; there are signs or instructions to indicate which operation or operations are to be performed. A problem, on the other hand, is an arithmetical situation which requires that the pupil first decide upon the operation or operations which are to be performed. Every problem yields one or more examples but a decision is required as to what these examples are.

Many teachers use these two terms synonymously. Other teachers seldom use the word "example" at all but call all examples "problems." The distinction is a convenient one, however, for it eliminates the necessity of explaining what kind of "problems" is meant when "problems" are being discussed, or for using such expressions as "word problems" and "verbal problems."

Some persons contend that this distinction between problems and examples is rather naïve. They argue that division with two- and three-digit divisors is a real problem to the pupil who is just learning it, but when learned, offers no more than a series of examples. What he must do in this subtraction example, may be much more of a "problem" to a pupil than "What will 2 pencils cost at 5 cents each?" It should be admitted that our distinction is, in a measure, an arbitrary one; but it is a useful one. In this chapter, then, we shall discuss the teaching of problem solving, meaning by "problem" a verbal statement which requires the pupil first to decide what operation or operations to perform and then to perform those operations.

$$\begin{array}{r} 600104 \\ \underline{385647} \end{array}$$

Problem solving in the primary grades. The problems which pupils in the primary grades solve are very simple problems. They are nearly all one-step problems. Because of their simplicity the task of teaching children to solve these problems is a relatively simple task. Many of the complexities which enter into problem solving in later grades are due to the necessity of performing two or more operations before the question which the problem asks is answered. The necessity of performing these operations must be appreciated and the pupil must also understand the order in which they are to be performed.

Most of the research which has been done on problem solving has been done in the fourth and later grades. Most of the suggestions which have been offered for assisting teachers in teaching problem solving do not apply to primary grade situations. This is no doubt due to the relative simplicity of problem solving in these grades. We shall consider a few matters pertaining to problems and problem solving in this chapter but the more serious consideration of this subject is left to Volume II.

Qualities of good problems. In selecting problems for pupils to solve, the teacher should keep in mind the main qualities which good problems possess. These may be stated as follows:

1. **Reality.** Good problems are real. They deal with conditions which are a part of the experiences of the pupils for which they are intended or in some cases, the experiences of others in whom these pupils are interested.

2. **Interest.** Good problems are interesting. They are derived from situations which are not only real but which make a strong appeal to the pupils who are to solve the problems.

3. **Language.** (a) The language of good problems is a language which pupils can understand. It is free from unknown words and unfamiliar forms of expression. (b) The language of good problems is a language which pupils like to hear and read. Good problems read like stories. They have an attractive style.

4. **Use of basic skills.** Good problems provide opportunities to put to use the fundamental skills which the pupils have been trying to acquire. They are intimately related to the program of lessons on the fundamental operations.

Reality in problems. One would think that the point that problems should be real would be taken for granted. There seems to be no justification for problems which represent conditions that do not exist in practical life situations. But such problems are found all too frequently in children's assignments. There seem to be three reasons for this.

1. It is sometimes difficult to find problems which apply some of the basic skills. Division, for instance, occurs relatively infrequently in the experiences of most people. Lacking a sufficient number of real problems, teachers and textbook makers have a tendency to manufacture problems which are unreal.

2. A second reason is the persistence of the doctrine of formal discipline. Those who hold to this doctrine believe that it matters little what problems a pupil solves if he has enough of them and they are sufficiently difficult. They believe that one problem will provide as good mental training as another and that, therefore, it does not matter whether the problems are real or unreal.

3. A third reason is inertia and a tendency to accept without question that to which we have for years been accustomed. Some teachers are so accustomed to unreal problems that they fail to detect them in a list to which their attention has been directed. For example, an experienced primary teacher was asked to criticize this problem: "Johnny lost one-half of his marbles and had 8 left. How many had he at first?" She replied that the problem was excellent for it dealt with marbles and all boys were interested in marbles. She failed completely to see that the problem belongs to the "Answer-known" type. One must know how many marbles Johnny had at first to know that 8 is one-half of them. Such a problem would never occur in the actual life experience of a marble-playing boy. It would occur only in a textbook or in a school room.

It is true that some pupils enjoy both unreal and real problems. They are the pupils who like arithmetic for its own sake. But there are many pupils whose interest in this subject soon wanes if they suspect that what they are learning will not be of service to them. They may find multiplication difficult and if the problems in which multiplication is used are unreal, fantastic creations designed only to provide practice on multiplication they may quite well show a disposition to give up in their efforts to learn a difficult subject.

In recent years, textbooks have been greatly improved. Problem material has been subjected to a careful examination and most of the unreal material has been eliminated. Several years ago, books frequently contained such problems as these.

1. Our electric light bill for January was $4.80. For July it was one-half as large. What was the bill for July?

2. Henry is 6 years old, and Robert is 4 times as old. How old is Robert?

3. Henry and John were reading the same book, and when Henry had read 58 pages he found that this was 25 more pages than John had read. How many pages had John read?

4. John brought 3 books from the library and read 18 pages in each that night. How many pages did he read?

The faults of these problems are obvious. There would be little justification in teaching arithmetic if it had no more worthy uses than is represented by problems such as these.

If a textbook is supplied to the pupils, the teacher should examine critically the problems which it contains. Even those of recent date sometimes contain problems which are not real. For example, there is the problem which tells about the 24 picture books which the pupils made and the fact that the boys made one-third of them. Finding how many the boys made is easily accomplished by finding one-third of 24 or by dividing 24 by 3, but in the real situation one would probably know that the boys made 8 before he knew that they made one-third of the total number.

In the typical primary school room there is a greater danger that unreal problems will be provided by the teacher than that they will be supplied by a textbook. Many teachers have not become so sensitive to unreality in problems as have textbook writers. It is well for the teacher to examine closely the problems which she prepares with this matter of reality only in mind before she gives them to pupils to be solved.

Problems having interest. There is no difficulty as to interest if the problems arise directly from the pupils' own activities. If we could be assured that such activities would provide sufficient problem material for a well-balanced arithmetic program, the matter of interest (and also the matter of reality) would take care of itself. But in most schools it seems to be necessary to provide practice materials in the form of examples and problems. These sometimes come in through the medium of a number book in the second grade and they usually come in textbook form in the third grade. They also come directly from the hands of the teacher in each of the primary grades.

Many children like arithmetic. They like it because its tasks are specific, they can see what they have accomplished, and they know when a task is well done. Some like it because of the puzzle element which it contains.

Some like it because they like to deal with numbers and they enjoy quantitative thinking. A few will continue to enjoy arithmetic however fantastic and unreal and apparently devoid of interest its problems may be.

Other children dislike arithmetic very heartily. The reason usually is found in the kind of arithmetic they have been taught and the manner in which they have been taught. As we pointed out in Chapter 1 this dislike is often due to the early abstract nature of the arithmetic experiences which they have had and to the fact that much of the material presented has been memorized but has not been understood. Any interest which such pupils have in the subject in later grades is likely to be interest in it only as a means to an end, a kind of toleration of a distasteful subject which is the means of attaining an objective which can not be attained without computation.

For many children, probably the majority, there is a close relationship between interest and reality. If problems are to be interesting, they must be real. A few may be interested in unreal problems but they will be as much interested in problems which are real provided that they are equal to the unreal problems in difficulty and other factors. If we are to guarantee interest, we should first guarantee reality.

There are problems which may seem at first glance to be real but which are almost wholly devoid of interest. Consider these:

1. A box has 8 corners. How many corners have 5 boxes?
2. George Washington was born in 1732 and died in 1799. How many years did he live?
3. A fly has 6 legs. How many legs have 7 flies?

4. One wall contains 5460 bricks. Another wall contains 2545 bricks. How many more bricks in the first wall than in the second?

These problems are real in the sense that a box does actually have 8 corners, Washington was born in 1732 and did die in 1799, etc. They may be said to be unreal to young children in that they do not grow in any natural way out of the experiences of young children. Whatever we may say about reality, little can be said for problems such as these from the standpoint of interest. Who cares how many corners 5 boxes have or how many legs 7 flies possess? Washington was 67 years of age when he died but what of it? Few people will care how many bricks there are in a wall and probably no one will be interested in the number of bricks in one wall in excess of the number in another.

Pupils may very profitably solve problems which occur in the experiences of their elders as well as those which occur in the experiences of themselves. Some of the arithmetic experiences of a child's father are interesting to the child himself. Consider, for example, the cost of 5 gallons of gasoline for Dad's car which was the subject of a problem used in Chapter 8. But other problems, drawn from the experiences of their parents, may be of no interest at all to children in the primary grades. For instance, a problem states that a man has $375.40 in the bank, draws out $139.75, and asks how much he has left in the bank. Problems of this kind occur rather frequently in textbooks and in the lists which are prepared by teachers. They probably do more to destroy than to stimulate interest in arithmetic.

The language of problems. Some problems, otherwise satisfactory, cause difficulty because of the unusual or hard words which they contain. Persons who are not in frequent contact with young children tend to forget their vocabulary limitations and to use words which the children do not know. For example, a problem tells that 38 *passengers* were riding on a street car and that 16 got off at a *transfer point.* The arithmetic of this problem is quite easy but the language is more difficult. It may be argued that a pupil should be able to solve this problem even though he is unfamiliar with passengers and transfer point, but the unfamiliar terms tend to confuse and to distract the pupil's attention from the arithmetic content.

Teachers may check on the probable difficulty of words by looking them up in Thorndike's[1] *The Teacher's Word Book* and Horn's[2] *A Basic Writing Vocabulary.* Thorndike's list includes 10,000 words which were found to occur most frequently in a tabulation from 41 sources including children's literature, English classics, school textbooks, newspapers, correspondence, etc. Horn's list, which also includes 10,000 words, is based upon studies of words most often used in adult writing. Naturally, the two lists disagree in many respects but they help in determining whether the vocabulary of a textbook or of the problems in a textbook contains rare or unusual words. For example a recently published third-grade textbook contains a problem in which the

[1] Thorndike, Edward L. *The Teacher's Word Book.* New York: Teachers College, Columbia University, 1921. 134 pp.

[2] Horn, Ernest. *A Basic Writing Vocabulary.* Iowa City, Iowa: University of Iowa, 1926. 225 pp.

word "empress" occurs. Thorndike's list contains nearly six thousand words which were found to occur more frequently than the word "empress." Horn's list does not include the word at all. Thus, the two lists support the opinion which one would probably have had when he read the problem to the effect that the word "empress" should not be used in a problem written for pupils in the third grade.

The words which can be used in problems prepared by the teacher vary considerably from one community to another. Words which the pupils in a third-grade class in one community will know may be entirely unknown to the pupils in a third-grade class in another community. Consider, for example, the word "cistern" which was found in an arithmetic problem. Cisterns are so common in some small town and rural areas that all third-grade pupils are familiar with the word. But in many large cities the word "cistern" is almost never heard by young children.

It is frequently contended that the teacher should strive to increase the pupil's vocabulary no matter what the subject which is being taught and that arithmetic problems should contain unknown words in order that the pupils may learn these words. True, the teacher does have this responsibility. However, there are so many words which belong to arithmetic for the pupil to learn that he can hardly be expected to take on such words as *empress* and *cistern* in an arithmetic problem. This might also be said for such words as *cashier, diagnostic test, festival,* and *wampum,* all of which were found in a few minutes' examination of recently published third-grade texts.

The vocabulary of arithmetic textbooks is difficult enough at the best. Buswell and John[3] report in considerable detail the vocabulary difficulties which are found in arithmetic textbooks. The particular burden of a third-grade text depends much upon the text; texts differ greatly in the words they use. Furthermore, the words used in a textbook may occur so infrequently that the pupil has little opportunity to learn them.

The story element in problems. The opinion prevails that pupils will be more successful in solving problems if these problems are worded in an attractive story-like manner than if they are worded in the dry, concise language so often characteristic of the problems which appear in textbooks. Wilson[4] says, "The first step in teaching children to read problem-material is one of making the story in the problem so real and so vivid that the pupil realizes the situation."

Myers made a study of "How problems designed to stimulate vivid imagination compare in difficulty with very similar problems of the dry, concise, traditional sort."[5] He gave 12 problems to 486 pupils in the upper grades of the elementary school, the high school, and the normal school. Six of these were worded in the usual formal fashion and six others were designed to have an imaginative appeal. Each formal problem was intended to be equivalent to a corresponding imaginative problem

---

[3] Buswell, G. T. and John, Lenore. *The Vocabulary of Arithmetic.* Chicago: The University of Chicago, 1931. 146 pp.

[4] Wilson, Estaline. "Improving the Ability to Read Arithmetic Problems." *Elementary School Journal,* XXII: 380-386, January, 1922.

[5] Myers, Garry Cleveland. *The Prevention and Correction of Errors in Arithmetic.* Chicago: The Plymouth Press, 1925, p. 65.

so far as the intrinsic arithmetical difficulty was concerned. In five of the six cases, the imaginative problem was solved correctly by a larger number of pupils than was the corresponding formal problem. In the sixth case, the number of correct solutions was equal for the two problems.

Although no pupils in the primary grades were included in this experiment, we may very properly examine some of the problems. Here are two:

1. Laura, whose grandmother gave her $1.50, saved 5 cents each school day from her lunch money. How many school days before Laura will have enough money to buy a book which costs $2.50?

2. Little Betty wanted to surprise her mother on Christmas. She knew that her mother needed a good pair of scissors. The old ones would not cut well. One day Betty went with her daddy to a big store to see what a good pair of scissors would cost. She saw one for $2.00. Betty had 95 cents which her grandmother had given her. "I shall save 5 cents every day from my school money." After ———— school days she bought the scissors, which lay at the foot of the Christmas tree on Christmas morning marked, "To my dear mother, from Betty."

The first of these problems was solved correctly by 181 pupils, or 37 per cent of all those who took the test. The second was solved correctly by 320 pupils, or 66 per cent of those tested.[6]

This seems to be a decided victory for the imaginative problem. The results on the other four pairs in which the imaginative problem came out ahead were somewhat

[6] Myers, Garry Cleveland, *op. cit.*, pp. 65-67.

less favorable to the problem of the imaginative type. For all six pairs, the average per cent correct on the formal problems was 61 and on the imaginative problems, 76.

Wheat[7] obtained results which are in disagreement with those of Myers. He gave an elaborate battery of tests, including most of the problems in the Myers test, to several hundred pupils in grades 5 to 8, inclusive. The results fail to show any significant advantage for the imaginative problems. In fact, the pupils did better on the conventional problems than on the imaginative problems when time limits were imposed. The results seem to suggest that the longer and more elaborate statements of the imaginative problems were a hindrance to the pupils rather than a help. More time was required to read them and there was a suggestion to the effect that the verbiage of the imaginative problems beclouded the facts which they presented and the questions which they asked.

The Wheat study seems to have been set up more carefully and more elaborately than was the Myers study and, for this reason, its results probably should be given the greater weight. There may have been errors in the handling of the results of the Myers tests and some of the apparent advantage of the imaginative problems may have been a matter of chance. Nevertheless, many teachers testify that a greater interest in problems is developed if there is a story element running through the statement of them and that this is particularly true in the lower

[7] Wheat, Harry Grove. *The Relative Merits of Conventional and Imaginative Types of Problems in Arithmetic.* New York: Teachers College, Columbia University, 1929. 123 pp.

grades. It will be noted that neither Myers nor Wheat gave the tests which have been reported to pupils in the third and the fourth grades. We need further studies of the successes of pupils, especially of pupils in grades three and four, on problems of various kinds before we can conclude just what kind of problem statement is best.

In the mean time, the author suggests that problems be stated in simple, easy language; that the sentences not be very long; and that there be a story element in the problem or in a series of problems. Statements and facts which are utterly irrelevant to the problem should be excluded. The second Myers problem which we have quoted can be much more briefly stated and still be interesting. For instance, why say, "The old ones would not cut well?"

Recently published textbooks contain much better problem statements than did those of a generation ago. In the older books, problems such as the following were very common:

Find the cost of two loaves of bread at 12 cents each. This is simple, brief, and very much to the point. But there was a tiresome sameness about these for there would be a whole page with no variation except in the objects bought and the price paid for each. The very sameness of the language soon came to suggest multiplication without thought. Such problems after a time become hardly more than examples. There was a dreary monotony which tended to kill what interest the pupil may have had when he began work on such a list.

The modern tendency is for this problem to appear in some such form as the following:

Mary Jane went to the bakery for her mother. Bread cost 12 cents a loaf. How much did she pay for two loaves?

This too is brief, but it has a more life-like and a more personal type of interest than has the other. It is not a mere arithmetic assignment; it suggests a type of experience in which many pupils engage and with which most of them are acquainted. Furthermore, the language of others in the same list will be different from the language of this. Other persons will be named and other situations will be described. Also, there may be several problems which are derived from a single situation as was suggested for problems on the addition and the subtraction facts in Chapter 4.

Problems for practice on basic skills. We have indicated that each of the basic skills which is acquired should be promptly put to use in a series of problems. There should be problems for the addition facts, for easy column addition, for addition with carrying, for the subtraction facts, for subtraction without and with borrowing, and for similar detailed phases of multiplication and division. We have said that problems provide a valuable form of practice on these fundamental skills and that they motivate the work in the fundamentals by showing that these skills are useful skills.

When one states that problems should be deliberately provided for the purpose of helping with the learning of the fundamental processes of arithmetic he may seem to be getting "the cart before the horse." For, is it not true that the activities in which children engage provide problems and that these problems require for their solution the ability to perform the fundamental operations?

This is true, and this point has been made repeatedly in the preceding chapters. Each new phase of a fundamental process should be introduced through the medium of a problem and this problem should be a real problem, one which would normally arise in life's affairs. But when the new process has been taught and practice on this process is being provided we should swing back to problems again for the reasons stated in the preceding paragraph.

A classification of problems. The problems which pupils solve in school may be conveniently grouped into three classes. The first class includes those which are based upon situations which are actually present to the pupils' senses. When the pupils engage in any kind of activity singly or as a cooperative enterprise, such as playing store, planning a school garden, building a doll-house, deciding which side won in a game or contest, etc., the problems arising from such enterprises may be said to be first-class problems. Because of the realistic appeal which problems of this class make pupils will attack them with greater enthusiasm and usually will be more successful in solving them than will be the case with problems drawn from the affairs of others. They are less likely to engage in purely random manipulations, such as adding all of the numbers if there are three or more of them, or dividing when a quotient without a remainder can be obtained, than if the problems are less realistic and, hence, less well understood.

Ideally, all of the problems should belong to this first class. Ideally every problem solved should come from an enterprise or activity which is worth while for its own sake and which, for its successful prosecution, requires the solution of problems. The problems which most adults solve belong to this class. But, actually a satisfactory arithmetic course for children requires additional problem material to supplement that which the activities provide and to round out a better balanced program.

Secondly, there are those problems which are based upon situations which are not actually present to the pupils' senses but which they can readily imagine. When pupils make their plans for the future or live in their imaginations the experiences of others whom they hear about or read about, the problems which arise may make almost as strong an appeal as if they came from their own actual present or past experiences. Pupils plan for parties, week-end excursions, and camping trips, they estimate how long it will take them to save enough money to buy some toy or other article, and they listen with interest to the accounts of the experiences of their friends or other associates; good problems arise out of such experiences. Problems based upon hypothetical hikes, camping trips, automobile tours, fishing trips, etc., are problems of the second class. They can not be problems of the first class unless the pupils actually take the trip, make the hike, etc., but because of the resemblance of the conditions to experiences which the pupils have had, and because of the interest which they have in such experiences they easily imagine the conditions assumed in the problems and delight in solving them.

There should be no shortage of this second class of problems. Any teacher who knows the kinds of experiences which her pupils have, who is familiar with their ruling interests, and who possesses a reasonable degree of imagination, should be able to prepare problems which pupils will enjoy and which will supplement in a desirable way their arithmetic experiences.

The third class of problems includes those which are mere verbal descriptions of situations which the pupil does not readily imagine and in which he has little, if any, interest. Since the situations assumed in problems of this class are not situations which are real to the pupils and since they are not situations which they can readily imagine themselves experiencing, they will have only a partial understanding of them, they will be slightly, if at all, interested in them, and they will, as a consequence, make poor progress as they undertake to solve them. Many of the difficulties which both pupils and teachers experience in learning and teaching problem-solving can be charged to the use of problems which are neither real nor interesting, problems which are mere verbal descriptions of situations and conditions foreign to the interests and experiences of children. What little success pupils attain with problems of this class is of little value for life problems are not problems of this kind.

Obviously, these three classes of problems have been stated in the order of their desirability. The first class is the best and the third class is the poorest. But many schools which still use the older type of textbook have a preponderance of third-class problems, for the order in which these classes are stated is the reverse order of the frequency of their occurrence in many such textbooks.

Textbooks can hardly be expected to provide first-class problems. Problems which are real to one child or group of children cannot be better than second-class problems to another pupil or class, unless the latter have had identically the same experiences as the former. First-class problems will have to come from the immediate environment and experiences of the pupils of the group and will be initiated by the pupils and the teacher. We can, however, expect our texts to contain an abundance of problems of the second class—those which make a strong appeal to the imaginations of children. The desirable text will strive for the complete elimination of problems of class three, will contain an abundance of problems of class two, and will offer many suggestions and hints for the use of problems of class one.

Method in problem solving. Much has been written in recent years on the technique of training children to solve problems. However, nearly all of this applies to the intermediate and the upper grades. For a review of the experimental evidence and a discussion of this subject, the reader is referred to Volume II of this work. The teacher in the primary grades will do well to have as many problems as possible arise directly out of children's own experiences and to see to it that those which are presented in printed or written form deal with situations which children can readily imagine because of their acquaintance with and interest in them. She will also try to avoid vocabulary and other language difficulties and will maintain a proper correlation between the basic skills the children have acquired and the problems they are to solve.

QUESTIONS AND REVIEW EXERCISES

1. Do you agree that the distinction between a problem and an example which is made in this chapter is a desirable one for teachers to observe?

2. Is this a problem or an example? "Find the sum of 437 and 296."

3. Which is the more important, the ability to solve examples or the ability to solve problems?

4. Some teachers say that the ability to reason is not sufficiently well developed in children in the primary grades to permit them to solve problems. What is your reaction to this statement?

5. How do you account for the fact that most of the research which has been done on problem solving has had to do with problem solving in grades higher than the third?

6. Examine critically the problems in a textbook designed for use in the third grade. Are they real? Are they real in the lives of children or in the lives of adults?

7. Criticize the problems in the same text from the point of view of interest.

8. Has it been your observation that if children like arithmetic, they like it well, and if they dislike it, they dislike it heartily? How do you account for the extreme likes and dislikes which sometimes develop toward this subject?

9. What is meant by "Answer-known" problems? Can they be real? Are they often found in schools?

10. If you were unable to find real problems for practising division, would you use unreal problems? If not, what would you do?

11. What is the doctrine of formal discipline? What differences will the acceptance or rejection of this doctrine make in the kind of arithmetic which children have?

12. Are real problems always interesting? Are unreal problems ever interesting? If so, to whom?

13. A second-grade class was asked, "How many pachydermata are 8 pachydermata and 5 pachydermata?" Many who knew that 8 and 5 are 13 failed to answer. Shouldn't second-grade pupils answer, "Thirteen," to this question whether or not they know the word "pachydermata"?

14. What is the advantage in having several problems based upon the same general situation with a story element running through the list?

15. Look through a third-grade text for problems which seem to be stated in particularly interesting language. Do you find others the language of which you could improve?

16. What did Myers conclude about the value of problems worded so as to have a strong imaginative appeal? What did Wheat conclude? Can you account for the differences in their results?

17. What are the three classes of problems described in this chapter? Which of these classes has to be found largely in local pupil and school situations? Which class should be most abundant in textbooks?

18. How may problems be both a means of motivating the pupil's work in the fundamental operations and a means of practising these skills when they have been acquired?

CHAPTER TEST

Read these statements and decide whether they are true or false. A scoring key will be found on page 406.

1. In a problem, the operation to be performed is indicated.
2. Most of the research which has been done on problem solving has been done in the primary grades.
3. Children in the third grade are too immature to solve problems which appear in printed form.
4. Each new phase of a process should be introduced through the medium of a problem.

5. Problems in the primary grades are usually one-step problems.

6. Pupils are interested in problems which arise out of their own experiences.

7. No pupils enjoy unreal problems.

8. Real problems requiring the use of division are of less frequent occurrence in the lives of most people than are real problems requiring the use of multiplication.

9. In the typical school, the acceptance of the doctrine of formal discipline would probably mean an improvement in the quality of the arithmetic problems.

10. This is a real problem: "When Ruth had walked 4 blocks she was half way to school. How many blocks are there from Ruth's home to her school?"

11. Problems of the "Answer-known" type are unreal.

12. The quality of the problems in textbooks recently published is better than that in the older textbooks.

13. Children who dislike arithmetic usually have had a poor brand of arithmetic, or poor teaching, or both.

14. For many children, there is a close relationship between interest and reality.

15. Pupils may profitably solve problems which occur in the experiences of their elders.

16. Arithmetic problems should be worded so as to increase the pupils' vocabularies.

17. The Teacher's Word Book was prepared by Myers.

18. No two problems in a list should be based upon the same general situation.

19. Wheat and Myers agreed that problems having an imaginative appeal are better than others.

20. Problems of Class I are those which are based upon situations present to the pupils' senses.

21. If the majority of the problems in a textbook are not Class I problems, the book should not be adopted for class use.

22. Problem solving is more important than example solving.

SELECTED REFERENCES

1. Buswell, G. T. and John Lenore. *The Vocabulary of Arithmetic.* Chicago: The University of Chicago, 1931. 146 pp. Reports the findings of a thorough investigation of the vocabulary of arithmetic textbooks and the difficulty of the words for the pupils. Surveys other vocabulary studies to date.

2. Chase, Sara E. "Waste in Arithmetic." *Teachers College Record,* XVIII: 360-370, September, 1917. Vocabulary tests made up from words found in arithmetic texts were given to pupils in Grades IV and V. Many of the words were unknown to the pupils.

3. Clark, John R., Otis, Arthur S., and Hatton, Caroline. *First Steps in Teaching Number.* Yonkers-on-Hudson, New York: World Book Company, 1929. 225 pp. Chapter XV is devoted to discussion of problem solving in the second grade.

4. Horn, Ernest. *A Basic Writing Vocabulary.* Iowa City, Iowa: University of Iowa, 1926. 225 pp. A valuable list of 10,000 words commonly used in adult writing.

5. Myers, Garry Cleveland. *The Prevention and Correction of Errors in Arithmetic.* Chicago: The Plymouth Press, 1925. 75 pp. Chapter XI is entitled, "An Experimental Study of Imagination in Arithmetic." Other portions of the booklet are also interesting.

6. Thorndike, Edward Lee. *The New Methods in Arithmetic.* Chicago: Rand McNally and Company, 1921. 260 pp. Chapter VII, pages 125-146, is devoted to a discussion of problem solving.

7. Thorndike, Edward L. *The Teacher's Word Book.* New York: Teachers College, Columbia University, 1921. 134 pp.

Gives a list of 10,000 more commonly used English words. This is the most frequently used word list.

8. Wheat, Harry Grove. *The Relative Merits of Conventional and Imaginative Types of Problems in Arithmetic.* New York: Teachers College, Columbia University, 1929. 123 pp. Indicates that lengthy statements of problems worded so as to make an imaginative appeal are no better than the briefer, more conventional statements.

9. Wilson, Estaline. "Improving the Ability to Read Arithmetic Problems." *Elementary School Journal,* XXII: 380-386, January, 1922. Suggests that the story of a problem must be real and vivid if the pupils are to understand it.

CHAPTER 12

THE COURSE OF STUDY

In recent years, there has been a wide interest in curriculum making and curriculum revision. Hundreds of city, county, and other school districts have discarded their old courses and written new or have so thoroughly rewritten and supplemented their old courses that the products are essentially new courses.

Preparing a course of study—the old method. According to the older method of preparing a course of study, it was written by one person and that person was the superintendent of schools. Reeder,[1] in an autobiographical account, tells how a young superintendent, newly elected to a position, proceeded to revise the course of study. Without considering whether such a revision was needed or whether he was particularly well qualified to produce it, the new superintendent promptly proceeded to discard the course already in use and to write a new one.

The new course which the superintendent turned out was a patch-work affair, portions of it being adapted from courses in use in districts, especially the large city districts, located in all parts of the United States. Such a course was not suited to any community, certainly not to the community for which it was prepared.

No one person is well qualified to produce a course of study for all grades and for all subjects. The course

[1] Reeder, Ward G. *The Fundamentals of Public School Administration.* New York: The Macmillan Company, 1930, pp. 420-423.

should be the work of many specialists—specialists in arithmetic, specialists in reading, specialists in primary education, etc. The superintendent may be a specialist in one of the elementary or secondary school subjects, or in the work of the primary or the intermediate grades, but he can hardly be a specialist in all of the subjects or in the work of all of the grades.

A one-man course of study is likely to fail utterly to serve the purposes which a course of study should serve. It will provide a brief outline of the work by subjects and by grades and will make references to adopted textbooks but it will be deficient in helpful suggestions to teachers as to how the subjects are to be developed and how the textbooks are to be used. Such teaching helps as are included will be characterized by vagueness and indefiniteness rather than by clearness and concreteness. This kind of course may be the pride of its author but it will not be a cherished possession of the teachers.

Unfortunately, this old-fashioned type of course is still in use in many communities. Furthermore, editions of it are still being turned out. In some instances the superintendent receives assistance from a few of his close associates. Thus, a county superintendent may assign portions of the course to local superintendents in the county for revision. In other cases, the superintendent persists in doing the entire task himself.

Preparing a course of study—the new method. The courses of study which have attracted favorable attention in the last decade or two have not been the courses which were turned out by the method just described. Instead, the modern course is the result of the co-operative labors of many members of the school staff. These include the superintendent, the principals, the supervisors, the teachers, and all other educational employees, such as assistant superintendents, the director of curriculum, the director of research, etc.

The prevailing plan is the committee plan. If the school system is a very small system, all of the teachers may serve on a single committee under the direction of the superintendent. But in a large system, many committees will be appointed. There may be a committee for each subject in each grade. Thus, there may be a committee on first-grade reading, a committee on second-grade number work, etc. For each committee, the best educated and most expert teachers in the system will be chosen. In making up a committee for second-grade number work, for example, those second-grade teachers who have made the most intensive study of number work in the primary grades and who have achieved outstanding success in teaching number in the second grade will be selected.

Those whose responsibility it is to prepare a course for number work in the second grade may be a subcommittee of a larger committee which prepares the entire arithmetic course of study. This committee will include in its membership, in addition to teachers who are expert and well-informed, at least one principal and one supervisor. This larger committee as a whole will prepare statements on the place of arithmetic in the curriculum of the elementary school and the objectives to be accomplished. It will review critically the work of the various sub-committees and will see that the courses which they prepare are properly integrated. There must be no serious overlappings of the courses for consecutive grades and, of course, there must be no gaps.

If a committee has been appointed to develop a course of study in arithmetic, this committee should be organized under the leadership of an aggressive and able chairman. The chairman must be well read in the recent literature on curriculum making, must know the technique of curriculum construction in general, and must be well informed on curriculum standards and tendencies in arithmetic in particular. He must preside over meetings of the committee, must stimulate and direct discussion, and must be able to offer leads and helpful suggestions to the members of the various sub-committees. He must keep himself informed on the progress of the sub-committees and must be able to stimulate them to continued activity if necessary. So important is the work of the chairman that he should be relieved from a part or all of his teaching or other duties while the most intensive work of his committee is under way.

The committee should have at its disposal an extensive library. This library should include books, monographs, and articles on curriculum making in general; books on principles of education and general methods of teaching; books dealing specifically with the teaching of arithmetic; arithmetic textbooks; courses of study from the more progressive school systems; yearbooks of national societies, such as *The Twenty-Ninth Yearbook of the National Society for the Study of Education* and *The Tenth Yearbook of the National Council of Teachers of Mathematics;* files of recent issues of several educational journals such as *The Elementary School Journal, The Journal of Educational Research, The Journal of Educational Method, The Catholic Education Review, Childhood Education, The Mathematics Teacher, The Educational Research Bulletin* (Ohio State University), *School and Society, The Grade Teacher, American Childhood,* and others; doctoral dissertations and research monographs dealing with special phases of arithmetic, several of which have been listed in the Selected References given with the preceding chapters; summaries of research in arithmetic such as the Buswell-Judd monograph published by the University of Chicago, the later annual summaries published by Buswell in *The Elementary School Journal,* and the summaries published by the American Educational Research Association in *The Review of Educational Research;* and other available sources of information.

Occasionally, the committee should have the benefit of the counsel of a nationally known authority in arithmetic. Such an authority should be brought to the city whose curriculum is being revised to confer with and advise the committee when their work is just getting under way and on occasions as they develop their program. Between visits, he should keep in touch with the committee through their chairman by mail, should answer specific questions put to him, and should receive for review and criticism the units of the course as they are completed.

When the course has been prepared, it should be submitted to all of the teachers, principals, and supervisors for trial. The course should not be printed when first completed but mimeographed. During this period of trial, criticisms and suggestions for revision should be solicited by the committee. Thus, every teacher who uses the course has an opportunity to criticize it and to participate in its revision. The course is then, finally, the joint product of all who are to use it rather than the product of a single individual or a restricted group of individuals.

Continuous revision necessary. A good course of study is not a static thing but dynamic; it must ever be revised to incorporate better materials, to provide for better placement of those materials, and to suggest better methods of instruction. As has been indicated in preceding chapters, there are topics in arithmetic toward which a very tentative attitude must be taken as regards grade placement, organization, and methods of instruction.

For example, no one knows just what value rote counting has in developing an understanding of number, what the best order is for teaching the combinations in any one of the four fundamental operations, what the best method is in subtraction, what the best method is for rationalizing new processes, in what grade or at what mental age the elements of division should first be introduced, etc. As evidence accumulates on these controversial points, it should modify prevailing practices and the course of study should be revised accordingly.

After a trial period, the course of study is usually printed and made available to all interested persons. It may be better, however, to leave it in mimeographed form and supply it to teachers in a loose-leaf container or, if printed, to print it in loose-leaf form. Then revisions can be made easily and the revised sheets can be placed by each teacher in her own copy in the places of those which have become out of date.

Provision for individual differences. Children differ greatly in the rate at which they learn and in the age at which a given type of arithmetical experience is meaningful to them. They not only differ in native intelligence but also in the variety and richness of their out-of school experiences. This means that they will be of varying ages when the different kinds of number experiences can be profitably introduced, that they will get varying amounts of meaning from these experiences, and that they will show marked differences in the rate of their progress. A typical second-grade class, composed of pupils whose average chronological age is, say, seven and one-half years, will contain some pupils whose mental age is ten years or more, and others whose mental age is five years or less. The I.Q.'s of the former are, of course, 133 or more, and of the latter, 67 or less. Such a range of mental ages presents an extremely difficult problem for the teacher.

Many teachers, who develop the fundamentals of arithmetic by mass instruction undertake to adapt their teaching to the average ability and experience level found in their classes. The majority of the pupils may get along very well with such instruction, if it is skilful, but the extreme deviates will gain little, if any, advantage from such teaching. The dull will be unable to keep pace with their classmates and, as they lag behind, will become less and less interested and more and more discouraged or indifferent. The gifted will find the assigned tasks easy, will probably be bored with explanations which they do not need, and will turn their attention to other and more interesting activities.

The modern course of study makes very definite provision for individual differences. In the first place, it provides that the pupils shall be studied and taught as individuals, or, when there is group instruction, the groups be homogeneous. There will usually be at least three groups—a slow group, an average group, and a rapid group. The slow group will include pupils who cover less than a year's work in a year's time but who do their work as far as they go better than they could if they tried to keep pace with their faster classmates. The rapid group will contain pupils who, eventually, may be accelerated in their progress through the grades, completing the six grades of the elementary school in five, or possibly four, years.

In the second place, there will be differences in the material assigned to these groups. The slow group will cover just the minimum essentials, while the rapid group will have more difficult number experiences including, sometimes, topics and methods of solution beyond those in the usual course of study. This method of providing for individual differences, however, will be found less frequently in the primary grades than in the intermediate and upper grades. In the primary grades, only those types of experience which are important in the lives of all will find a place in the course of study.

In the third place, methods of instruction will be varied to suit the abilities of the pupils in the various groups. The slow group will require explanations in the simplest, most concrete form and will need to have these explanations frequently repeated, with variations in the approach and in the nature of the illustrative materials. The bright group, on the other hand, will see reasons and will understand processes more quickly.

In teaching slow groups, it is sometimes necessary that the "why" of a procedure be omitted entirely, or that a less thorough and less complete explanation of it be given, and that the pupils be permitted to devote themselves entirely or more extensively to the "how"—to gaining skill in the process. In teaching carrying in multiplication, for example, it is sometimes best for dull pupils to learn the process by imitation rather than through rationalization. Of course, the reasons should be supplied and seen, if the pupils are able to comprehend them.

Arithmetic in activities. Many of the activities in which children engage require knowledge of, and skill in, arithmetic. Although it is frequently necessary that the pupil devote his attention exclusively to the processes of arithmetic in order that there may be sufficient opportunity for practice on the fundamental operations, much of what is learned in arithmetic will be learned through actual use in an activity of real and lifelike character.

The course of study should indicate very definitely how opportunities for the development of number concept and skill in the fundamental operations may be found in worth-while activities. Usually, the opportunities are present in a well-selected list of activities but too often the teacher fails to make the most effective use of them. The course of study should give specific suggestions, with illustrations, for the teacher's guidance. Naturally, much must be left to the teacher so far as the selection of activities and the use of those activities in teaching the fundamentals of arithmetic is concerned, but the course of study should provide helpful suggestions.

ARITHMETIC IN THE FIRST GRADE

In Chapter 2, we considered the place of arithmetic in the curriculum of the primary grades. We indicated that in recent years zealous reformers, in their very commendable desire to improve the program of the primary grades, have gone so far as to eliminate arithmetic entirely. We reviewed the evidence to the effect that young children make considerable progress toward an understanding of number in their out-of-school activities, we suggested that situations requiring some use of number are present on every hand in the school and out-of-school experiences of these children whether we like it or not, and we recommended that the primary teacher make very definite provision for correcting the erroneous ideas which children sometimes acquire and provide them with experiences which will guarantee opportunity for growth in number concept. We said that arithmetic may appear to the pupils to be quite incidental but that to the teacher it will represent a very definite plan.

Just what arithmetic experiences should be planned for first-grade pupils will depend upon several factors, the chief of which are: (1) their out-of-school experiences; (2) their mental maturity; (3) their interest in activities involving number; and (4) the extent to which they have already acquired number ideas. It is impossible to prescribe wisely for all first-grade classes. We shall simply indicate here the chief types of number experience which may be provided for typical first-grade pupils.

Counting and reading and writing numbers. It was indicated in Chapter 2 that the typical pupil can do rote counting to 25 or 30 and rational counting to 20 when he enters the first grade. It seems to be reasonable, then, to expect the first-grade teacher to set up definite goals for counting. The typical pupil may learn to count objects as far as this skill is required in his activities; this will rarely be beyond 50. He may also learn rote counting to 100 as he becomes better and better acquainted with number system.

He may also learn to count to 100 by 5's and 10's and to 20 by 2's. Counting by 2's may go beyond 20 if need for it arises. Suggestions for accomplishing this have been given in Chapter 3.

First-grade pupils may learn to read numbers as various uses arise. Page numbers in the books which they use may go to 100 or farther. They will probably have less use for writing numbers than for reading them but they may learn to write the one-digit numbers and many of those having two digits.

They may also learn to identify the number in a small group without counting and they may have occasion to use a few of the ordinals. Just how far this is to go will have to be left to the discretion of the teacher but if the teacher is alert she will find many opportunities for using ordinals and for recognizing the number in small groups.

Measurement. It has been suggested that many phases of measurement are important in the early number experiences of children. They are less important than counting but they should not be overlooked by the first-grade teacher.

Measures of time should include the days of the week, some or all of the months, and the day of the month. Such terms as *yesterday, today,* and *tomorrow* are learned. Important dates such as Thanksgiving, Christmas, Valentine Day, and the birthdays of the pupils, are recognized and discussed.

Each pupil should own and use his own foot rule and should come to recognize the *inch* and the *foot* and the fact that there are 12 inches in a foot. The foot rules in use should be graduated in half-inch divisions. Various activities will require the use of the rule in measuring materials.

Liquid measures will include the *pint,* the *quart* and the *glass* or *cup.* Pupils will learn that two glassfuls or two cupfuls make a pint and that two pints make a quart. The application of these measures to milk will be seen and discussed.

First-grade pupils will learn to recognize the more common coins and their interrelationships. These will include the cent (penny), the nickel, the dime, and the quarter. They will learn to make change in the school store and elsewhere and will learn that there are five cents in a nickel; 10 cents in a dime, and 25 cents in a quarter. The signs, ¢ and $, will be recognized and read as they are encountered on price tags.

The terms *dozen* and *half-dozen* will be learned and associated with the numbers 6 and 12.

There will be concrete representations of fractions. As was pointed out in Chapter 10, first-grade pupils often have wrong ideas of the most common fraction, one-half. They will learn this fraction better and may become acquainted with other fractions, especially one-fourth.

There will be frequent opportunities to make comparisons. These will lead to the use of such words as *larger, smaller, bigger, littler, taller, shorter, longer, shorter, higher, lower, heavier, lighter, nearer, farther, more, less,* etc. Typical uses for these terms have been suggested in Chapter 10.

Addition and subtraction. Pupils' activities lead naturally to the beginnings of addition and subtraction in the first grade. No definite goal should be set as to the number of addition and subtraction facts to be learned in this grade and there should be no abstract drills on the facts as such. But we saw in Chapter 2 that entering first-grade pupils frequently show considerable acquaintance with the easier addition facts so it would seem that the teacher should make the best of such opportunities as arise to give the pupils a still better grasp of some of the simpler additions. There will also be opportunities for developing an acquaintance with subtraction and for finding differences or remainders for small numbers.

Problems and activities. Simple, numerical problems will arise frequently. The kinds of situations which produce them have been mentioned in several of the preceding chapters. The solving of such problems will be oral except, perhaps, the writing of the numbers involved.

The activities of children which require the use of number are many and varied. These range in elaborateness and complexity all the way from the simplest activities incident to the performance of routine schoolroom duties, such as distributing materials and keeping various room records, to the life-like activity which may last through several days or weeks, such as developing and operating "Our Sweet Shop" or planning and conducting "A Doll Sale." The following are a few suggestions:

1. Keeping score in games.
2. Keeping various room records.
3. Counting pupils, materials, etc., and distributing materials to pupils and groups of pupils.
4. Comparing distances, sizes, ages, etc.
5. Measuring materials, lengths of objects, etc.
6. Finding pages in books, numbers on lockers, etc.
7. Building and operating a candy store, a flower shop, a toy shop, conducting a doll sale, a second-hand sale, etc.
8. Buying and selling the school milk supply, planning lunches to be purchased at the school cafeteria, etc.
9. Making and operating a bus, a boat, a train, an airplane, etc.
10. Caring for a library, checking the books, etc.

ARITHMETIC IN THE SECOND GRADE

Much of the informal type of arithmetic which is prominent in the first grade will be continued in the second grade. Many of the items enumerated there and many of the suggestions offered should be incorporated in the second-grade program.

The second-grade teacher's first responsibility is to ascertain precisely what arithmetic the pupils already know and what skills they already possess. In the light of what we have discovered as to what the typical pupil knows about arithmetic when he enters the first grade, it is reasonable to expect him to have made considerably greater progress by the time he is ready for the second grade, whatever the first-grade program may have been. But a well ordered first-grade program will provide for definite attention to certain fundamentals that all six-year-olds need and are able to understand. What is done in the first grade will not be of standard and uniform amount, however, so it is necessary that the teacher in the second grade begin by taking a careful inventory of the knowledge and skills which her pupils have already acquired. She will find that one group will differ from another and she will find that the members of a group differ greatly from each other.

The first-grade program was decidedly informal. The second-grade program should be informal also. We suggested that the work of the first grade should be planned quite definitely by the teacher although it might seem to the pupil to be incidental to something else. It is even more important that the second-grade teacher make definite plans for the arithmetic program of the year. A more precise schedule of minimum essentials can be set up for the second grade than for the first.

Counting and reading and writing numbers. Counting by 1's, 5's, and 10's should go beyond 100 as far as necessary in gaining an understanding of the number system. Above 100, the pupils may count by 100's to 1000. Counting by 2's may go beyond 20 as far as need requires. Rote counting by 2's may go to 100.

Practice in reading and writing numbers in the hundreds but not beyond 1000 should be provided. Part of this will be necessary for practical needs and part to gain a better appreciation of the number system. Thus, the pupil may write all numbers from 338 to 365, etc.

Work with numbers in the second grade may include some work with Roman numerals. If these are taught in this grade, they should be taught as far as XII. Suggestions on this topic have been given in Chapter 10.

Addition. If the pupils in the second grade have had in the first grade a rich experience with situations involving number, they will be ready for a program which includes the addition combinations. The zeros should be omitted until two-digit addends are introduced, for reasons indicated in Chapter 4, and it may not be advisable to include all of the combinations of one-digit numbers without zeros, but very definite provision can be made for most if not all of the combinations. We have seen that entering first-grade pupils have already acquired considerable familiarity with the easier combinations.

Late in the second year, pupils should be able to profit from drill exercises on the addition combinations such as those described in Chapter 4. Of course, care should be taken to see that the drill lessons do not become instances of mere meaningless repetition. It should also be remembered that we have in mind normal average second-grade pupils; dull or retarded pupils may not be ready for this kind of arithmetic even though they are classified in the second grade.

Provision may also be made for the adding of two-digit numbers, and possibly three-digit numbers, without carrying and for the adding of single columns of three and four one-digit numbers without higher decade addition. Zeros may be introduced at this time. The terms, *add* and *sum,* may be used and also the signs, + and =.

Subtraction. In Chapter 4, we recommended that the addition facts and the subtraction facts be taught together as teaching units. If this is done, pupils in the second grade will carry their work in subtraction as far as their work in addition. For average pupils with a proper background of number experience in the first grade, this may mean all 45 of the subtraction combinations (81 subtraction facts) but it may mean less than this number.

Examples having two-digit numbers, and possibly three-digit numbers also, as minuends and as subtrahends may be used. Such examples will include the zero facts in subtraction. The terms, *subtract, difference,* and *remainder* and the sign, –, may be learned.

Measurement. All of the measurement items listed for the first grade should receive further attention in the second grade or should be introduced in the second grade if they have not already been learned. In addition to these, it is suggested that the following items be added.

Measures of time may be extended to include the *hour,* the *half-hour,* the *quarter-hour,* the *minute,* and the *year.* The first four of these will be used by the pupils as they learn to tell time. The last will naturally come into use as the calendar is given further study and as ages are mentioned.

To the measures of length mentioned in the first-grade list, we may add the *yard.* Yardsticks should be available and should lead to the discovery that there are three feet in a yard. We may also use the terms *half-inch* and *quarter-inch.* Foot rules and yardsticks should be graduated in quarter-inch divisions.

The pupil's knowledge of liquid measures may be extended to include the *gallon* if need for it is readily found. He will learn that there are four quarts in a gallon. He will also learn *half-gallon* and will recognize that this is the same as two quarts. The pupil's frequent observations of purchases of gasoline and motor oil by gallons and quarts may well be used here.

Money measures will include the *dollar* and the *half-dollar.* The quarter will take on new meaning when it is recognized as a quarter of a dollar.

The *pound* may be learned as a measure of weight. This may also lead to the use of *half-pound* and *quarter-pound* in connection with purchases of candy, butter, and other commodities purchased by the pupils or by their parents.

We mentioned the fraction, one-half, in the first-grade outline and suggested that the fraction, one-fourth, might also be included. Both of these fractions should be used frequently in the second grade. It will be noted that we have applied them to the hour, the inch, the gallon, the dollar, and the pound. They will have many other uses. Some second-grade teachers include other fractions, especially three-fourths and one-third, but it seems well to limit the minimum list to one-half and one-fourth.

Problems and activities. Problems will occupy a place of gradually increasing prominence in the course of study in arithmetic for the primary grades. In the second grade many problems involving the addition and the subtraction facts may be solved. These will be, for the most part, simple one-step problems although some involving two steps may be used if the numbers are small and the combinations quite well known. For example, Mary buys 2 three-cent postage stamps and wants to know how much change she should have left from a dime.

Many, if not most, of the problems used in the second grade will occur in the form of oral statements but written problems may also be used. These may be found in published number books, or they may be written on the blackboard, or they may be typed or mimeographed on sheets of paper. Great care should be exercised to see that the words used in problem statements are in the reading vocabulary of the pupils.

Almost all of the activities which were suggested for use in Grade 1 are also suitable for use in Grade 2. Certain obvious modifications will be made to adapt the activities to the changing interests and increasing abilities of the pupils and to prevent loss of interest through monotony, but many of these activities are repeated through the years of a child's school life, occurring sometimes as routine parts of the day's work. They may quite well be utilized in developing a knowledge and an understanding of number and in increasing number skills.

A few suggestions are given simply to indicate the kinds which are of greatest usefulness.

1. Measuring the heights of pupils, using the appropriate apparatus.
2. Finding weights of pupils.
3. Keeping monthly records of heights and weights.
4. Telling time.
5. Reading the thermometer.
6. Looking up dates on the calendar and counting the number of days, or weeks, or months, to dates or occurrences which are of interest.
7. Finding house numbers, room numbers, locker numbers, numbers of coat hooks, post office box numbers, seat

numbers, etc.; looking up telephone numbers; locating cars by license numbers.

8. Counting and passing out books, pencils, paper, and other materials.

9. Playing number games giving practice on the fundamentals of addition and subtraction.

10. Comparing attendance records, counting the number who have been absent, counting the number who have been tardy, counting the number who have been neither absent nor tardy.

11. Finding differences between ages.

12. Finding differences in the number of blocks pupils have to walk to school.

13. Buying, selling, and making change; real and imaginary problems about costs, differences in prices, total costs, and amounts received as change.

ARITHMETIC IN THE THIRD GRADE

In any grade, the teacher's plans for teaching arithmetic should be built upon a sure knowledge of the number experiences which the pupils have already had. To build a third-grade program upon the theory that third-grade pupils *should* be able to profit from certain types of arithmetic instruction is often to court disaster. The third-grade teacher must know the extent to which the pupils who come to her have already developed an understanding of number and she must not overestimate the arithmetic knowledge which they have already acquired or the skills which they have gained.

The suggestions which have been offered for the course in the first and second grades are admittedly tentative. It is believed that the number experiences which have been suggested for the first grade will be profitable experiences for pupils of average intelligence if their out-of-school experiences follows the lines indicated in this book. Likewise, the second-grade suggestions are based upon the presumption that the outlined first-grade course has been followed and, again, that the pupils are of average intelligence.

In many schools, a definite program is outlined for the third grade with too little regard for what has been done in grades one and two. Schools which make no provision at all for arithmetic in the first two grades usually find that the progress which the pupils have made by the time they come to grade three has depended very much upon the teachers they have had. Those teachers who are alert to the opportunities for developing number appreciation in the first and the second grades do far more for their pupils than do those teachers whose interest is largely restricted to other aspects of the pupil's activities. It follows, then, that the third-grade teacher should first take an inventory of what the pupils understand, know, and can do. This inventory should be an individual affair; marked differences will be found. Each pupil should begin where he is, not where his teacher thinks he should be.

The grade placement of arithmetic topics. In recent years there has been much interest in the proper grade placement of arithmetic topics. The work of Washburne and his Committee of Seven[2] has attracted widespread

---

[2] Washburne, Carleton. "Grade Placement of Arithmetic Topics." National Society for the Study of Education, *Twenty-Ninth Yearbook.* Bloomington, Illinois: Public School Publishing Company, 1930, pp. 641-670.

Washburne, Carleton. "Mental Age and the Arithmetic Curriculum:

attention and has doubtless had a large effect upon courses of study. This Committee found that first graders can master the addition facts whose sums do not exceed 10 and that second-grade pupils are able to learn the remaining addition facts. The results for multiplication were less definite but there was a suggestion to the effect that a greater degree of mental maturity is necessary for this subject than is usually found in third-grade pupils.

Schools are still experimenting with this matter of grade placement. What the final outcome will be as regards multiplication and other topics commonly found in grade three remains to be seen. We shall proceed to outline a course which will include all that may be desired but considerably more than many schools will offer. While discussing multiplication and division in Chapters 7, 8, and 9, we indicated that the material treated might quite well be more extensive than that which the ideal course of study would include for the third grade.

The author suggests that this matter of grade placement is conditioned upon other things than mental age. Mental age, of course, is important, perhaps the most important of all factors. But readiness also depends upon former experiences. In the preceding chapters, we have emphasized repeatedly the importance of a rich and an extensive experience with number situations, of the con-

---

A Summary of the Committee of Seven Grade Placement Investigations to Date. *Journal of Educational Research,* XXIII: 210-231, March, 1931.

Washburne, Carleton. "The Values, Limitations, and Applications of the Findings of the Committee of Seven." *Journal of Educational Research,* XXIX: 694-707, May, 1936.

crete before the abstract, and of the development of teaching methods which will permit the new to be apprehended through its relationship to the old. Such practices may well modify otherwise sound conclusions as to the proper grade placement of arithmetic topics.

Most of the arithmetic textbooks in use in this country are planned to be used in the third grade. Some schools use number primers or number readers in the second grade and even in the first grade, but it is probable that more children make their first acquaintance with an arithmetic text in grade three than in any other grade of the elementary school. This means that the arithmetic taught in the third grade depends to no small extent upon what is contained in the adopted text.

There is a current tendency to modify the content of third-grade texts by moving upward to the fourth grade a considerable portion of the work traditionally done in grade three. Whereas, the older texts, and some of those recently published, provided for the learning of all of the multiplication and the division facts and for considerable work with one-digit multipliers and one-digit divisors in the third grade, some modern texts include in the third-grade assignment only the barest beginning of these two processes. Whether or not this tendency is a good one is not yet known. Nor do we know the extent to which the more difficult phases of what has been thought to be third-grade material should be moved ahead to the fourth grade, if this trend is desirable. Some authors of textbooks admit the uncertain condition here by issuing a dual set of textbooks, one containing the traditional content grade by grade and the other offering a stepped-up program.

Reading and writing numbers. There should be further practice in reading and writing numbers through those having four digits, or as far as 10,000. Counting by 100's should be practised as a means of helping the pupil to see how hundreds are related to thousands. Also, there may be counting by 1000's to 10,000.

There should be further study of Roman notation. It will probably be sufficient to go as far as XXX.

Addition. The addition facts should be reviewed and completed if they were not all learned in the second grade. As column addition is extended, higher decade addition will be taught. This will be carried rather systematically into the thirties with enough practice in higher decades to enable the pupils to generalize on these combinations. Special emphasis will be given to those requiring bridging. If multiplication with carrying is taught, there will be special emphasis also upon those higher decade addition combinations which are used in carrying in multiplication.

Carrying will be taught. Examples may consist of two-digit, three-digit, and four-digit addends. Zeros will be included. There will be some concern over attention span as single columns containing as many as six or seven addends are added. Pupils will be taught to check their answers.

Subtraction. All of the subtraction facts will be taught or reviewed. Examples having two-digit, three-digit, and four-digit minuends and subtrahends will be given for practice. All of the zero facts will be included. Borrowing (or carrying) will be taught. Pupils will be taught to check their answers.

Multiplication. Multiplication will be introduced and

will be carried as far as circumstances seem to warrant. This will probably include the 2's, 3's, 4's, and 5's and other combinations having products less than some assigned number, as 40, and may include all of the multiplication facts to 9 × 9. Two-digit and three-digit multiplicands will probably be used with one-digit multipliers but carrying may and may not be taught. Zeros may occur in the multiplicand. The terms, *multiply* and *product* and the sign ×, will be learned.

Division. The division combinations should be carried as far as the multiplication combinations as was indicated in Chapter 7. Also division examples which correspond to the multiplication examples in use may be given. All work will be done by the long division form. Answers will be checked. The terms, *divide* and *quotient* and the sign ÷, may be learned.

Measurement and fractions. The units of measurement listed in the outlines for the first and second grades should be reviewed and should have much additional practice in the third grade. In addition to these, we may add the *mile* for length and the *ounce* for weight. Further facts about the relationships between monetary units, such as the number of dimes in a dollar and the number of cents in a dollar, will also be learned.

There will be considerable new experience with fractions. Many such opportunities will arise in connection with comparisons of pints with quarts, quarts with gallons, feet with yards, days with weeks, etc. Also, the division facts which are taught may be represented in fraction form as was indicated in Chapter 9. Thus, the unit fractions, one-half to one-ninth, inclusive, may be used. Most of the work with fractions, however, should be confined to the fractions in more common use, such as one-half, one-fourth, one-third, and one-eighth, with some attention to one-fifth and one-sixth. A few additional fractions, particularly three-fourths and two-thirds may also be used.

Problems and activities. In the third grade, there will be many problems whose solutions require the use of addition and subtraction. There will also be problems leading to multiplication and division as far as these operations are learned. Teachers will find it necessary to supplement the texts in use by supplying many additional problems which are drawn from local situations.

Problems involving two operations should occur rather frequently in the third grade. Such problems occur in the affairs of children in their ordinary life experiences.

Many of the activities suggested for the second grade will be suitable for the third grade also. In addition to these, the following suggestions as to activities particularly suitable for third-grade pupils are offered:

1. Planning a school picnic.
2. Planning a party.
3. Planning a trip: expenditures for gasoline, meals, etc.
4. Playing number games giving practice on the fundamentals of the various operations.
5. Ordering from a catalog.
6. Earning and spending money. Planning Christmas expenditures, etc.
7. Comparing heights and weights: finding the difference in inches between the tallest and the shortest, the difference in weight between the heaviest and the lightest, etc.
8. Computing the cost of a new outfit of clothing for a boy or a girl.

9. Making an inventory of various articles and materials in the schoolroom.
10. Making birthday books containing dates of birthdays of pupils in the room.
11. Making the school garden pay.
12. Building and operating a shop or store.
13. Building a boat, or airplane, or doll house, etc.

The trend toward a socialized curriculum. We have observed that there is a distinct trend toward a new and somewhat different grade placement of arithmetic topics. There has also been apparent for several years a trend toward an enriched and socialized arithmetic program. The older type of course of study frequently placed greater emphasis upon the computational function of arithmetic than upon any other function, but there is a tendency in the modern course to recognize the informational, the sociological, and the psychological functions without losing sight of the importance of the computational.

These four functions are discussed by Brueckner.[3] He emphasizes the point that all four of these functions are of importance, and that arithmetic is not a tool subject but is a means of making the pupils acquainted with the contributions which are made by number in the various aspects of our social organization. Buckingham[4] discusses the importance of informational arithmetic and Bus-

[3] Brueckner, Leo J. "Diagnosis in Arithmetic." National Society for the Study of Education, *Thirty-Fourth Yearbook*. Bloomington, Illinois: Public School Publishing Company, 1935, pp. 269-272.

[4] Buckingham, B. R. "Informational Arithmetic." National Council of Teachers of Mathematics, Tenth Yearbook, *The Teaching of Arithmetic*. New York: Teachers College, Columbia University, 1935, pp. 51-73.

well[5] shows the relation of social arithmetic to computational arithmetic.

It should not be inferred that the older type of course of study made no provision for the informational, the sociological, and the psychological functions of arithmetic. These current developments in the arithmetic curriculum are not entirely new developments. The present trend is in the direction of a changed emphasis. Computation will continue to be stressed; we can hardly get along without it. But computation will be far more meaningful and the whole arithmetic program will be far more valuable if due provision is made in the course of study for arithmetic as information, for arithmetic as a social study, and for those abilities which are implied by the psychological function of the subject.

QUESTIONS AND REVIEW EXERCISES

1. Examine your local course of study. Who prepared it? When was it published? How many pages are devoted to arithmetic? To the arithmetic of the first three grades? Aside from indicating the scope of the work to be done, is it a useful document to the teacher?

2. If the superintendent of schools has a more extensive education and a greater variety of types of experience than any of the classroom teachers, why should he not, single handed, undertake the preparation of a course of study?

3. Outline the procedure which you believe should be followed in preparing a course of study. What part should the superintendent play? The principals? The supervisors?

---

[5] Buswell, G. T. "The Relation of Social Arithmetic to Computational Arithmetic." National Council of Teachers of Mathematics, Tenth Yearbook, *The Teaching of Arithmetic.* New York: Teachers College, Columbia University, 1935, pp. 74-84.

The teachers? To what extent, if any, should outsiders participate?

4. While the preparation of a course of study is under way, should the chairmen of the committees of teachers have their teaching loads reduced?

5. You probably agree that a course of study should not be a "scissors and paste" affair. To what extent should books, monographs, other courses of study, etc., be used by those who produce a course of study?

6. When should a new course of study be printed?

7. How often should a course of study be revised? Why are revisions necessary in a factual subject such as arithmetic?

8. Should all pupils dull and bright, follow the same course? What, if any, differentiations should be made?

9. Can pupils learn all of the arithmetic they need to know through activities? If not what phases will require additional attention?

10. What advantage is there in providing the first-grade teacher with definite suggestions as to the arithmetic ideas her pupils should acquire? What disadvantage?

11. Scrutinize carefully the outline given in this chapter for the first grade. Are there any items among those suggested which you would omit? Are there any additional items which you would include?

12. In a similar manner, criticize the suggestions given for the second grade.

13. Prepare a list of activities which you believe to be suitable for the first grade and which provide opportunities for developing an understanding and appreciation of number.

14. Prepare a similar list for the second grade.

15. How much arithmetic is provided for by the third-grade course of study in use in your community? Is there any which you believe should be omitted? Is there any which you would add?

16. Review the articles dealing with the work of the Committee of Seven on grade placement. Summarize what you consider to be the valuable contributions made by this Committee. Have you any criticisms on the Committee's work and recommendations?

17. What do you understand by the four functions of arithmetic which are emphasized by Brueckner? In your opinion, is there danger of neglecting the computational as greater emphasis is placed upon the informational, the sociological, and the psychological?

18. One element of the psychological function given by Brueckner is "ability and disposition to use quantitative methods as the basis of precise, accurate, orderly thinking." Can this be developed without attention to the other three functions also? Suggest overlappings and interrelations among these four functions.

19. To what extent should the textbook be the course of study? To what extent should a course of study be a textbook? Which is used more in your community?

20. Would it be desirable for each state to have a uniform course of study in all school districts of the state? Would a national course of study be a good thing? Summarize the advantages and disadvantages of a state course; of a national course.

CHAPTER TEST

For each of these statements, select the best answer. A scoring key will be found on page 406.

1. The old fashioned course of study was usually written by (1) the teachers (2) the superintendent (3) outside authority.

2. The course of study should be prepared by (1) the teachers (2) the administrative authorities (3) all educational employees working co-operatively.

3. Course of study committees should use outside authori-

ties (1) to criticize their work and advise them on further progress (2) to write the course for them (3) to tell them how to write the course.

4. The best known periodical for summaries of research in arithmetic is (1) *The Elementary School Journal* (2) *School and Society* (3) *The Journal of Educational Research.*

5. The ideal plan is to revise the course of study (1) every ten years (2) every five years (3) continuously.

6. If a child has a chronological age of eight years and a mental age of ten years, his intelligence quotient is (1) 80 (2) 100 (3) 125.

7. The second-grade teacher in teaching arithmetic should use (1) the individual plan (2) the group plan (3) a combination of the individual and group plans.

8. The reasons for procedures should be omitted most often for (1) dull pupils (2) average pupils (3) bright pupils.

9. Activities as a means of learning arithmetic are usually (1) entirely adequate (2) entirely inadequate (3) somewhat inadequate.

10. Concerning the place of arithmetic in the first grade school authorities (1) disagree (2) agree that it should occupy a prominent place (3) agree that it should have no place.

11. The typical pupil when he enters the first grade (1) can do rote counting as far as rational counting (2) can do rote counting farther than rational counting (3) can do rational counting farther than rote counting.

12. It was suggested that the first-grade pupil learn to count to (1) 10 (2) 100 (3) 1000.

13. It was recommended that attention first be given to fractions in (1) the first grade (2) the second grade (3) the third grade.

14. Most of the problems used in the first grade should come to the pupils (1) in print (2) orally (3) in script.

15. The second-grade teacher should begin by (1) reteaching the work of the first grade (2) testing the pupils to see

what they already know (3) developing the work assigned to the second grade.

16. It was suggested that the first work in Roman notation be given in (1) the first grade (2) the second grade (3) the third grade.

17. In the typical school, an arithmetic textbook is first used in (1) the first grade (2) the second grade (3) the third grade.

18. The Committee of Seven was most interested in (1) the proper grade placement of arithmetic topics (2) the development of effective methods of teaching (3) the construction of valid arithmetic tests.

19. The current tendency in arithmetic is (1) to move topics from the third grade to the fourth (2) to move topics from the fourth grade to the third (3) to make the work of the third grade more difficult.

20. It was suggested that Roman notation in the third grade go as far as (1) XII (2) XXX (3) L.

21. It was suggested that third-grade pupils learn the term (1) *multiplicand* (2) *multiplier* (3) *product.*

22. We recommended that the plus sign (+) be introduced in (1) the first grade (2) the second grade (3) the third grade.

23. In the older type of curriculum the most emphasized function of arithmetic was (1) the computational (2) the informational (3) the sociological.

24. The course outlined for the third grade suggests (1) a minimum program (2) an average program (3) a maximum program.

SELECTED REFERENCES

1. Brueckner, Leo J. "Diagnosis in Arithmetic." National Society for the Study of Education *Thirty-Fourth Yearbook.* Bloomington, Illinois: Public School Publishing Company, 1935, pp. 269-302. This yearbook is devoted to the subject of Educational Diagnosis and is all worth reading. A dis-

cussion of the four major functions of arithmetic will be found on pages 270-271.

2. Buckingham, B. R. "Informational Arithmetic." National Council of Teachers on Mathematics, Tenth Yearbook, *The Teaching of Arithmetic.* New York: Teachers College, Columbia University, 1935, pp. 51-73. Teachers will find it worth while to read this entire yearbook. Buckingham's chapter stresses the value of arithmetic as information.

3. Buswell, G. T. "The Relation of Social Arithmetic to Computational Arithmetic." National Council of Teachers of Mathematics, Tenth Yearbook, *The Teaching of Arithmetic.* New York: Teachers College, Columbia University, 1935, pp. 74-84. Stresses the value of social arithmetic. The reader will do well to read this reference along with the two listed above.

4. Curriculum Journal. Published by the Society for Curriculum Study. Columbus, Ohio: Bureau of Educational Research, Ohio State University. The reader will find the issues of this periodical a valuable source of information on many curriculum problems, some of which pertain to the primary grades.

5. Losh, Rosamond and Weeks, Ruth Mary. *Primary Number Projects.* Boston: Houghton Mifflin Company, 1923, pp. 174-196. Although an older reference, this volume contains many excellent suggestions. The pages cited refer specifically to a course of study in number for the kindergarten, the first grade, and the second grade.

6. Reeder, Ward G. *The Fundamentals of Public School Administration.* New York: The Macmillan Company, 1931, pp. 418-441. A chapter entitled "Making and Using the Curriculum." It is written from the administration point of view. Gives valuable general suggestions in brief form and a bibliography.

7. Reid, Florence E. "Incidental Number Situations in First Grade." *Journal of Educational Research,* XXX: 36-43,

September, 1936. A report of a study on incidental number situations which may be found in the experiences of first-grade pupils.

8. *Review of Educational Research.* Published by the American Educational Research Association. Washington, D.C.: National Educational Association. Volume I, pp. 1-64 (January, 1931), Volume IV, pp. 121-252 (April, 1934), and Volume VII, pp. 113-236 (April, 1937) summarize research bearing upon the curriculum. Additional summaries will appear at three-year intervals.

9. Thiele, C. L. "The Mathematical Viewpoint Applied to the Teaching of Elementary School Arithmetic." National Council of Teachers of Mathematics, Tenth Yearbook, *The Teaching of Arithmetic.* New York: Teachers College, Columbia University, 1935, pp. 212-232. A stimulating article treating arithmetic as a series of meaningful, interrelated experiences.

10. Washburne, Carleton. "Grade Placement of Arithmetic Topics." National Society for the Study of Education, *Twenty-Ninth Yearbook.* Bloomington, Illinois: Public School Publishing Company, 1930, pp. 641-670. An earlier report of the Committee of Seven.

11. Washburne, Carleton. "Mental Age and the Arithmetic Curriculum: A Summary of the Committee of Seven Grade Placement Investigations to Date." *Journal of Educational Research,* XXIII: 210-231, March, 1931. Stresses the importance of the placement of arithmetic topics in terms of mental age rather than school grade and summarizes the investigations to date.

12. Washburne, Carleton. "The Value, Limitations, and Applications of the Findings of the Committee of Seven." *Journal of Educational Research,* XXIX: 694-707, May, 1936. Discusses in perspective the work of the Committee of Seven to the date of writing. Gives a complete bibliography.

ANSWERS FOR CHAPTER TESTS

CHAPTER 1. 1. True. 2. False. 3. False. 4. True. 5. False. 6. False. 7. True. 8. False. 9. True. 10. False. 11. False. 12. True. 13. True. 14. True. 15. True. 16. True. 17. True. 18. False. 19. False. 20. True. 21. True. 22. True. 23. False. 24. True. 25. False.

CHAPTER 2. 1. (3). 2. (3). 3. (3). 4. (1). 5. (1). 6. (2). 7. (2). 8. (2). 9. (3). 10. (1). 11. (2). 12. (1). 13. (2). 14. (3). 15. (3). 16. (3). 17. (2). 18. (1). 19. (1). 20. (2).

CHAPTER 3. 1. (2). 2. (1). 3. (1). 4. (2). 5. (3). 6. (1). 7. (3). 8. (2). 9. (3). 10. (1). 11. (2). 12. (1). 13. (3). 14. (2). 15. (3). 16. (3). 17. (3). 18. (1). 19. (2). 20. (3).

CHAPTER 4. 1. False. 2. True. 3. False. 4. False. 5. False. 6. False. 7. True. 8. False. 9. False. 10. True. 11. False. 12. False. 13. True. 14. True. 15. True. 16. False. 17. True. 18. True. 19. False. 20. False. 21. True. 22. True. 23. True. 24. True. 25. True. 26. True. 27. False. 28. True. 29. False. 30. False. 31. True. 32. True. 33. False. 34. False. 35. False. 36. True. 37. True. 38. False. 39. True. 40. False.

CHAPTER 5. 1. False. 2. True. 3. False. 4. True. 5. False. 6. True. 7. True. 8. False. 9. False. 10. False. 11. False. 12. True. 13. True. 14. False. 15. False. 16. False. 17. True. 18. True. 19. True. 20. True. 21. True. 22. False. 23. False. 24. True. 25. True. 26. False. 27. False. 28. True. 29. False. 30. False. 31. False. 32. True. 33. True. 34. True. 35. False. 36. True. 37. True. 38. False. 39. True. 40. False.

CHAPTER 6. 1. (1). 2. (3). 3. (1). 4. (1). 5. (2). 6. (1). 7. (2). 8. (3). 9. (3). 10. (2). 11. (1). 12. (2). 13. (2). 14. (2). 15. (3). 16. (3). 17. (1). 18. (3). 19. (1). 20. (1). 21. (2). 22. (2). 23. (3). 24. (1). 25. (3). 26. (3). 27. (2). 28. (1). 29. (3). 30. (2).

CHAPTER 7. 1. True. 2. True. 3. True. 4. True. 5. False. 6. True. 7. False. 8. True. 9. True. 10. False. 11. False. 12. False. 13. False. 14. True. 15. True. 16. False. 17. True. 18. True. 19. True. 20. False. 21. False. 22. True. 23. True.

24. False. 25. False. 26. False. 27. False. 28. False. 29. True. 30. False. 31. False. 32. False. 33. True. 34. True. 35. True.

CHAPTER 8. 1. True. 2. False. 3. False. 4. True. 5. False. 6. True. 7. True. 8. False. 9. False. 10. True. 11. True. 12. True. 13. True. 14. False. 15. False. 16. True. 17. False. 18. False. 19. True. 20. False.

CHAPTER 9. 1. (2). 2. (1). 3. (3). 4. (1). 5. (2). 6. (3). 7. (1). 8. (3). 9. (1). 10. (2). 11. (3). 12. (2). 13. (3). 14. (2). 15. (2). 16. (3). 17. (3). 18. (1). 19. (1). 20. (3). 21. (2). 22. (1).

CHAPTER 10. 1. True. 2. False. 3. False. 4. True. 5. False. 6. False. 7. False. 8. True. 9. True. 10. True. 11. False. 12. True. 13. False. 14. True. 15. True. 16. True. 17. True. 18. False. 19. False. 20. False.

CHAPTER 11. 1. False. 2. False. 3. False. 4. True. 5. True. 6. True. 7. False. 8. True. 9. False. 10. False. 11. True. 12. True. 13. True. 14. True. 15. True. 16. False. 17. False. 18. False. 19. False. 20. True. 21. False. 22. True.

CHAPTER 12. 1. (2). 2. (3). 3. (1). 4. (1). 5. (3). 6. (3). 7. (3). 8. (1). 9. (3). 10. (1). 11. (2). 12. (2). 13. (1). 14. (2). 15. (2). 16. (2). 17. (3). 18. (1). 19. (1). 20. (2). 21. (3). 22. (2). 23. (1). 24. (3).

INDEX

Activity program, 42-49
Addition, teaching of, 76-122, 123-169; when to begin, 77-78; how to begin, 78-79; combinations and facts, 79-82; zero combinations, 82-84; flash cards, 98-101; games and drill devices, 101-107; problem solving in, 107-110; tests in, 110-114; easy column, 123-128; up or down, 128-129; longer columns in, 130-131; zeros in, 131; higher decade, 131-151; carrying in, 152-156; unequal length addends in, 157-159; speed in, 159-160; checks in, 160-162; attention span in, 162; in the first grade, 382; in the second grade, 385; in the third grade, 393
Answers for chapter tests, 405-406
Arithmetic, place of, 26-56; in readers, 34-35, 321-324; in the first grade, 379-383; in the second grade, 383-389; in the third grade, 389-396
Austrian method, 180

Ballard, P. B., 11, 23, 182, 286, 319
Beatty, Willard W., 186, 211
Beckmann, 32
Behrens, Minnie S., 85, 121
Beito, E. A., 86, 120
Benezet, L. P., 26
Betz, William B., 48-49, 54
Borrowing, in subtraction, 190-192
Brown, J. C., 24, 121, 257
Brownell, William A., 2, 23, 25, 74, 95, 120, 167
Brueckner, Leo J., 86, 120, 167, 396, 401
Buckingham, B. R., 27-29, 39, 40-42, 54, 76, 86, 120, 128, 129, 168, 186, 211, 286, 320, 396, 402
Buswell, G. T., 134, 168, 194, 211, 356, 368, 397, 402

Capacity, measures of, 334
Cardinal numbers, 63-65
Carrying, in addition, 152-156; in multiplication, 262-265; in division, 297-306
Chapter tests, 22-23, 52-53, 72-74, 117-120, 165-167, 208-211, 254-256, 278-279, 318-319, 343-344, 366-368, 399-401
Chase, Sara E., 368
Chazal, Charlotte B., 95, 120
Checks, in addition, 160-162; in subtraction, 201-202; in multiplication, 274-275; in division, 314-315
Children's knowledge of number, 27-35
Clapp, Frank L., 84, 120, 225, 256
Clark, John R., 74, 344, 368
Cobb, Stanwood, 43-44, 55
Cole, Lawrence W., 128
Collective terms, 335
Combinations, addition and subtraction, 76-122; multiplication and division, 216-235
Comparisons, 329-330
Complementary method, 180-181
Conant, L. L., 9, 23
Concrete number experiences, need for, 2-6
Counting, 57-63, 379-380, 384
Course of study, the, 370-404; old method of preparing, 370-371; new method of preparing, 371-375; revision of, 375; provision for individual differences in, 376-378; for the first grade, 379-383; for the second grade, 383-389; for the third grade, 389-396

Decomposition, method of, 177
De May, Amy J., 3, 5, 12, 24
Denominate measures, 331-335
Descoeudres, 32
Difficulty of combinations, 84-85, 225-226

Division, teaching of, 213-257, 281-320; zeros in, 214-216, 306-314; combinations and facts, 216-235; games and practice exercises, 236-245; flash cards, 239-240; solving problems in, 246-249, 315; tests in, 249-250; as measurement, 283; as partition, 283-285; short *versus* long, 285-289; difficulty steps in, 289-290; without carrying, 290-292; facts with remainders, 292-297; with carrying, 297-306; remainders in, 302-303; checks in, 314-315; in the third grade, 394
Drill, need for, 6, 96-98
Drummond, Margaret, 5, 24, 60, 74

Effect, Law of, 205
Eldredge, E. C., 24, 121, 257
Equal additions, method of, 178
Exercise, Law of, 204-205

Facts, addition and subtraction, 81-82; multiplication and division, 213-220
Flash cards, 98-101, 239-240
Fowlkes, John Guy, 215, 225, 226
Fractions, children's knowledge of, 32; in division, 282-284; developing an understanding of, 335-341; in the second grade, 386-387; in the third grade, 394-395
Freeman, F. M., 6, 24
Functions of arithmetic, 396-397

Games and drill devices, 101-107, 236-246
Ginsburg, Jekuthial, 8, 25, 75
Glazier, Harriet E., 168
Grade placement of arithmetic topics, 390-392
Grossnickle, Foster E., 287, 320
Gunderson, Agnes G., 34-35, 55, 321-324, 344

Hanna, Paul R., 44-47, 55
Harris, Alice L., 35-37
Hatton, Caroline, 74, 344, 368
Herbst, R. L., 184
Higher decade addition, 131-151; in multiplication, 135-137; how to teach, 137-140; practice in, 140-151
Higher decade subtraction, 202-205
Holloway, Harry Vance, 84, 121
Horn, Ernest, 354, 368

Individual differences, 59-61, 376-378

John, Lenore, 134, 168, 286, 320, 356, 368
Johnson, J. T., 184, 186, 211, 285
Judd, Charles Hubbard, 74, 194, 211

Karpinski, Louis Charles, 279
Kennedy, Agnes, 256
Kindergarten, arithmetic in, 35-37
Klapper, Paul, 168, 211, 256, 279, 320
Knight, F. B., 75, 84, 86, 121, 225, 257

Length, measures of, 331-332
Lennes, N. J., 279
Lockhart, Lovine, 24, 121, 257
Losh, Rosamond, 24, 121, 257, 402

MacLatchy, Josephine, 27-29, 39, 54, 55, 76, 79, 87, 120, 121, 168
McClelland, William W., 182
McLaughlin, Katherine, 32, 35
Manuel, H. T., 129
Mead, Cyrus D., 183, 186, 211, 212
Measurement, 330-335; in the first grade, 380-382; in the second grade, 386-387; in the third grade, 394
Morton, Robert L., 24, 75, 168
Multiple counting, 61-62
Multiplication, teaching of, 213-257, 258-280; zeros in, 214-216, 270-273; combinations and facts, 216-235; tables, 220-221; relation to addition, 224-227; games and practice exercises, 236-246; flash cards, 239-240; solving problems in, 246-249, 273-274; tests in, 249-250; without carrying, 259-262; with carrying, 262-270; checks

in, 274-275; up or down, 275-276; in the third grade, 393-394
Myers, Garry Cleveland, 286, 320, 356-359, 368

Norem, G. M., 225-227
Number comprehension, 1-25, 57-74

Oftedal, Laura, 257
Olander, Herbert T., 86, 122
Ordinal numbers, 63-65
Osburn, W. J., 182, 212
Otis, Arthur S., 74, 344, 368

Partition, 283-285
Polkinghorne, Ada R., 32, 56, 284, 320, 336-338, 344
Primitive man and number, 8-10
Problems, and examples, 346-347; in primary grades, 347-348; qualities of, 348-361; reality in, 348-351; interest in, 351-353; language of, 354-360; story element in, 356-360; for practice on basic skills, 360-361; classification of, 361-364; method in solving, 364
Problem solving, 107-110, 202, 246-249, 273-274, 315, 346-369

Questions and review exercises, 20-21, 50-51, 70-72, 114-117, 162-165, 206-208, 251-254, 276-278, 316-317, 341-343, 365-366, 397-399

Rational counting, 57-62
Readers, arithmetic in, 34-35, 321-324
Readiness, Law of, 47, 206
Reading and writing numbers, 65-69, 379-380, 384, 393
Recognizing groups without counting, 62-63
Reeder, Ward G., 370, 402
References, 23-25, 54-56, 74-75, 120-122, 167-169, 211-212, 256-257, 279-280, 319-320, 344-345, 368-369, 401-403
Reid, Florence E., 56, 402
Rhymes, 18-20
Roantree, William F., 169, 279, 345
Roman numerals, 324-329, 384, 393
Rote counting, 57-62
Ruch, G. M., 183, 212, 257
Russell, Ned M., 24

Sears, Isabel, 186, 211
Smith, David Eugene, 8, 25, 75, 219, 257
Smith, Nila B., 33-34, 56, 331, 345
Socialized curriculum, trend toward, 396-397
Stages of number understanding, 12-18
Stone, John C., 181, 183, 212
Stretch, Lorene B., 6, 25
Subtraction, teaching of, 76 122, 170-212; combinations, 79-82; zero combinations, 82-84; flash cards, 98-101; games and drill devices, 101-107; problem solving in, 107-110, 202; tests in, 110-114; without borrowing, 172-176; zeros in, 173-175; methods in, 176-188; disputes in, 181-188; type problems of, 188-190; borrowing in, 190-192; habits in, 192-196; types of examples in, 196-199; crutches in, 199-200; checks in, 201-202; higher decade, 202-205; cardinal points in, 204-206; in the first grade, 382; in the second grade, 385-386; in the third grade, 393

Taylor, Joseph S., 186, 212
Taylor, Mary S., 169, 279, 345
Tests, 110-114, 249-250
Thiele, C. L., 96, 122, 403
Thorndike, Edward L., 25, 75, 162, 279, 294, 320, 354, 368
Time, measures of, 332-334

Vogel, Mabel, 122, 257

Washburne, Carleton, 42, 56, 87, 122, 257, 390, 391, 403
Weeks, Ruth Mary, 24, 121, 257, 402
Weight, measures of, 334-335

Wesley, Marion, 75
Wheat, Harry Grove, 7, 25, 75, 91, 122, 358-359, 369
Wilson, Esteline, 356, 369
Wilson, Guy M., 183, 212
Winch, W. H., 182, 192-194, 212
Woody, Clifford, 29-31, 56

Writing numbers, 69, 380, 384

Zero, 66-67; combinations, 82-84, 214-216; in column addition, 131; in subtraction, 197-198; in multiplication, 270-273; in division, 306-314